Collins

Student Book

Approved by AQA

NEW GCSE MATHS
AQA Modular
Fully supports the 2010 GCSE Specification

an Speed • Keith Gordon • Kevin Evans • Trevor Senior • Chris Pearce

CONTENTS

RECALL

UNIT 3: Geometry and Algebra

INTRODUCTION

Welcome to Collins New GCSE Maths for AQA Modular Higher Book 2. The first part of this book covers the Recall content you will have learnt in Unit 1 and Unit 2. You will also need some content covered in this section for your Unit 3 exam. The second part covers the content specific to Unit 3.

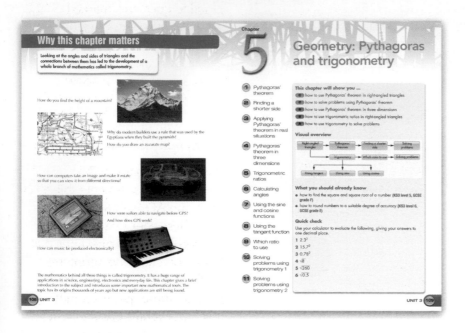

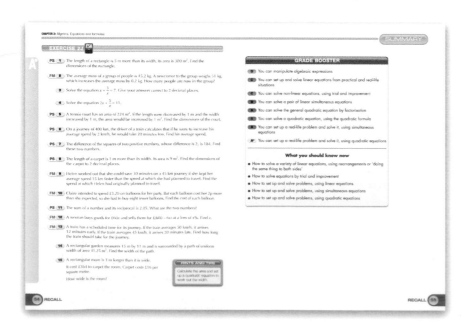

Why this chapter matters

Find out why each chapter is important through the history of maths, seeing how maths links to other subjects and cultures, and how maths is related to real life.

Chapter overviews

Look ahead to see what maths you will be doing and how you can build on what you already know.

Colour-coded grades

Know what target grade you are working at and track your progress with the colour-coded grade panels at the side of the page.

Use of calculators

Questions where you must or could use your calculator are marked with 🖩 icon.

Explanations involving calculators are based on *CASIO fx–83ES*.

Grade booster

Review what you have learnt and how to get to the next grade with the Grade booster at the end of each chapter.

Worked examples

Understand the topic before you start the exercise by reading the examples in blue boxes. These take you through questions step by step.

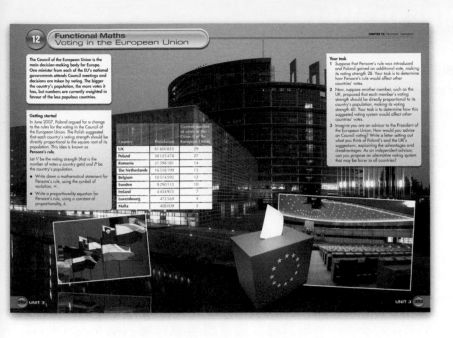

Functional maths

Practise functional maths skills to see how people use maths in everyday life. Look out for practice questions marked **FM**. There are also extra functional-maths and problem-solving activities at the end of every chapter to build and apply your skills.

New Assessment Objectives

Practise new parts of the curriculum (Assessment Objectives AO2 and AO3) with questions that assess your understanding marked **AU** and questions that test if you can solve problems marked **PS**. You will also practise some questions that involve several steps and where you have to choose which method to use; these also test AO2. There are also plenty of straightforward questions (AO1) that test if you can do the maths.

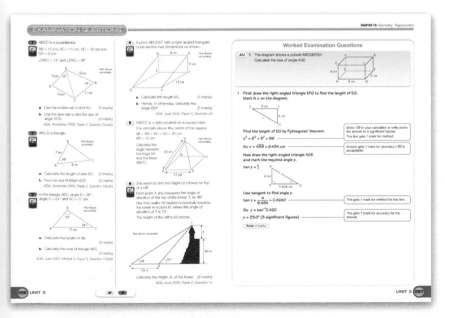

Exam practice

Prepare for your exams with past exam questions and detailed worked exam questions with examiner comments to help you score maximum marks.

Quality of Written Communication (QWC)

Practise using accurate mathematical vocabulary and writing logical answers to questions to ensure you get your QWC (Quality of Written Communication) marks in the exams. The Glossary and worked exam questions will help you with this.

Why this chapter matters

Technology is increasingly important in our lives. It helps us do many things more efficiently than we could without it.

Modern **calculators** take away the need to perform long calculations by hand. They can help to improve accuracy – but a calculator is only as good as the person using it. If you press the buttons in the wrong order when doing a calculation then you will get the wrong answer. That is why learning to use a calculator effectively is important.

The earliest known calculating device was a **tally stick**, which was a stick with notches cut into it so that small numbers could be recorded.

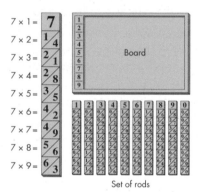

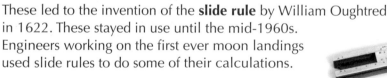

In about 2000 BC the **abacus** was invented in Eygpt.

Abacuses are still used widely in China today and they were used widely for almost 3500 years, until John Napier devised a calculating aid called **Napier's bones**.

These led to the invention of the **slide rule** by William Oughtred in 1622. These stayed in use until the mid-1960s. Engineers working on the first ever moon landings used slide rules to do some of their calculations.

In the mid-16th century the first **mechanical calculating machines** were produced. These were based on a series of cogs and gears and so were too expensive to be widely used.

The first **electronic computers** were produced in the mid-20th century. Once the transistor was perfected, the power increased and the cost and size decreased until the point where the average scientific calculator that students use in schools has more computing power than the first craft that went into space.

1

Number: Using a calculator

1 Basic calculations and using brackets

2 Adding and subtracting fractions with a calculator

3 Multiplying and dividing fractions with a calculator

This chapter will show you ...

to **G** **D** how to use a calculator effectively

Visual overview

Basic calculations (+, −, ×, ÷) → Inputting fractions → Calculating with fractions

What you should already know

- How to add, subtract, multiply and divide with whole numbers and decimals **(KS3 level 5, GCSE grade E)**
- How to simplify fractions and decimals **(KS3 level 5, GCSE grade E)**
- How to convert improper fractions to mixed numbers or decimals and vice versa **(KS3 level 6, GCSE grade E)**
- The rules of BIDMAS/BODMAS with decimals **(KS3 level 5, GCSE grade E)**
- How to add and subtract fractions and decimals **(KS3 level 6, GCSE grade D)**

Quick check

1 Complete these calculations. Do not use a calculator.

   a $48 + 89$ **b** $102 - 37$ **c** 23×7

   d $336 \div 8$ **e** $3.6 + 2.9$ **f** $8.4 - 3.8$

   g 3×4.5 **h** $7.8 \div 6$

2 a Convert these mixed numbers into improper fractions.

   i $2\frac{2}{5}$ **ii** $3\frac{1}{4}$ **iii** $1\frac{7}{9}$

   b Convert these improper fractions into mixed numbers.

   i $\frac{11}{6}$ **ii** $\frac{7}{3}$ **iii** $\frac{23}{7}$

3 Work these out without using a calculator.

   a $2 + 3 \times 4$ **b** $(2 + 3) \times 4$

   c $6 + 4 - 3^2$ **d** $6 + (4 - 3)^2$

4 Work these out without using a calculator.

   a $\frac{2}{3} + \frac{3}{4}$ **b** $\frac{1}{5} + \frac{2}{7}$

   c $\frac{4}{5} - \frac{1}{4}$ **d** $2\frac{1}{3} - 1\frac{2}{5}$

This section will show you how to:
- use some of the important keys, including the bracket keys, to do calculations on a calculator

Key words
brackets
equals
function key
key
shift key

Most of the calculations in this unit are carried out to find the final answer of an algebraic problem or a geometric problem. The examples are intended to demonstrate how to use some of the **function keys** on the calculator. Remember that some functions will need the **shift key** SHIFT to make them work. When you have **keyed** in the calculation, press the **equals** key = to give the answer.

Some calculators display answers to fraction calculations as fractions. There is always a key to change this to a decimal. In examinations, an answer given as a fraction or a decimal will always be acceptable unless the question asks you to round to a given accuracy.

Most scientific calculators can be set up to display the answers in the format you want.

EXAMPLE 1

These three angles are on a straight line.

To find the size of angle **a**, subtract the angles 68° and 49° from 180°.

You can do the calculation in two ways.

$180 - 68 - 49$ or $180 - (68 + 49)$

Try keying each calculation into your calculator.

$180 - 68 - 49$

The display will show 63.

$180 - (68 + 49)$

Again, the display should show 63.

It is important that you can do this both ways.

You must use the correct calculation or use **brackets** to combine parts of the calculation.

A common error is to work out $180 - 68 + 49$, which will give the wrong answer.

> You will learn more about angles in Chapter 6.

FM Functional Maths **AU** (AO2) Assessing Understanding **PS** (AO3) Problem Solving

EXAMPLE 2

Work out the area of this trapezium,
where $a = 12.3$, $b = 16.8$ and $h = 2.4$.

To work out the area of the trapezium, you use
the formula:

$$A = \tfrac{1}{2}(a + b)h$$

Remember, you should always substitute into a
formula before working it out.

$$A = \tfrac{1}{2}(12.3 + 16.8) \times 2.4$$

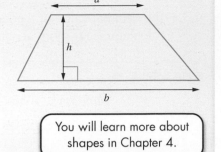

> You will learn more about
> shapes in Chapter 4.

Between the brackets and the numbers at each end there is an assumed
multiplication sign, so the calculation is:

$$\tfrac{1}{2} \times (12.3 + 16.8) \times 2.4$$

Be careful, $\tfrac{1}{2}$ can be keyed in lots of different ways:

- As a division

  [1] [÷] [2] [=]

  The display should show 0.5.

- Using the fraction key and the arrows

  [▤] [1] [▼] [2] [=]

  The display should show $\tfrac{1}{2}$.

Keying in the full calculation, using the fraction key:

[▤] [1] [▼] [2] [▶] [×] [( ] [1] [2] [•] [3] [+] [1] [6] [•] [8] [ )] [×] [2] [•] [4] [=]

The display should show 34.92 or $\dfrac{873}{25}$.

Your calculator has a power key [$x^{\blacksquare}$] and a cube key [x^3].

EXAMPLE 3

Find the value of $4.5^3 - 2 \times 4.5$.

Try keying in:

[4] [•] [5] [x^3] [3] [−] [2] [×] [4] [•] [5] [=]

The display should show 82.125 or $\dfrac{657}{8}$.

> You often have to work out
> calculations like this in trial
> and improvement
> questions. You will learn
> more about trial and
> improvement in Chapter 2.

Most calculations involving circles will involve the number π (pronounced 'pi'), which has its own calculator button $\boxed{\pi}$.

> You will learn more about π and circles in Chapter 4.

The decimal value of π goes on for ever. It has an approximate value of 3.14 but the value in a calculator is far more accurate and may be displayed as 3.1415926535 or π.

EXAMPLE 4

Work out: **a** $\pi \times 3.2^2$ **b** $2 \times \pi \times 4.9$

Give your answers to 1 decimal place.

a Try keying in:

$\boxed{\pi}\ \boxed{\times}\ \boxed{3}\ \boxed{\cdot}\ \boxed{2}\ \boxed{x^2}\ \boxed{=}$

The display should show 32.16990877 or $\frac{256}{25}\pi$. (Convert this to a decimal.)

This is 32.2 to 1 decimal place.

b Try keying in:

$\boxed{2}\ \boxed{\times}\ \boxed{\pi}\ \boxed{\times}\ \boxed{4}\ \boxed{\cdot}\ \boxed{9}\ \boxed{=}$

The display should show 30.78760801 or $\frac{49}{5}\pi$. (Convert this to a decimal.)

This is 30.8 to 1 decimal place.

EXERCISE 1A

Use your calculator to work out the following.

Try to key in the calculation in as one continuous set, without writing down any intermediate values.

1 Work these out.

　　a $(10 - 2) \times 180 \div 10$

　　b $180 - (360 \div 5)$

2 Work these out.

　　a $\frac{1}{2} \times (4.6 + 6.8) \times 2.2$

　　b $\frac{1}{2} \times (2.3 + 9.9) \times 4.5$

3 Work out the following and give your answers to 1 decimal place.

　　a $\pi \times 8.5$　　　　**b** $2 \times \pi \times 3.9$　　　　**c** $\pi \times 6.8^2$　　　　**d** $\pi \times 0.7^2$

FM 4 At Sovereign garage, Jon bought 21 litres of petrol for £21.52.

At the Bridge garage he paid £15.41 for 15 litres.

At which garage is the petrol cheaper?

AU **5** A teacher asked her class to work out $\dfrac{2.3 + 8.9}{3.8 - 1.7}$.

Abby keyed in:

(2 . 3 + 8 . 9) ÷ 3 . 8 − 1 . 7 =

Bobby keyed in:

2 . 3 + 8 . 9 ÷ 3 . 8 − 1 . 7 =

Col keyed in:

(2 . 3 + 8 . 9) ÷ (3 . 8 − 1 . 7) =

Donna keyed in:

2 . 3 + 8 . 9 ÷ (3 . 8 − 1 . 7) =

They each rounded their answers to 3 decimal places.

Work out the answer each of them found.

Who had the correct answer?

PS **6** Show that a speed of 31 metres per seconds is approximately 70 miles per hour.

You will need to know that 1 mile ≈ 1610 metres.

7 Work the vale of each of these, if $a = 3.4$, $b = 5.6$ and $c = 8.8$.

  a abc **b** $2(ab + ac + bc)$

8 Work out the following giving your answer to 2 decimal places.

  a $\sqrt{(3.2^2 - 1.6^2)}$ **b** $\sqrt{(4.8^2 + 3.6^2)}$

9 Work these out.

  a $7.8^3 + 3 \times 7.8$ **b** $5.45^3 - 2 \times 5.45 - 40$

1.2 Adding and subtracting fractions with a calculator

This section will show you how to:	Key words	
• use a calculator to add and subtract fractions	fraction	mixed number
	improper fraction	proper fraction
	key	shift key

In this lesson, questions requiring calculation of **fractions** are set in a context linked to other topics, such as algebra or geometry.

You will recall from Unit 2 that a fraction with the numerator bigger than the denominator is an **improper fraction** or a *top-heavy fraction*.

You will also recall that a **mixed number** is made up of a whole number and a **proper fraction**.

For example:

$$\tfrac{14}{5} = 2\tfrac{4}{5} \text{ and } 3\tfrac{2}{7} = \tfrac{23}{7}$$

Using a calculator with improper fractions

Check that your calculator has a fraction key. Remember, for some functions, you may need to use the **shift key** SHIFT.

To **key** in a fraction, press .

Input the fraction so that it looks like this:

$$\tfrac{9}{5} \text{ or } 9\lrcorner5$$

Now press the equals key = so that the fraction displays in the answer
part of the screen.

Pressing shift and the key S⇔D will convert the fraction to a mixed number.

$$1\lrcorner4\lrcorner5$$

This is the mixed number $1\tfrac{4}{5}$.

Pressing the equals sign again will convert the mixed number back to an improper fraction.

- Can you see a way of converting an improper fraction to a mixed number without using a calculator?

- Test your idea. Then use your calculator to check it.

Using a calculator to convert mixed numbers to improper fractions

To input a mixed number, press the shift key first and then the fraction key ▤.

Pressing the equals sign will convert the mixed number to an improper fraction.

- Now key in at least 10 improper fractions and convert them to mixed numbers.

- Remember to press the equals sign to change the mixed numbers back to improper fractions.

- Now input at least 10 mixed numbers and convert them to improper fractions.

- Look at your results. Can you see a way of converting a mixed number to an improper fraction without using a calculator?

- Test your idea. Then use your calculator to check it.

EXAMPLE 5

A water tank is half full. One-third of the capacity of the full tank is poured out.

What fraction of the tank is now full of water?

The calculation is $\frac{1}{2} - \frac{1}{3}$.

Keying in the calculation gives:

The display should show $\frac{1}{6}$.

The tank is now one-sixth full of water.

EXAMPLE 6

Work out the perimeter of a rectangle $1\frac{1}{2}$ cm long and $3\frac{2}{3}$ cm wide.

To work out the perimeter of this rectangle, you can use the formula:

$P = 2l + 2w$

where $l = 1\frac{1}{2}$ cm and $w = 3\frac{2}{3}$ cm.

$P = 2 \times 1\frac{1}{2} + 2 \times 3\frac{2}{3}$

Keying in the calculation gives:

The display should show $10\frac{1}{3}$.

So the perimeter is $10\frac{1}{3}$ cm.

EXERCISE 1B

1 Use your calculator to work these out. Give your answers as mixed numbers.

Try to key in the calculation as one continuous set, without writing down any intermediate values.

a $4\frac{3}{4} + 1\frac{4}{5}$ b $3\frac{5}{6} + 4\frac{7}{10}$ c $7\frac{4}{5} + 8\frac{9}{20}$ d $9\frac{3}{8} + 2\frac{9}{25}$

e $6\frac{7}{20} + 1\frac{3}{16}$ f $2\frac{5}{8} + 3\frac{9}{16} + 5\frac{3}{5}$ g $6\frac{9}{20} - 3\frac{1}{12}$ h $4\frac{3}{4} - 2\frac{7}{48}$

i $8\frac{11}{32} - 5\frac{1}{6}$ j $12\frac{4}{5} + 3\frac{9}{16} - 8\frac{2}{3}$ k $9\frac{7}{16} + 5\frac{3}{8} - 7\frac{1}{20}$ l $10\frac{3}{4} + 6\frac{2}{9} - 12\frac{3}{11}$

2 A water tank is three-quarters full. Two-thirds of a full tank is poured out.

What fraction of the tank is now full of water?

D

C

3

a What is the distance between Wickersley and Redbrook, using these roads?

b How much further is it to Redbrook than to Wickersley?

FM 4 Here is a calculation.

$$\frac{3}{25} + \frac{7}{10}$$

Imagine that you are trying to explain to someone how to use a calculator to do this.

Write down what you would say.

FM 5 There are the same number of boys and girls in a school.

Because of snow $\frac{4}{5}$ of the boys are absent and $\frac{5}{12}$ of the girls are absent.

What fraction of the students are present?

PS 6 **a** Use your calculator to work out $\frac{18}{37} - \frac{23}{43}$.

b Explain how your answer tells you that $\frac{23}{43}$ is greater than $\frac{18}{37}$.

AU 7 Jon is working out $\frac{9}{32} + \frac{5}{7}$ without using a calculator.

He adds the numerators and the denominators to get an answer of $\frac{14}{39}$ which is not correct.

a Use a calculator to work out the correct answer.

b Work out $\frac{14}{39} - \frac{9}{32}$ on your calculator.

c Work out $\frac{14}{39} - \frac{5}{7}$ on your calculator.

d Explain why your answers to parts **b** and **c** show that $\frac{14}{39}$ is a fraction between $\frac{9}{32}$ and $\frac{5}{7}$.

AU 8 **a** Choose two other fractions to add together.

Write down the incorrect answer that Jon would get.

Repeat the steps of question **7** for these fractions.

b Is Jon's answer between your two fractions?

AU 9 To work out the perimeter of a rectangle the following formula is used.

$$P = 2l + 2w$$

Work out the perimeter when $l = 5\frac{1}{8}$ cm and $w = 4\frac{1}{3}$ cm.

PS 10 A shape is rotated 90° clockwise and then a further 60° clockwise.

What fraction of a turn is needed to return it to its original position.

Give both possible answers.

Multiplying and dividing fractions with a calculator

This topic will be assessed in Unit 3.

This section will show you how to:
- use a calculator to multiply and divide fractions

Key words
fraction
key
shift key

In this lesson, questions requiring calculation of **fractions** will be set in a context linked to other topics such as algebra or geometry. Remember, for some functions, you may need to use the **shift key** SHIFT.

EXAMPLE 7

Work out the area of a rectangle of length $3\frac{1}{2}$ m and width $2\frac{2}{3}$ m.

The formula for the area of a rectangle is:

area = length × width

Keying in the calculation, where length = $3\frac{1}{2}$ and width = $2\frac{2}{3}$ gives:

SHIFT ⊟ 3 ▶ 1 ▼ 2 → × SHIFT ⊟ 2 ▶ 2 ▼ 3 ▶ =

The display should show $9\frac{1}{3}$.

The area is $9\frac{1}{3}$ cm^2.

EXAMPLE 8

Work out the average speed of a bus that travels $20\frac{1}{4}$ miles in $\frac{3}{4}$ hour.

The formula for the average speed is:

$$\text{average speed} = \frac{\text{distance}}{\text{time}}$$

You will learn more about distance, speed and time in Chapter 3.

Use this formula to work the average speed of the bus, where distance is $20\frac{1}{4}$ and time is $\frac{3}{4}$.

Keying in the calculation gives:

SHIFT ⊟ 2 0 ▶ 1 ▼ 4 ÷ ⊟ 3 ▼ 4 ▶ =

The display should show 27.

The average speed is 27 mph.

EXERCISE 1C

1 Use your calculator to work these out. Give your answers as fractions.

Try to key in the calculation as one continuous set, without writing down any intermediate values.

a $\frac{3}{4} \times \frac{4}{5}$

b $\frac{5}{6} \times \frac{7}{10}$

c $\frac{4}{5} \times \frac{9}{20}$

d $\frac{3}{8} \times \frac{9}{25}$

e $\frac{7}{20} \times \frac{3}{16}$

f $\frac{5}{8} \times \frac{9}{16} \times \frac{3}{5}$

g $\frac{9}{20} \div \frac{1}{12}$

h $\frac{3}{4} \div \frac{7}{48}$

i $\frac{11}{32} \div \frac{1}{6}$

j $\frac{4}{5} \times \frac{9}{16} \div \frac{2}{3}$

k $\frac{7}{16} \times \frac{3}{8} \div \frac{1}{20}$

l $\frac{3}{4} \times \frac{2}{9} \div \frac{3}{11}$

2 The formula for the area of a rectangle is:

area = length × width

Use this formula to work the area of a rectangle of length $\frac{2}{3}$ m and width $\frac{1}{4}$ m.

3 Some steps are each $\frac{1}{5}$ m high. How many steps are needed to climb 3 m?

AU 4 **a** Use your calculator to work out $\frac{3}{4} \times \frac{9}{16}$.

b Write down the answer to $\frac{9}{4} \times \frac{3}{16}$.

AU 5 **a** Use your calculator to work out $\frac{2}{3} \div \frac{5}{6}$.

b Use your calculator to work out $\frac{2}{3} \times \frac{6}{5}$.

c Use your calculator to work out $\frac{4}{7} \div \frac{3}{4}$.

d Write down the answer to $\frac{4}{7} \times \frac{4}{3}$.

6 Use your calculator to work these out. Give your answers as mixed numbers.

Try to key in the calculation as one continuous set, without writing down any intermediate values.

a $4\frac{3}{4} \times 1\frac{4}{5}$

b $3\frac{5}{6} \times 4\frac{7}{10}$

c $7\frac{4}{5} \times 8\frac{9}{20}$

d $9\frac{3}{8} \times 2\frac{9}{25}$

e $6\frac{7}{20} \times 1\frac{3}{16}$

f $2\frac{5}{8} \times 3\frac{9}{16} \times 5\frac{3}{5}$

g $6\frac{9}{20} \div 3\frac{1}{12}$

h $4\frac{3}{4} \div 2\frac{7}{48}$

i $8\frac{11}{32} \div 5\frac{1}{6}$

j $12\frac{4}{5} \times 3\frac{9}{16} \div 8\frac{2}{3}$

k $9\frac{7}{16} \times 5\frac{3}{8} \div 7\frac{1}{20}$

l $10\frac{3}{4} \times 6\frac{2}{9} \div 12\frac{3}{11}$

7 The formula for the area of a rectangle is:

area = length × width

Use this formula to work the area of a rectangle of length $5\frac{2}{3}$ m and width $3\frac{1}{4}$ m.

8 The volume of a cuboid is $26\frac{3}{4}$ cm^3. It is cut into eight equal pieces.

Work out the volume of one of the pieces.

9 The formula for the distance travelled is:

distance = average speed × time taken

Work out how far a car travelling at an average speed of $36\frac{1}{4}$ mph will travel in $2\frac{1}{2}$ hours.

10 Glasses are filled from litre bottles of water.

Each glass holds $\frac{1}{2}$ pint.

1 litre = $1\frac{3}{4}$ pints

How many litre bottles are needed to fill 10 glasses?

PS FM **11** The ribbon on a roll is $3\frac{1}{2}$ m long. Joe wants to cut pieces of ribbon that are each $\frac{1}{6}$ m long.

He needs 50 pieces.

How many rolls will he need?

GRADE BOOSTER

D You can use BIDMAS or BODMAS to carry out operations in the correct order

D You can use a calculator to add, subtract, multiply and divide fractions

C You can use a calculator to add, subtract, multiply and divide mixed numbers

What you should know now

● How to use a calculator effectively, including the brackets and fraction keys

1 Ahmed uses $\frac{2}{3}$ of a litre of milk each day.

He buys milk in 2-litre bottles.

What is the least number of bottles that he needs to buy for one week?

You **must** show your working.

AQA, June 2009, Module 3, Question 18

2 A train travels 350 miles in $4\frac{3}{4}$ hours. Work out the average speed of the train in miles per hour.

3 A painter has 40 litres of paint.

The paint is in 2.5-litre tins.

How many tins of paint does he have?

4 The diagram shows a trapezium.

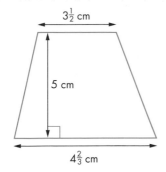

$3\frac{1}{2}$ cm

5 cm

$4\frac{2}{3}$ cm

Work out the area of the trapezium.

Hint: Area $= \frac{1}{2}(a + b)h$

5 Matt counts 40 strides as he walks 30 m.

a How long is each stride?

b How many strides would he take if he walked 75 m?

c He decides that to get enough exercise he will do 3000 strides.

How far will he need to walk?

6 a A parallelogram has base $7\frac{1}{2}$ cm and perpendicular height $7\frac{1}{2}$ cm.

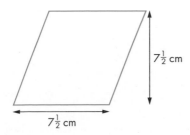

$7\frac{1}{2}$ cm

$7\frac{1}{2}$ cm

Work out the area.

Hint: Area of a parallelogram = base × perpendicular height

b The perimeter of the parallelogram is $35\frac{1}{2}$ cm.

How long is one of the sloping sides?

7 Calculate $\dfrac{5.6 \times 7.8}{4.3 - 2.1}$

a Write down your full calculator display. *(1 mark)*

b Write your answer to part **a** to one decimal place. *(1 mark)*

AQA, June 2008, Module 3, Question 1

8 Calculate $\sqrt{8.17^3 + 4.39^2}$

a Give **all** the figures on your calculator display. *(1 mark)*

b Give your answer to an appropriate degree of accuracy. *(1 mark)*

AQA, November 2007, Paper 2 Question 1b

9 Work out $\dfrac{21.6 \times 64}{35.1 + 9.57}$

a Write down your full calculator display. *(1 mark)*

b Write your answer to two decimal places. *(1 mark)*

AQA, June 2009, Module 3, Question 1

10 Work out as a decimal $\dfrac{4.6^2}{8.6 - 2.7}$

a Write down your full calculator display. *(1 mark)*

b Write your answer to three significant figures. *(1 mark)*

AQA, March 2008, Module 3, Question 4

11 a A cuboid has length $5\frac{1}{2}$ cm, width $3\frac{1}{2}$ cm and height 4 cm.

Work out the volume.

Hint: Volume of a cuboid = length × width × height

b The volume of a cuboid is 50 cm³.

One edge is $2\frac{1}{2}$ cm long.

Work out a pair of possible lengths for the other edges.

12 A square of side $3\frac{1}{2}$ cm is shown.

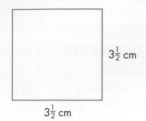

$3\frac{1}{2}$ cm

$3\frac{1}{2}$ cm

Chris is working out the area.

He works out $3\frac{1}{2} \times 3\frac{1}{2}$.

He says the answer is $9\frac{1}{4}$ cm^2.

He is wrong.

Use a calculator to work out the correct answer. Explain his mistake.

13 The area of the cross-section of a prism is $6\frac{1}{4}$ cm^2.

The volume of the prism is 25 cm^3.

Work out the length of the prism.

Hint: Volume of a prism = area of cross-section × length

Worked Examination Questions

AU **1** The perimeter of a rectangle is $32\frac{1}{2}$ cm.

Work out a pair of possible values for the length and the width of the rectangle.

1   Perimeter is 2 × length + 2 × width

Length + width = $32\frac{1}{2}$ ÷ 2

> This gets 1 mark for the method.

Length + width = $16\frac{1}{4}$ cm

> This gets a mark for an accurate calculation.

Possible length and width are:

Length = 10 cm

Width = $6\frac{1}{4}$ cm

> Any two values with a sum of $16\frac{1}{4}$ would score the final mark.

Total: 3 marks

FM **2** A driver is travelling 200 miles.

He sets off at 10 am.

He stops for a 20-minute break.

His average speed when travelling is $42\frac{1}{2}$ mph.

He wants to arrive before 3 pm.

Is he successful?

2   Time travelling = distance ÷ average speed

= 200 ÷ $42\frac{1}{2}$

> This gets 1 mark for method.

= $4\frac{12}{17}$ or 4.7058...

20 minutes = $\frac{1}{3}$ hour or 0.33

> This is the next step and gets 1 mark for method.

$4\frac{12}{17}$ + $\frac{1}{3}$ or 4.7058... + 0.33...

= $5\frac{2}{51}$ hours 5.039 hours

> This gets 1 mark for accuracy.

10 am to 3 pm is 5 hours so he arrives after 3 pm

> A statement giving the correct conclusion from correct working would get 1 mark for quality of written communication (QWC).

Total: 4 marks

You have been asked by your Business Studies teacher to set up a jewellery stall selling beaded jewellery at an upcoming Young Enterprise fair. There will be 50 stalls at this fair (many of which will be selling jewellery) and it is expected that there will be 500 attendees.

You will be competing against every other stall to sell your products to the attendees, either as one-off purchases or as bulk orders. In order to be successful in this you must carefully plan the design, cost and price of your jewellery, to ensure that people will buy your products and that you make a profit.

Getting started

Answer these questions to begin thinking about how beads can be used to make a piece of jewellery.

1 How many 6 mm beads are needed to make a bracelet?

2 How many 8 mm beads are needed to make an anklet?

3 How many 10 mm beads are needed to make a short necklace?

4 How many 10 mm beads are needed to make a long necklace?

5 You are asked to make a bracelet with beads of two different lengths. You decide to use 6 mm red beads and 8 mm blue beads. How many would you need if you used them alternately?

How to make beaded jewellery

Beads are sold in different sizes and wire is sold in different thicknesses, called the gauge. To make a piece of jewellery the beads are threaded onto the wire.

Step 1 Choose a gauge of wire and cut the length required.

Step 2 Put a fastening on one end.

Step 3 Thread on beads of different sizes in a pattern.

Step 4 Put a fastener on the other end.

Your jewellery is now complete.

Cost of materials

Here are the costs of the raw materials that you will need to make your jewellery.

6 mm beads	10p each
8 mm beads	12p each
10 mm beads	15p each
24-gauge wire	10p per centimetre
20-gauge wire	8p per centimetre
Fasteners for both ends: 30p per item of jewellery	

Advice

For bracelets and anklets use 20-gauge wire.

For necklaces use 24-gauge wire.

Beads are available in three lengths: 6 mm, 8 mm and 10 mm.

Beads are available in three colours, green, blue and red.

Your task

With a partner, draw up a business plan for your jewellery stall, to ensure you produce high quality beaded jewellery that will turn a good profit. In your plan, you should include:

- an outline of who you expect to buy your jewellery (your 'target market')
- a design for at least one set of jewellery that will appeal to your target market
- a list of all the materials you will need
- the cost of your designs
- a fair price at which to sell your jewellery
- a discounting plan for bulk orders, or if you must reduce your prices on the day
- an expected profit.

Use all the information given on these pages to create your business plan.

Be sure to justify your plan, using appropriate mathematics and describing the calculations that you have done.

Present your business plan as a report to the Young Enterprise committee.

Standard lengths for bracelets and necklaces

Bracelet	17 cm
Anklet	23 cm
Short necklace	39 cm
Long necklace	46 cm

Why this chapter matters

Mathematicians are interested in the way that numbers work, rather than just looking at specific calculations. Using letters to represent numbers, they can use formulae and solve the very complicated equations that occur in modern technology. Without the use of algebra, mankind would not have developed aircraft or walked on the Moon.

2000 BC — The Babylonians discover that the ratio of the circumference of a circle to its diameter is approximately 3.125. This is the first time an approximation to π is used.

The Chinese made the first reference to negative numbers.

100 AD — Heron of Alexandria did some work that led to the need for the square root of a negative number but this was dismissed for many centuries as something that was impossible.

1500 AD — Italian mathematicians came across formulae that could only be solved if the square root of –1 was used.

1550 AD — Rafael Bombelli was the first mathematician to introduce the notation $\sqrt{-1} = i$.

1618 AD — When doing work on logarithms, the Scottish mathematician John Napier published a list of 'natural logarithms' that were based on a number with a value of about 2.718, although this number was not quoted.

1680 AD — A Swiss mathematician, Jacob Bernoulli, found the value 2.71828… which is the limit of $(1 + \frac{1}{n})^n$. (Try this on your calculator with a big number for n. If $n = 1000$, then $1.001^{1000} = 2.71692…$)

1727 AD — Another Swiss mathematician, Leonhard Euler, gave the value the letter e.

1748 AD — Euler publishes his famous formula $\ln_e(\cos x + i\sin x) = ix$ which can also be expressed as $e^{i\pi} = -1$.

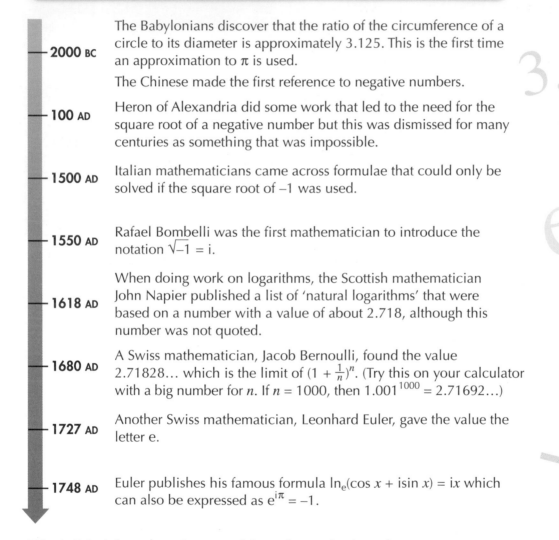

Why is Euler's formula so important? Any advanced culture, be it human or alien, would need a counting system that included a unit of 1. It would also need a symbol to record zero. Circles occur all over the Universe, so the ratio π would be familiar. The same is true for would e, which is a constant that occurs naturally. So Euler's formula really is universal. Many people even think it proves the existence of God.

However, other people think that the fact that five of the most important numbers in mathematics, 0, 1, e, i and π, all occur in such a neat formula is pure coincidence.

$$e^{i\pi} + 1 = 0$$

Chapter

Algebra: Equations and formulae

This chapter will remind you ...

- how to solve linear equations
- how to solve simultaneous equations
- how to solve quadratic equations

This chapter will show you ...

C how to set up and solve linear equations

A how to solve quadratic equations, using the quadratic formula

B how to set up and solve simultaneous equations

to **A** **A*** how to set up and solve problems, using quadratic equations

Visual overview

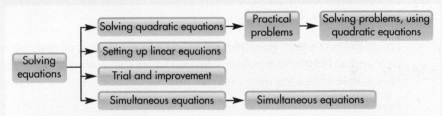

What you should already know

- The basic language of algebra **(KS3 level 5, GCSE grade E)**
- How to collect together like terms **(KS3 level 5, GCSE grade E)**
- How to multiply terms such as $2m \times 3m$ **(KS3 level 5, GCSE grade E)**
- How to solve simple equations **(KS3 level 6, GCSE grade E/D)**

Quick check

1 Expand the following.

   a $3(x - 5)$ **b** $2(x + 7)$ **c** $7(2x - 3)$

2 Simplify the following.

   a $5y + 2y - y$ **b** $4x + 2 + 3x - 5$ **c** $3(x + 1) - 2(x - 1)$

3 Simplify the following.

   a $4 \times 2x$ **b** $6y \times 3y$ **c** $x^2 \times 3x$

4 Solve the following equations.

   a $x + 3 = 7$ **b** $5x = 30$ **c** $\frac{x}{8} = 8$

   d $2x + 5 = 3$ **e** $4x - 3 = 13$ **f** $\frac{x}{3} - 2 = 9$

This section will remind you how to:
- apply the rules of algebra
- simplify algebraic expressions by multiplying terms
- simplify algebraic expressions by collecting **like terms**
- **expand and simplify** brackets
- factorise expressions
- **substitute** numbers into expressions and formulae

Key words

brackets	factorisation
coefficient	formula
constant term	identity
equation	like terms
expand	simplify
expand and simplify	substitute
expression	terms
factor	variable

Here are some words used in algebra that you need to know.

Variable: This is what the letters used to represent numbers are called. They can take on any value so they 'vary'.

Coefficient: This is the number in front of a letter, so in $2x$ the coefficient of x is 2.

Expression: This is any combination of letters and numbers. For example, $2x + 4y$ and $\frac{p-6}{5}$ are expressions.

Equations: You will have met these in Book 1. These contain, as the name suggests, an equals sign and at least one variable. The important fact is that a value can be found for the variable. This is called *solving the equation*.

Formula: You may already have seen many formulae (the plural of formula). These are like equations in that they contain an equals sign, but there is more than one variable and they are rules for working out things such as area or the cost of taxi fares.

For example, $V = x^3$, $A = \frac{1}{2}bh$ and $C = 3 + 4m$ are formulae.

Identity: This looks like a formula, but the important fact about an identity is that it is true for all values, whether numerical or algebraic. For example, $5n \equiv 2n + 3n$ and $(x + 1)^2 \equiv x^2 + 2x + 1$ are identities. Note that the special sign $\equiv$ is used in an identity.

Terms: These are the separate parts of expressions, equations, formulae and identities. In $3x + 2y - 7$, there are three terms, $3x$, $+ 2y$ and -7. Expressions inside **brackets** are treated as a single term in calculations, although they can be multiplied out in expansions.

Constant term: This is any single number in an expression or equation, so in $x^2 + 3x + 7$, the constant term is 7.

EXAMPLE 1

Expand   **a** $3(2x + 7)$ **b** $2x(3x - 4y)$

a $3 \times 2x + 3 \times 7 = 6x + 21$

b $2x \times 3x - 2x \times 4y = 6x^2 - 8xy$

EXAMPLE 2

Expand and **simplify** $6(2x + 5) - 3(3x - 1)$

$$6(2x + 5) - 3(3x - 1) = 12x + 30 - 9x + 3$$
$$= 12x - 9x + 30 + 3$$
$$= 3x + 33$$

EXAMPLE 3

Factorise the following expressions.

a $3x + 6$ b $4my + 12mx$ c $5kp - 10k^2p + 15kp^2$

a The common **factor** is 3, so $3x + 6 = 3(x + 2)$

b The common factor is $4m$, so $4my + 12mx = 4m(y + 3x)$

c The common factor is $5kp$, so $5kp - 10k^2p + 15kp^2 = 5kp(1 - 2k + 3p)$

EXAMPLE 4

The formula for the perimeter of a rectangle is $P = 2l + 2w$

Work out the perimeter when $l = 4.5$ cm and $w = 1.75$ cm

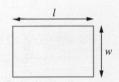

$P = 2(4.5) + 2(1.75) = 9 + 3.5 = 12.5$ cm

EXAMPLE 5

State whether each of the following is an expression (E), equation (Q), formula (F) or identity (I).

A: $x^2 - 5x$ B: $c = \sqrt{(a^2 + b^2)}$ C: $2x - 3 = 1$ D: $4n - 3n = n$

A is an expression (E) with two terms.

B is a formula (F). This is the formula for finding the hypotenuse of a right-angled triangle with short sides of a and b.

C is an equation (Q) which can be solved to give $x = 2$.

D is an identity (I).

EXERCISE 2A

AU 1 a Which of the following expressions are equivalent?

$$3m \times 8n \qquad 2m \times 12n \qquad 4n \times 6m \qquad m \times 24n$$

b The expressions $\frac{x}{2}$ and x^2 are the same for only one positive value of x.

What is the value?

2 Expand these expressions.

a $5(3 - m)$

b $3(2x + 7)$

c $x(x + 2)$

d $2m(5 - m)$

e $5s(s + 3)$

f $3n(m - p)$

3 Factorise the following expressions.

a $18 - 3m$

b $6x + 12$

c $x^2 + 5x$

d $10m - m^2$

e $15s^2 + 3$

f $3n - pn$

AU 4 Find the missing terms to make these equations true.

a $8x + 12y - \boxed{} - \boxed{} = 5x + 4y$

b $3a - 5b - \boxed{} + \boxed{} = a - b$

PS 5 ABCDEF is an L-shape.

AB = DE = x

AF = $4x - 1$ and EF = $3x + 1$

a Explain why the length BC = $3x - 1$.

b Find the perimeter of the shape in terms of x.

c If $x = 6$ cm what is the perimeter of the shape?

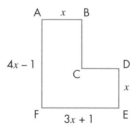

PS 6 A square and a rectangle have the same perimeter.

The rectangle has one side that is three times as long as the other.

The square has a side of 8 cm.

What are the dimensions of the rectangle?

7 Find the value of each of these expressions when $x = 1.4$, $y = 2.5$ and $z = 0.8$.

a $\dfrac{3x + 4}{2}$

b $\dfrac{x + 2y}{z}$

c $\dfrac{y}{z} + x$

AU 8 The formula for the area, A, of a square with side x is $A = x^2$.

The formula for the area, T, of a triangle with base b and height h is $T = \frac{1}{2}bh$.

Find **different** values of x, b and h so that $A = T$.

9 The formula for the gas bill each quarter in a household is £17.50 + £0.12 per unit.

A family uses 6250 units in a quarter.

  a How much is their total bill?

  b The family pay a direct debit of £220 per month towards their gas costs.

    By how much will they be in credit or debit after the quarter?

AU 10 x and y are different prime numbers.

Choose values for x and y so that the formula $5x + 2y$

  a evaluates to an even number

  b evaluates to an odd number.

AU 11 Kaz knows that x, y and z have the values 3, 6 and 9 but he does not know which variable has which value.

  a What is the maximum value that the expression $x + 3y - 5z$ could have?

  b What is the minimum value that the expression $2x - y + 3z$ could have?

FM 12 A car costs £90 per day to rent.

Some friends decide to rent the car for five days.

  a Which of the following formulae would represent the cost per day if there are n people in the car and they share the cost equally?

$$\frac{450}{5n} \qquad \frac{450}{n+5} \qquad \frac{450}{n}$$

  b Three friends rent the car.

    When they get the bill they find that there is a special discount for a five-day rental.

    They each find it cost them £20 less than they expected.

    How much does a five-day rental cost?

13 Expand these expressions.

  a $4p^2(3p - q)$ **b** $5t^2(2t^2 + 7)$ **c** $5x(2x + 7y)$

  d $2m^2(5 - m^3)$ **e** $8s^3(s + 3t)$ **f** $6nm^2(m - n)$

14 The local supermarket is offering £2 off a large box of chocolates.

Madge wants four boxes.

  a If the normal price of one box is £t, write down the expressions below that represent how much it will cost Madge to buy four boxes.

$$4(t - 2) \qquad 4t - 1 \qquad 4t - 4 \qquad 4t - 8$$

  b The original price of a box of chocolates was £8.50.

    How much will Madge actually pay?

15 Expand and simplify the following expressions.

   a $5(4x + 1) + 3(x + 2)$ **b** $4(y - 2) + 5(y + 3)$ **c** $2(3x - 2) - 4(x + 1)$

   d $5(2x + 3) + 6(2x - 1)$ **e** $6x(2x - 3) + 2x(x + 4)$ **f** $3(4x^2 - 3) + x^2(5 + 2x)$

16 Factorise the following expressions.

   a $9p^2 + 6pt$ **b** $12mp - 8m^2$ **c** $16a^2b + 4ab$

   d $4a^2 - 6a + 2$ **e** $20xy^2 + 10x^2y + 5xy$ **f** $8mt^2 - 4m^2t$

AU 17 Darren wrote the following:

$$2(3x - 5) = 5x - 3$$

Darren has made two mistakes.

Explain the mistakes that Darren has made.

> **HINTS AND TIPS**
>
> It is not enough to give the right answer. You must try to explain why Darren wrote 5 for 2×3 instead of 6.

PS 18 The expansion $3(x + 4) = 3x + 12$ can be shown by the diagram.

   a What expansion is shown in this diagram?

   b Write down an expansion that is shown on this diagram.

19 In Highville school there are 2000 students. One day a student returns from abroad with an infectious disease. The following day the student is off school. The following day three more students are off school with the disease and then each day three times more students than the day before are off. How many days will it be before there are no students left in school?

> **HINTS AND TIPS**
>
> Fill in a table like this:
>
> | Day | 1 | 2 | 3 | 4 |
> |---|---|---|---|---|
> | Number off | 1 | 3 | 9 | 27 |
> | Total number off | 1 | 4 | 13 | 40 |

20 A three-carriage train has $2f$ first-class seats and $2s$ standard-class seats.

A four-carriage train has $3f$ first-class seats and $3s$ standard-class seats.

On a weekday six three-carriage trains and three four-carriage trains travel from Bristol to Bournemouth.

   a Write down an expression for the total number of first-class and standard-class seats available during the day.

FM

b On average in any day one-third of the first class seats are used at a cost of £45 each.
On average in any day four-fifths of the standard class seats are used at a cost of £30 each.

How much money does the rail company earn in an average day on this route?

Give your answer in terms of f and s.

c $f = 16$ and $s = 50$

It costs the rail company £30 000 per day to operate this route.

How much profit or loss do they make on an average day?

PS 21 A rectangle with sides 6 and $3x + 5$ has a smaller rectangle with sides 2 and $x - 2$ cut from it.

Work out the remaining area.

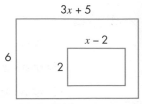

FM 22 Five friends have a meal together. They each have a main course costing £7.25 and a dessert costing £2.75.

Colin says that the bill will be 5 × £7.25 + 5 × £2.75.

Kim says that she has an easier way to work out the bill as 5 × £(7.25 + 2.75).

a Explain why Colin's and Kim's methods both give the correct answer.

b Explain why Kim's method is better.

c What is the total bill?

AU 23 Three students are asked to factorise the expression $16m - 4$.

These are their answers.

Alex	Aimee	Rebecca
$2(8m - 2)$	$4(4m - 1)$	$8m(2 - \frac{1}{2m})$

All the answers are accurately factorised but only one is the normally accepted answer.

a Which student gave the correct answer?

b Explain why the other two students' answers are not acceptable as correct answers.

PS 24 Explain why $7x - 9y$ cannot be factorised.

25 $3(x + 1) = 3x + 3$ is an identity.

a Substitute $x = 5$ in both sides to show that it is true for a numerical value.

b Substitute $x = n + 2$ and expand and simplify both sides to show that it is true for an algebraic expression.

Solving linear equations

This section will remind you how to:
- solve linear equations by rearrangement

Key words

do the same to both sides
inverse operations
rearrangement
solution
variable

Work through these examples to remind yourself how to solve equations.

Remember: to solve equations, you can **do the same to both sides**, use **inverse operations** or **rearrangement** to find the **solution** for the **variable**.

EXAMPLE 6

Solve the following equations.

a $\dfrac{y}{5} + 7 = 4$ 　　　　　 **b** $\dfrac{z+4}{3} = 5$

a Subtract 7 from both sides: 　　　　 $\dfrac{y}{5} = -3$

　　Multiply both sides by 5: 　　　　　 $y = -15$

　　Check: $-15 \div 5 + 7 = -3 + 7 = 4$ ✓

b Multiply both sides by 3: 　　　　　 $z + 4 = 15$

　　Subtract 4 from both sides: 　　　　 $z = 11$

　　Check: $(11 + 4) \div 3 = 15 \div 3 = 5$ ✓

Don't forget to check your answer in the original equation.

EXAMPLE 7

Solve the following equations.

a $2(x + 7) = 15$ 　　　　 **b** $4(y - 9) = 12$

a Expand the brackets: 　　　　　 $2x + 14 = 15$

　　Subtract 14 from both sides: 　　　 $2x = 1$

　　Divide both sides by 2: 　　　　　 $x = \dfrac{1}{2}$

　　Check: $2 \times (\dfrac{1}{2} + 7) = 2 \times 7\dfrac{1}{2} = 15$ ✓

b Expand the brackets: 　　　　　 $4y - 36 = 12$

　　Add 36 to both sides: 　　　　　 $4y = 48$

　　Divide both sides by 4: 　　　　　 $y = 12$

　　Check: $4 \times (12 - 9) = 4 \times 3 = 12$ ✓

EXAMPLE 8

Solve the following equations.

a $5x + 2 = 3x + 11$ **b** $6(x - 1) = 2x + 14$

a Rearrange the equations to get the x-terms on one side and the number terms on the other:

$$5x - 3x = 11 - 2$$

Collect like terms: $2x = 9$

Divide both sides by 2: $x = 4\frac{1}{2}$

Check: Left-hand side $5 \times 4\frac{1}{2} + 2 = 24\frac{1}{2}$

         Right-hand side $3 \times 4\frac{1}{2} + 11 = 24\frac{1}{2}$ = left-hand side   ✓

b Expand the brackets: $6x - 6 = 2x + 14$

Rearrange: $6x - 2x = 14 + 6$

Collect like terms: $4x = 20$

Divide both sides by 4: $x = 5$

Check: $6(5 - 1) = 24$, $2 \times 5 + 14 = 10 + 14 = 24$ ✓

EXERCISE 2B

Solve the equations in questions **1** to **4**.

1   **a** $\dfrac{x + 2}{5} = 3$ **b** $\dfrac{x - 7}{6} = 2$ **c** $\dfrac{x + 3}{2} = 1$ **d** $\dfrac{x - 1}{8} = 5$

2   **a** $3(x + 7) = 12$ **b** $4(x - 1) = 6$ **c** $5(3x + 9) = 45$ **d** $3(2x - 7) = 12$

3   **a** $7x + 9 = 2x + 19$ **b** $4x - 8 = 3x + 7$ **c** $3x + 5 = 5x - 9$ **d** $3x - 1 = 6 - 4x$

4   **a** $3(x + 9) = x + 3$ **b** $4(2x - 1) = 3(x + 7)$

      c $2(x + 8) + 3(x - 2) = x + 6$ **d** $5(x - 1) - 2(x - 7) = 4(x + 2)$

AU 5 The solution to this equation is $x = -1$.

$$ax + b = c$$

What is the relationship between a, b and c?

PS 6 A sequence is formed by multiplying each term by 2 and adding 3 to find the next term.

The first term of such a sequence is a and the fourth term is 41.

     a …   …   41

a Explain why $8a + 21 = 41$ **b** Find the value of a.

Setting up equations

This section will remind you how to:
- set up equations from given information, and then solve them

Key words
do the same to both sides
equation
rearrange
solve

Equations are used to represent situations, so that you can **solve** real-life problems. Many real-life problems can be solved by setting them up as linear equations. You can **do the same to both sides** or use **rearrangement** to **solve** the problem.

EXAMPLE 9

A milkman sets off from the dairy with eight crates of milk, each containing b bottles.

He delivers 92 bottles to a large factory and finds that he has exactly 100 bottles left on his milk float. How many bottles were in each crate?

The equation is:

$8b - 92 = 100$

$8b = 192$ (Add 92 to both sides.)

$b = 24$ (Divide both sides by 8.)

EXAMPLE 10

The rectangle shown has a perimeter of 40 cm.

Find the value of x.

The perimeter of the rectangle is:

$3x + 1 + x + 3 + 3x + 1 + x + 3 = 40$

This simplifies to: $\qquad 8x + 8 = 40$

Subtract 8 from both sides: $\qquad 8x = 32$

Divide both sides by 8: $\qquad x = 4$

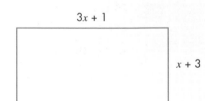

$3x + 1$

$x + 3$

EXERCISE 2C

Set up an equation to represent each situation described below. Then solve the equation. Remember to check each answer.

D

FM 1 A man buys a daily paper from Monday to Saturday for d pence. He buys a Sunday paper for £1.80. His weekly paper bill is £7.20.

What is the price of his daily paper?

2 The diagram shows a rectangle.

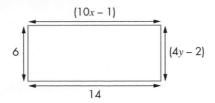

a What is the value of x?

b What is the value of y?

PS 3 In this rectangle, the length is 3 cm more than the width. The perimeter is 12 cm.

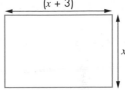

a What is the value of x?

b What is the area of the rectangle?

4 Mary has two bags, each of which contains the same number of sweets. She eats four sweets. She then finds that she has 30 sweets left. How many sweets were there in each bag to start with?

FM 5 A carpet costs £12.75 per square metre.

The shop charges £35 for fitting. The final bill was £137.

How many square metres of carpet were fitted?

FM 6 Moshin bought eight garden chairs. When he got to the till he used a £10 voucher as part payment. His final bill was £56.

a Set this problem up as an equation, using c as the cost of one chair.

b Solve the equation to find the cost of one chair.

FM 7 This diagram shows the traffic flow through a one-way system in a town centre.

Cars enter at A and at each junction the fractions show the proportion of cars that take each route.

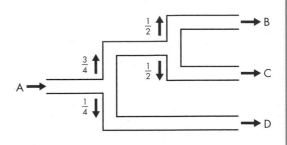

a 1200 cars enter at A. How many come out of each of the exits, B, C and D?

b If 300 cars exit at B, how many cars entered at A?

c If 500 cars exit at D, how many exit at B?

D

FM 8 A rectangular room is 3 m longer than it is wide.
The perimeter is 16 m.

Carpet costs £9.00 per square metre. How much will it
cost to carpet the room?

> **HINTS AND TIPS**
>
> Set up an equation to
> work out the length and
> width, then calculate
> the area.

C

PS 9 A boy is Y years old. His father is 25 years older than he is. The sum of their ages is 31.
How old is the boy?

PS 10 Another boy is X years old. His sister is twice as old as he is. The sum of their ages is 27.
How old is the boy?

11 The diagram shows a square.

Find x if the perimeter is 44 cm.

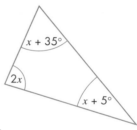

$(4x - 1)$

PS 12 Max thought of a number. He then multiplied his number by 3. He added 4 to the answer.
He then doubled that answer to get a final value of 38. What number did he start with?

13 The angles of a triangle are $2x$, $x + 5°$ and $x + 35°$.

a Write down an equation to show this.

b Solve your equation to find the value of x.

$x + 35°$

$2x$

$x + 5°$

FM 14 Five friends went for a meal in a restaurant. The bill was £x.
They decided to add a £10 tip and split the bill between them.

Each person paid £9.50.

a Set this problem up as an equation.

b Solve the equation to work out the bill before the tip was added.

AU 15 The diagram shows two number machines that
perform the same operations.

a Starting with an input value of 7, work through
the left-hand machine to get the output.

b Find an input value that gives the same value
for the output.

c Write down the algebraic expressions in the
right-hand machine for an input of n. (The first
operation has been filled in for you.)

d Set up an equation for the same input and
output and show each step in solving the
equation to get the answer in part b.

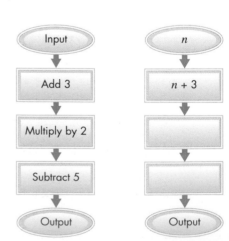

PS 16 A teacher asked her class to find three angles of a triangle that were consecutive even numbers.

Tammy wrote:
$$x + x + 2 + x + 4 = 180$$
$$3x + 6 = 180$$
$$3x = 174$$
$$x = 58$$

HINTS AND TIPS

Do the same type of working as Tammy did for a triangle. Work out the value of x. What happens?

So the angles are 58°, 60° and 62°.

The teacher then asked the class to find four angles of a quadrilateral that are consecutive even numbers.

Can this be done? Explain your answer.

FM 17 Mary has a large and a small bottle of cola. The large bottle holds 50 cl more than the small bottle.

From the large bottle she fills four cups and has 18 cl left over.

From the small bottle she fills three cups and has 1 cl left over.

How much cola does each bottle hold?

HINTS AND TIPS

Set up equations for both using x as the amount of pop in a cup. Put them equal but remember to add 50 to the small bottle equation to allow for the difference. Solve for x, then work out how much is in each bottle.

2.4 Trial and improvement

This topic will be assessed in Unit 3.

This section will show you how to:

- estimate the answers to some questions that do not have exact solutions, using the method of trial and improvement

Key words

comment
decimal place
guess
trial and improvement

Certain equations cannot be solved exactly. However, a close enough solution to such an equation can be found by the **trial-and-improvement** method. (Sometimes this is wrongly called the trial-and-error method.)

The idea is to keep trying different values in the equation to take it closer and closer to the 'true' solution. This step-by-step process is continued until a value is found that gives a solution that is close enough to the accuracy required.

The trial-and-improvement method is the way in which computers are programmed to solve equations.

EXAMPLE 11

Solve the equation $x^3 + x = 105$, giving the solution correct to 1 **decimal place**.

Step 1 You must find the two consecutive whole numbers between which x lies. You do this by intelligent guessing.

Try $x = 5$: $125 + 5 = 130$ Too high – next trial needs to be much smaller.
Try $x = 4$: $64 + 4 = 68$ Too low.

So now you know that the solution lies between $x = 4$ and $x = 5$.

Step 2 You must find the two consecutive 1-decimal-place numbers between which x lies. Try 4.5, which is halfway between 4 and 5.

This gives $91.125 + 4.5 = 95.625$ Too small.

Now attempt to improve this by trying 4.6.

This gives $97.336 + 4.6 = 101.936$ Still too small.
Try 4.7 which gives 108.523.   This is too high.
So the solution is between 4.6 and 4.7.

It looks as though 4.7 is closer but there is a very important final step.

Step 3 Now try the value that is halfway between the two 1-decimal-place values. In this case it is 4.65.

This gives 105.194 625.

This means that 4.6 is nearer the actual solution than 4.7.

Never assume that the one-decimal-place number that gives the closest value to the solution is the answer.

The diagram on the right shows why this is.

The approximate answer is $x = 4.6$ to 1 decimal place.

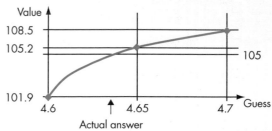

The best way to answer this type of question is to set up a table to show working. You will need three columns: **guess** (the trial), the equation to be solved and a **comment** – whether the value of the equation is too high or too low.

Guess	$x^3 + x$	Comment
4	68	Too low
5	130	Too high
4.5	95.625	Too low
4.6	101.936	Too low
4.7	108.523	Too high
4.65	105.194 625	Too high

EXERCISE 2D

1 Find the two consecutive *whole numbers* between which the solution to each of the following equations lies.

    a $x^2 + x = 24$ **b** $x^3 + 2x = 80$ **c** $x^3 - x = 20$

2 Copy and complete the table by using trial and improvement to find an approximate solution to:

    $x^3 + 2x = 50$

Give your answer correct to 1 decimal place.

Guess	$x^3 + 2x$	Comment
3	33	Too low
4	72	Too high

3 Copy and complete the table by using trial and improvement to find an approximate solution to:

    $x^3 - 3x = 40$

Give your answer correct to 1 decimal place.

Guess	$x^3 - 3x$	Comment
4	52	Too high

4 Use trial and improvement to find an approximate solution to:

    $2x^3 + x = 35$

Give your answer correct to 1 decimal place.

You are given that the solution lies between 2 and 3.

> **HINTS AND TIPS**
>
> Set up a table to show your working. This makes it easier for you to show method and the examiner to mark.

5 Use trial and improvement to find an exact solution to:

    $4x^2 + 2x = 12$

Do not use a calculator.

6 Find a solution to each of the following equations, correct to 1 decimal place.

    a $2x^3 + 3x = 35$ **b** $3x^3 - 4x = 52$ **c** $2x^3 + 5x = 79$

PS 7 A rectangle has an area of 100 cm^2. Its length is 5 cm longer than its width.

    a Show that, if x is the width, then $x^2 + 5x = 100$.

    b Find, correct to 1 decimal place, the dimensions of the rectangle.

8 Use trial and improvement to find a solution to the equation $x^2 + x = 40$.

> **HINTS AND TIPS**
>
> Call the length of the side with 'ratio 1' x, write down the other two sides in terms of x and then write down an equation for the volume = 500.

FM 9 Rob is designing a juice carton to hold $\frac{1}{2}$ litre (500 cm^3).

He wants the sides of the base in the ratio 1 : 2.

He wants the height to be 8 cm more than the shorter side of the base.

Use trial and improvement to find the dimensions of the carton.

AU 10 A cube of side x cm has a square hole of side $\frac{x}{2}$ and depth 8 cm cut from it.

The volume of the remaining solid is 1500 cm^3.

a Explain why $x^3 - 2x^2 = 1500$.

b Use trial and improvement to find the value of x to 1 decimal place.

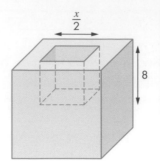

$\frac{x}{2}$

8

PS 11 Two numbers a and b are such that $ab = 20$ and $a + b = 10$.

Use trial and improvement to find the two numbers to 2 decimal places.

2.5 Solving simultaneous equations

This section will remind you how to:

- solve linear simultaneous equation in two variables

Key words

balance
check
coefficient
eliminate
simultaneous equations
substitute
variable

You will remember that these are the six steps in solving a pair of linear **simultaneous equations**.

Step 1: Balance the **coefficients** of one of the **variables**.

Step 2: Eliminate the variable by adding or subtracting the equations.

Step 3: Solve the resulting linear equation to find the value of one of the variables.

Step 4: Substitute this value into one of the original equations.

Step 5: Solve the resulting linear equation to find the value of the other variable.

Step 6: Check that the two values you have found work in both the original equations.

Work through these examples.

EXAMPLE 12

Solve the equations: $5x - y = 22$
$3x + y = 18$

Label the equations:
$$5x - y = 22 \quad (1)$$
$$3x + y = 18 \quad (2)$$

Step 1: As the coefficients of y are the same there is no need to balance the coefficients.

Step 2: Add the equations to eliminate y:

$(1) + (2)$ $\quad\quad\quad\quad\quad\quad\quad 8x = 40$

Step 3: Solve: $\quad\quad\quad\quad\quad\quad\quad\quad x = 5$

Step 4: Substitute into (2): $3 \times 5 + y = 18$

Step 5: Solve: $\quad\quad\quad\quad\quad\quad\quad\quad y = 3$

Step 6: Check: $\quad\quad\quad 5 \times 5 - 3 = 22$ and $3 \times 5 + 3 = 18$

EXAMPLE 13

In this example only one equation need be used to balance coefficients.

Solve the equations: $\quad 3x + y = 19 \quad (1)$
$\quad\quad\quad\quad\quad\quad\quad\quad 2x + 3y = 8 \quad (2)$

$(1) \times 3 \quad\quad\quad\quad\quad\quad 9x + 3y = 57 \quad (3)$

$(3) - (2) \quad\quad\quad\quad\quad\quad\quad 7x = 49$

$\quad\quad\quad\quad\quad\quad\quad\quad\quad\quad x = 7$

Substitute into (1): $\quad 3 \times 7 + y = 19$

Solve: $\quad\quad\quad\quad\quad\quad\quad\quad y = -2$

Check: $\quad\quad\quad 3 \times 7 - 2 = 19, \ 2 \times 7 - 3 \times 2 = 8$

EXAMPLE 14

In this example both equations need to be used to balance coefficients.

Solve the equations: $\quad 3x - 5y = 5 \quad\quad (1)$
$\quad\quad\quad\quad\quad\quad\quad\quad 5x - 3y = 15 \quad\quad (2)$

$(1) \times 5 \quad\quad\quad\quad 15x - 25y = 25 \quad\quad (3)$
$(2) \times 3 \quad\quad\quad\quad 15x - 9y = 45 \quad\quad (4)$

$(4) - (3) \quad\quad\quad\quad\quad\quad\quad 16y = 20$

$\quad\quad\quad\quad\quad\quad\quad\quad\quad\quad y = 1.25$

Substitute into (1): $\quad 3x - 6.25 = 5$

$\quad\quad\quad\quad\quad\quad\quad\quad\quad 3x = 11.25$

$\quad\quad\quad\quad\quad\quad\quad\quad\quad x = 3.75$

Check: $\quad\quad 3 \times 3.75 - 5 \times 1.25 = 5, \ 5 \times 3.75 - 3 \times 1.25 = 15$

EXERCISE 2E

Solve the following simultaneous equations.

1 $5x + 2y = 10$
   $7x - 2y = 20$

2 $3x + 5y = 22$
   $3x + 3y = 15$

3 $x + 4y = 11$
   $2x + 5y = 16$

4 $9x + 3y = 60$
   $3x + 2y = 19$

5 $3x - 2y = 19$
   $4x + y = 18$

6 $7x + 5y = 22$
   $3x - 2y = 26$

7 $3x - 4y = 18$
   $2x - 5y = 19$

8 $4x + 5y = 13$
   $3x + 2y = 8$

9 $3x + 2y = 4$
   $2x - 3y = 7$

10 $5x + 2y = 1$
   $3x + 3y = 6$

11 $3x - 7y = 29$
   $4x + 5y = 10$

12 $6x - 8y = 9$
   $x + y = 5$

13 $x - 5y = 15$
   $3x - 7y = 17$

14 $4x + 3y = 10$
   $5x - 2y = 24$

15 $5x - 3y = 10$
   $3x - y = 9$

2.6 Solving problems with simultaneous equations

This section will show you how to:
- solve problems, using simultaneous linear equations in two variables

Key words
balance
check
coefficient
eliminate
simultaneous equations
substitute
variable

You are now going to meet a type of problem that has to be expressed as a pair of simultaneous equations so that it can be solved. The next example shows you how to tackle such a problem.

EXAMPLE 15

On holiday last year, I was talking over breakfast to two families about how much it cost them to go to the theatre. They couldn't remember how much was charged for each adult or each child, but they could both remember what they had paid altogether.

The Advani family, consisting of Mr and Mrs Advani with their daughter Rupa, paid £23.

The Shaw family, consisting of Mrs Shaw with her two children, Len and Sue, paid £17.50.

How much would I have to pay for my wife, my four children and myself?

RECALL

Make a pair of simultaneous equations from the situation, as follows.

Let x be the cost of an adult ticket, and y be the cost of a child's ticket. Then

$2x + y = 23$ for the Advani family

and $x + 2y = 17.5$ for the Shaw family

Now solve these equations just as you have done in the previous examples, to obtain:

$x = £9.50$ and $y = £4$.

You can now find the cost, which will be $(2 \times £9.50) + (4 \times £4) = £35$.

EXERCISE 2F

Read each situation carefully, then make a pair of simultaneous equations in order to solve the problem.

PS 1 Amul and Kim have £10.70 between them. Amul has £3.70 more than Kim. Let x be the amount Amul has and y be the amount Kim has. Set up a pair of simultaneous equations. How much does each have?

FM 2 The two people in front of me at the Post Office were both buying stamps. One person bought 10 second-class and five first-class stamps at a total cost of £4.20. The other bought eight second-class and 10 first-class stamps at a total cost of £5.40.

    a Let x be the cost of a second-class stamp and y be the cost of a first-class stamp. Set up two simultaneous equations.

    b How much did I pay for three second-class and four first-class stamps?

3 At a local tea room I couldn't help noticing that at one table, where the customers had eaten six buns and had three teas, the bill came to £4.35. At another table, the customers had eaten 11 buns and had seven teas at a total cost of £8.80.

    a Let x be the cost of a bun and y be the cost of a cup of tea. Show the situation as a pair of simultaneous equations.

    b My family and I had five buns and six teas. What did it cost us?

PS 4 The sum of my son's age and my age this year is 72.

Six years ago my age was double that of my son.

Let my age now be x and my son's age now be y.

    a Explain why $x - 6 = 2(y - 6)$.   **b** Find the values of x and y.

5 In a tea shop, three teas and five buns cost £8.10

In the same tea shop three teas and three buns cost £6.30

    a Using t to represent the cost of a tea and b to represent the cost of a bun, set up the above information as a pair of simultaneous equations.

    b How much will I pay for four teas and six buns?

6 Three chews and four bubblies cost 72p. Five chews and two bubblies cost 64p. What would three chews and five bubblies cost?

FM 7 On a nut-and-bolt production line, all the nuts had the same mass and all the bolts, the same mass. An order of 50 nuts and 60 bolts had a mass of 10.6 kg. An order of 40 nuts and 30 bolts had a mass of 6.5 kg. What should the mass of an order of 60 nuts and 50 bolts be?

FM 8 My local taxi company charges a fixed amount plus so much per mile. When I took a six mile journey the cost was £3.70. When I took a 10 mile journey the cost was £5.10. My next journey is going to be eight miles. How much will this cost?

FM 9 Two members of the same church went to the same shop to buy material to make Christingles. One bought 200 oranges and 220 candles at a cost of £65.60. The other bought 210 oranges and 200 candles at a cost of £63.30. They only needed 200 of each. How much should it have cost them?

FM 10 When you book Bingham Hall for a conference you pay a fixed booking fee plus a charge for each delegate. AQA booked a conference for 65 delegates and was charged £192.50. OCR booked a conference for 40 delegates and was charged £180. EDEXCEL wants to book for 70 delegates. How much will they be charged?

FM 11 My mother-in-law uses this formula to cook a turkey:

$$T = a + bW$$

where T is the cooking time (minutes), W is the weight of the turkey (kg) and a and b are constants. She says it takes 4 hours 30 minutes to cook a 12 kg turkey, and 3 hours 10 minutes to cook an 8 kg turkey. How long will it take to cook a 5 kg turkey?

FM 12 Four sacks of potatoes and two sacks of carrots weigh 188 pounds.

Five sacks of potatoes and one sack of carrots weigh 202 pounds.

Baz buys seven sacks of potatoes and eight sacks of carrots.

Will he be able to carry them in his trailer, which has a safe working load of 450 pounds?

> **HINTS AND TIPS**
>
> Set up two simultaneous equations using p and c for the weight of a sack of potatoes and carrots respectively.

FM 13 Five bags of bark chipping and four trays of pansies cost £24.50.

Three bags of bark chippings and five trays of pansies cost £19.25.

Camilla wants six bags of bark chippings and eight trays of pansies.

She has £30. Will she have enough money?

> **HINTS AND TIPS**
>
> Set up a pair of simultaneous equations using b and p for the cost of bark chippings and pansies and solve them.

AU 14 A teacher asks her class to solve these two simultaneous equations.

$$y = x + 4 \qquad (1)$$
$$2y - x = 10 \qquad (2)$$

Carmen says to Jeff, "Let's save time, you work out the x-value and I'll work out the y-value." Jeff says, "Great idea."

This is Carmen's work.

$$y - x = 4 \quad (3)$$
$$2y - x = 10 \quad (2)$$
$$(2) - (3) \quad 3y = 6$$
$$y = 2$$

This is Jeff's work.

Substitute (1) into (2)

$$2(x + 4) - x = 10$$
$$2x + 8 - x = 10$$
$$3x = 18$$
$$x = 6$$

When the teacher reads out the answer as "two, six" the students mark their work correct.

Explain all the mistakes that Carmen and Jeff have made.

2.7 Solving quadratic equations

This section will show you how to:
● solve quadratic equations by factorisation

Key words
brackets
factorisation
quadratic expansion
solve

A quadratic equation is an equation of the form:

$$ax^2 + bx + c = 0$$

where a is a positive integer and b and c are integers.

Work through the following examples to recall the methods of **solving** quadratic equations.

Remember: to solve a quadratic equation by **factorisation**, set the **quadratic expansion** equal to zero, in two **brackets**, then **solve** each bracket.

EXAMPLE 16

Solve the following quadratic equations.

a $x^2 + 10x + 21 = 0$ **b** $x^2 - 2x - 24 = 0$

Recall that when the coefficient of x^2 is 1, there are a lot of clues you can use to find the factors.

Assume that the **factorisation** for $x^2 + px + q = 0$ is $(x + a)(x + b) = 0$

Clue 1: $a + b = p$ and $ab = q$

Clue 2: If the signs are $x^2 + px + q = 0$, the **brackets** will be $(x + a)(x + b) = 0$

Clue 3: If the signs are $x^2 - px + q = 0$, the brackets will be $(x - a)(x - b) = 0$

Clue 4: If the signs are $x^2 \pm px - q = 0$, the brackets will be $(x + a)(x - b) = 0$

EXAMPLE 16 (continued)

a
$$x^2 + 10x + 21 = 0$$
$$(x + 3)(x + 7) = 0$$
$$x + 3 = 0 \Rightarrow x = -3$$
$$x + 7 = 0 \Rightarrow x = -7$$
So the solution is $x = -3$ or $x = -7$

b
$$x^2 - 2x - 24 = 0$$
$$(x - 6)(x + 4) = 0$$
$$x - 6 = 0 \Rightarrow x = 6$$
$$x + 4 = 0 \Rightarrow x = -4$$
So the solution is $x = 6$ or $x = -4$

EXAMPLE 17

Solve the following quadratic equations.

a $3x^2 - 7x + 2 = 0$ **b** $6x^2 + 15x - 9 = 0$

When the coefficient of x^2 is greater than 1 then you have to consider all possible alternatives. The same rules on the signs apply as in Example 16.

a Split the x^2 term. This can only be $3x \times x$ so the brackets must be $(3x - a)(x - b)$.

Split the constant term. This can only be -1×-2.

This gives two possible alternatives: $(3x - 2)(x - 1) = 3x^2 - 5x + 2$

or: $(3x - 1)(x - 2) = 3x^2 - 7x + 2$

So $3x^2 - 7x + 2 = 0 \Rightarrow (3x - 1)(x - 2) = 0$

$$3x - 1 = 0 \Rightarrow x = \tfrac{1}{3}$$

$$x - 2 = 0 \Rightarrow x = 2$$

So the solution is $x = \tfrac{1}{3}$ or $x = 2$

b Split the x^2 term. There are two possibilities: $x \times 6x$ or $2x \times 3x$.

Split the constant term. There are two possibilities: 1×9 or 3×3.

This gives, with different signs, six alternatives.

Write a matrix like this:

x^2			Constant	
1	2		1	3
6	3		9	3

and work out which combination will give +15.

The combination that works is $+2 \times 9 + 3 \times -1$.

This gives the factorisation $(2x - 1)(3x + 9) = 6x^2 + 15x - 9$.

This method is cumbersome but with practice you can soon focus on the correct combination.

The important thing to remember is to expand your brackets to check they give the required quadratic expression.

$$6x^2 + 15x - 9 = 0 \Rightarrow (2x - 1)(3x + 9) = 0$$

$$2x - 1 = 0 \Rightarrow x = \tfrac{1}{2}$$

$$3x + 9 = 0 \Rightarrow x = -3$$

So the solution is $x = \tfrac{1}{2}$ or $x = -3$

Special cases

$b = 0$

When $b = 0$ in the quadratic equation we get $ax^2 + c = 0$.

Rearranging this equation gives $x = \pm \sqrt{\dfrac{-c}{a}}$.

This will only work if c is negative as it is not possible (at GCSE level) to find the square root of a negative number.

EXAMPLE 18

Solve the equations.

a $2x^2 - 7 = 0$ **b** $4x^2 - 9 = 0$

a $x^2 = \dfrac{7}{2}$ **b** $x = \pm \sqrt{\dfrac{9}{4}} = \pm \dfrac{3}{2}$

$x = \pm \sqrt{\dfrac{7}{2}}$

Difference of two squares

Part (b) of the last example is the difference of two squares.

Whenever an expression is of the form $a^2 - b^2$ it can be factorised into $(a + b)(a - b)$.

So, $4x^2 - 9 = (2x)^2 - 3^2 = (2x - 3)(2x + 3)$

EXAMPLE 19

Solve the equations.

a $4x^2 - 81 = 0$ **b** $2x^2 - 18 = 0$

a Recognise this as the difference of two squares.

$4x^2 - 81 = 0 \Rightarrow (2x - 9)(2x + 9) = 0$

$2x - 9 = 0 \Rightarrow x = 4\tfrac{1}{2}$

$2x + 9 = 0 \Rightarrow x = -4\tfrac{1}{2}$

So the solution is $x = 4\tfrac{1}{2}$ or $x = -4\tfrac{1}{2}$

b This is not the difference of two squares but if you divide all the terms by 2, the equations becomes $x^2 - 9 = 0$.

$x^2 - 9 = 0 \Rightarrow (x - 3)(x + 3) = 0$

$x - 3 = 0 \Rightarrow x = 3$

$x + 3 = 0 \Rightarrow x = -3$

So the solution is $x = 3$ or $x = -3$

$c = 0$

When $c = 0$ in the quadratic equation we get $ax^2 + bx = 0$.

This can be factorised as $x(ax + b) = 0$.

One solution will always be $x = 0$.

EXAMPLE 20

Solve the equations.

a $3x^2 - x = 0$ b $4x^2 + 6x = 0$

a $3x^2 - x = 0 \Rightarrow x(3x - 1) = 0$

    $3x - 1 = 0 \Rightarrow x = \frac{1}{3}$

   So the solution is $x = 0$ or $x = \frac{1}{3}$

b $4x^2 + 6x = 0 \Rightarrow 2x(2x + 3) = 0$

    $2x + 3 = 0 \Rightarrow x = \frac{3}{2}$

   So the solution is $x = 0$ or $x = \frac{3}{2}$

$(x + p)^2 = 0$

The quadratic expression $4x^2 - 4x + 1$ factorises to $(2x - 1)(2x - 1) = (2x - 1)^2$.

So the equation $4x^2 - 4x + 1 = 0$ becomes $(2x - 1)^2 = 0$.

There is only one solution: $x = \frac{1}{2}$

EXAMPLE 21

Solve the equations.

a $x^2 + 4x + 4 = 0$ b $9x^2 - 12x + 4 = 0$

a $x^2 + 4x + 4 = 0 \Rightarrow (x + 2)(x + 2) = 0$

    $(x + 2) = 0 \Rightarrow x = -2$

   So the solution is $x = -2$

b $9x^2 - 12x + 4 = 0 \Rightarrow (3x - 2)^2 = 0$

    $3x - 2 = 0 \Rightarrow x = \frac{2}{3}$

   So the solution is $x = \frac{2}{3}$

EXERCISE 2G

Solve the quadratic equations in questions **1** to **20**.

1 $x^2 + 5x + 4 = 0$ **2** $x^2 + 5x - 24 = 0$ **3** $x^2 - 5x - 6 = 0$

4 $x^2 - 13x - 30 = 0$ **5** $x^2 - 7x + 10 = 0$ **6** $x^2 - 9 = 0$

7 $2x^2 - 5 = 0$ **8** $4x^2 - 100 = 0$ **9** $27x^2 - 12 = 0$

10 $x^2 - 5x = 0$ **11** $3x^2 + 7x = 0$ **12** $12x^2 - 5x - 2 = 0$

13 $5x^2 - 11x + 2 = 0$ **14** $x^2 + 6x + 9 = 0$ **15** $6x^2 + 10x - 4 = 0$

RECALL

16 $4x^2 + 20x + 25 = 0$ **17** $3x^2 - 16x + 16 = 0$ **18** $6x^2 + 13x - 5 = 0$

19 $4x^2 + 4x - 3 = 0$ **20** $12x^2 + 13x - 4 = 0$

AU 21 **a** Find the **quadratic** equation for which the solution is $x = 1$.

b Find the **quadratic** equation for which the solutions are $x = \pm \dfrac{3}{2}$.

PS 22 Find the coordinates of the minimum point on the graph of the quadratic equation that cuts the x-axis at $x = 0$ and $x = -3$.

2.8 The quadratic formula

This topic will be assessed in Unit 3.

This section will show you how to:
- solve a quadratic equation by using the quadratic formula

Key words
coefficient
constant term
quadratic formula
soluble
solve

Many quadratic equations cannot be solved by factorisation because they do not have simple factors. Try to factorise, for example, $x^2 - 4x - 3 = 0$ or $3x^2 - 6x + 2 = 0$. You will find it is impossible.

One way to **solve** this type of equation is to use the **quadratic formula**. This formula can be used to solve *any* quadratic equation that is **soluble**. (Some are not, which the quadratic formula would immediately show.)

The solution of the equation $ax^2 + bx + c = 0$ is given by:

$$x = \frac{-b \pm \sqrt{b^2 - 4ac}}{2a}$$

where a and b are the **coefficients** of x^2 and x respectively and c is the **constant** term.

This is the quadratic formula. It is given on the formula sheet of GCSE examinations but it is best to learn it.

The symbol $\pm$ states that the square root has a positive and a negative value, *both* of which must be used in solving for x.

EXAMPLE 22

Solve $5x^2 - 11x - 4 = 0$, giving solutions correct to 2 decimal places.

Take the quadratic formula:

$$x = \frac{-b \pm \sqrt{b^2 - 4ac}}{2a}$$

and put $a = 5$, $b = -11$ and $c = -4$, which gives:

$$x = \frac{(-11) \pm \sqrt{(-11)^2 - 4(5)(-4)}}{2(5)}$$

Note that the values for a, b and c have been put into the formula in brackets. This is to avoid mistakes in calculation. It is a very common mistake to get the sign of b wrong or to think that -11^2 is -121. Using brackets will help you do the calculation correctly.

$$x = \frac{11 \pm \sqrt{121 + 80}}{10} = \frac{11 \pm \sqrt{201}}{10}$$

$$\Rightarrow x = 2.52 \text{ or } -0.32$$

Note: The calculation has been done in stages. With a calculator it is possible just to work out the answer, but make sure you can use your calculator properly. If not, break the calculation down. Remember the rule 'if you try to do two things at once, you will probably get one of them wrong'.

Examination tip: If you are asked to solve a quadratic equation to one or two decimal places, you can be sure that it can be solved only by the quadratic formula.

EXERCISE 2H

Use the quadratic formula to solve the equations in questions **1** to **15**. Give your answers to 2 decimal places.

HINTS AND TIPS

Use brackets when substituting and do not try to work two things out at the same time.

1 $2x^2 + x - 8 = 0$

2 $3x^2 + 5x + 1 = 0$

3 $x^2 - x - 10 = 0$

4 $5x^2 + 2x - 1 = 0$

5 $7x^2 + 12x + 2 = 0$

6 $3x^2 + 11x + 9 = 0$

7 $4x^2 + 9x + 3 = 0$

8 $6x^2 + 22x + 19 = 0$

9 $x^2 + 3x - 6 = 0$

10 $3x^2 - 7x + 1 = 0$

11 $2x^2 + 11x + 4 = 0$

12 $4x^2 + 5x - 3 = 0$

13 $4x^2 - 9x + 4 = 0$

14 $7x^2 + 3x - 2 = 0$

15 $5x^2 - 10x + 1 = 0$

FM 16 A rectangular lawn is 2 m longer than it is wide.

The area of the lawn is 21 m^2. The gardener wants to edge the lawn with edging strips, which are sold in lengths of $1\frac{1}{2}$ m. How many will she need to buy?

AU **17** Shaun is solving a quadratic equation, using the formula.

He correctly substitutes values for a, b and c to get:

$$x = \frac{3 \pm \sqrt{37}}{2}$$

What is the equation Shaun is trying to solve?

PS **18** Terry uses the quadratic formula to solve $4x^2 - 4x + 1 = 0$.

June uses factorisation to solve $4x^2 - 4x + 1 = 0$.

They both find something unusual in their solutions.

Explain what this is, and why.

2.9 ## Solving problems with quadratic equations

This topic will be assessed in Unit 3.

This section will show you how to:
- recognise why some quadratic equations cannot be factorised
- solve practical problems, using quadratic equations

Key words
discriminant

Quadratic equations with no solution

The quantity $(b^2 - 4ac)$ in the quadratic formula is known as the **discriminant**.

When $b^2 > 4ac$, $(b^2 - 4ac)$ is positive. This has been the case in almost all of the quadratics you have solved so far and it means there are two solutions.

When $b^2 = 4ac$, $(b^2 - 4ac)$ is zero. This has been the case in some of the quadratics you have solved so far. It means there is only one solution (the repeated root).

When $b^2 < 4ac$, $(b^2 - 4ac)$ is negative. So you need to find the square root of a negative number.

Such a square root cannot be found (at GCSE level) and therefore there are no solutions. You will not be asked about this in examinations but if it happens then you will have made a mistake and should check your working.

EXAMPLE 23

Find the discriminant $b^2 - 4ac$ of the equation $x^2 + 3x + 5 = 0$ and explain what the result tells you.

$$b^2 - 4ac = (3)^2 - 4(1)(5) = 9 - 20 = -11.$$

This means there are no solutions for x.

You will meet quadratic graphs in Chapter 11. All quadratic equations can be shown as graphs that have a characteristic shape known as a parabola.

Here are the graphs of the three types of quadratic equations: one with two solutions ($b^2 - 4ac > 0$), one with one solution ($b^2 - 4ac = 0$) and one with no solutions ($b^2 - 4ac < 0$).

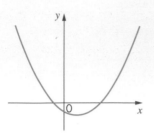 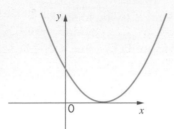 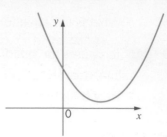

$b^2 - 4ac > 0$ two solutions, crosses the x-axis twice

$b^2 - 4ac = 0$ one solution, just touches the x-axis

$b^2 - 4ac < 0$ no solution, does not cross the x-axis

EXERCISE 2I

Work out the discriminant $b^2 - 4ac$ of the equations in questions **1** to **12**. In each case say how many solutions the equation has.

1 $3x^2 + 2x - 4 = 0$ **2** $2x^2 - 7x - 2 = 0$ **3** $5x^2 - 8x + 2 = 0$

4 $3x^2 + x - 7 = 0$ **5** $16x^2 - 23x + 6 = 0$ **6** $x^2 - 2x - 16 = 0$

7 $5x^2 + 5x + 3 = 0$ **8** $4x^2 + 3x + 2 = 0$ **9** $5x^2 - x - 2 = 0$

10 $x^2 + 6x - 1 = 0$ **11** $17x^2 - x + 2 = 0$ **12** $x^2 + 5x - 3 = 0$

PS 13 Bill works out the discriminant of the quadratic equation $x^2 + bx - c = 0$ as $b^2 - 4ac = 13$.

There are four possible equations that could lead to this discriminant. What are they?

Problems solved by quadratic equations

You are likely to have to solve a problem which involves generating a quadratic equation and finding its solution.

EXAMPLE 24

Find the sides of the right-angled triangle shown in the diagram.

The sides of a right-angled triangle are connected by Pythagoras' theorem, which says that $c^2 = a^2 + b^2$.

$$(x + 5)^2 + (x - 2)^2 = 13^2$$
$$(x^2 + 10x + 25) + (x^2 - 4x + 4) = 169$$
$$2x^2 + 6x + 29 = 169$$
$$2x^2 + 6x - 140 = 0$$

Divide by a factor of 2: $\quad x^2 + 3x - 70 = 0$

This factorises to: $\quad (x + 10)(x - 7) = 0$

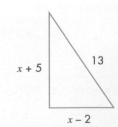

This gives $x = -10$ or 7.

Reject the negative value as it would give negative lengths.

Hence the sides of the triangle are 5, 12 and 13.

Note: You may know the Pythagorean triple 5, 12, 13 and guessed the answer but you would be expected to show working. Most 'real-life' problems will end up with a quadratic that factorises, as the questions are complicated enough without expecting you to use the quadratic formula.

EXAMPLE 25

Solve this equation. $\qquad\qquad\qquad 2x - \dfrac{3}{x} = 5$

Multiply through by x to give: $\qquad\quad 2x^2 - 3 = 5x$

Rearrange into the general form: $\quad 2x^2 - 5x - 3 = 0$

This factorises to: $\qquad\qquad\quad (2x + 1)(x - 3) = 0$

So $x = -\dfrac{1}{2}$ or $x = 3$.

EXAMPLE 26

A coach driver undertook a journey of 300 km. Her actual average speed turned out to be 10 km/h less than expected. Therefore, she took 1 hour longer over the journey than expected. Find her actual average speed.

Let the driver's actual average speed be x km/h.

So the estimated speed would have been $(x + 10)$ km/h.

Time taken $= \dfrac{\text{distance travelled}}{\text{speed}}$

At x km/h, she did the journey in $\dfrac{300}{x}$ hours.

At $(x + 10)$ km/h, she would have done the journey in $\dfrac{300}{x + 10}$ hours.

Since the journey took 1 hour longer than expected, then:

time taken $= \dfrac{300}{x + 10} + 1 = \dfrac{300 + x + 10}{x + 10} = \dfrac{300 + x}{x + 10}$

So $= \dfrac{300}{x} = \dfrac{310 + x}{x + 10} \Rightarrow 300(x + 10) = x(310 + x) \Rightarrow 300x + 3000 = 310x + x^2$

Rearranging into the general form gives: $x^2 + 10x - 3000 = 0$

This factorises into: $\qquad\qquad\qquad (x + 60)(x - 50) = 0 \Rightarrow x = -60$ or 50

The coach's average speed could not be -60 km/h, so it has to be 50 km/h.

EXERCISE 2J

PS 1 The length of a rectangle is 5 m more than its width. Its area is 300 m². Find the dimensions of the rectangle.

FM 2 The average mass of a group of people is 45.2 kg. A newcomer to the group weighs 51 kg, which increases the average mass by 0.2 kg. How many people are now in the group?

3 Solve the equation $x + \dfrac{3}{x} = 7$. Give your answers correct to 2 decimal places.

4 Solve the equation $2x + \dfrac{5}{x} = 11$.

PS 5 A tennis court has an area of 224 m². If the length were decreased by 1 m and the width increased by 1 m, the area would be increased by 1 m². Find the dimensions of the court.

PS 6 On a journey of 400 km, the driver of a train calculates that if he were to increase his average speed by 2 km/h, he would take 20 minutes less. Find his average speed.

PS 7 The difference of the squares of two positive numbers, whose difference is 2, is 184. Find these two numbers.

PS 8 The length of a carpet is 1 m more than its width. Its area is 9 m². Find the dimensions of the carpet to 2 decimal places.

FM 9 Helen worked out that she could save 30 minutes on a 45 km journey if she kept her average speed 15 km faster than the speed at which she had planned to travel. Find the speed at which Helen had originally planned to travel.

FM 10 Claire intended to spend £3.20 on balloons for her party. But each balloon cost her 2p more than she expected, so she had to buy eight fewer balloons. Find the cost of each balloon.

PS 11 The sum of a number and its reciprocal is 2.05. What are the two numbers?

FM 12 A woman buys goods for £60x and sells them for £(600 − 6x) at a loss of x%. Find x.

FM 13 A train has a scheduled time for its journey. If the train averages 50 km/h, it arrives 12 minutes early. If the train averages 45 km/h, it arrives 20 minutes late. Find how long the train should take for the journey.

14 A rectangular garden measures 15 m by 11 m and is surrounded by a path of uniform width of area 41.25 m². Find the width of the path.

15 A rectangular room is 3 m longer than it is wide.

It cost £364 to carpet the room. Carpet costs £16 per square metre.

How wide is the room?

> **HINTS AND TIPS**
>
> Calculate the area and set up a quadratic equation to work out the width.

GRADE BOOSTER

D You can manipulate algebraic expressions

C You can set up and solve linear equations from practical and real-life situations

C You can solve non-linear equations, using trial and improvement

B You can solve a pair of linear simultaneous equations

A You can solve the general quadratic equation by factorisation

A You can solve a quadratic equation, using the quadratic formula

A You can set up a real-life problem and solve it, using simultaneous equations

A* You can set up a real-life problem and solve it, using quadratic equations

What you should know now

- How to solve a variety of linear equations, using rearrangements or 'doing the same thing to both sides'
- How to solve equations by trial and improvement
- How to set up and solve problems, using linear equations
- How to set up and solve problems, using simultaneous equations
- How to set up and solve problems, using quadratic equations

1 A quadrilateral has one right angle.

The other angles are $2x$, $3x - 12$ and $x - 6$

Not drawn accurately

a Write down an equation in terms of x.

(1 mark)

b Solve your equation and find the size of the largest angle in the quadrilateral. *(3 marks)*

AQA, June 2007, Paper 1, Question 3(b)

2 The sketch shows the graph of $y = x^3 - 3x - 8$

The graph passes through the points $(2, -6)$ and $(3, 10)$

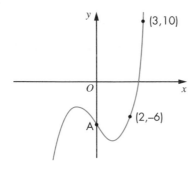

a The graph crosses the y-axis at the point A.

Write down the coordinates of the point A.

(1 mark)

b Use trial and improvement to find the solution of

$$x^3 - 3x - 8 = 0$$

Give your answer to 1 decimal place.

(4 marks)

AQA, November 2008, Paper 2, Question 13

3 ABC is an isosceles triangle.

The lengths, in cm, of the sides are

$AB = 4a + 3$, $BC = 2b + 5$ and $AC = 2a + b$

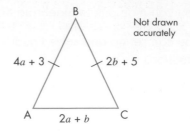

Not drawn accurately

a AB = BC

Show that $2a - b = 1$ *(2 marks)*

b The perimeter of the triangle is 32 cm.

Find the values of a and b. *(4 marks)*

AQA, November 2005, Paper 2, Question 14

4 In this 'magic' triangle each side has a total of 24

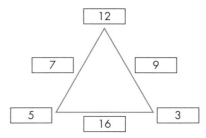

Here is another 'magic' triangle in which the sum of the three expressions on each of the three sides is the same.

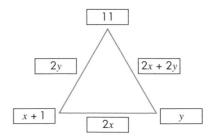

a By considering the left hand side and the right hand side, show that $x + y = 1$

(2 marks)

b By considering the left hand side and the bottom of the triangle, show that

$2x - y = 11$ *(2 marks)*

A* A B C

c Solve the simultaneous equations

$$x + y = 1$$
$$2x - y = 11 \qquad \text{(2 marks)}$$

You **must** show your working.

d Complete the 'magic' triangle. *(1 mark)*

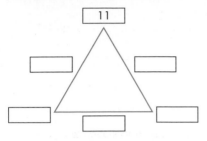

AQA, November 2008, Paper 1, Question 16

5 Solve the equation $2x^2 + 3x - 7 = 0$

Give your answers correct to 2 decimal places.

You **must** show your working. *(3 marks)*

AQA, June 2008, Paper 2, Question 20

6 Solve the equation $x^2 - 2x - 6 = 0$

Give your answer to two decimal places.

(3 marks)

AQA, June 2009, Paper 2, Question 26

7 The diagram shows a garden in the shape of a rectangle measuring 10 m by 8 m.

On two sides of the garden there is a path x metres wide.

The remaining area is covered by grass.

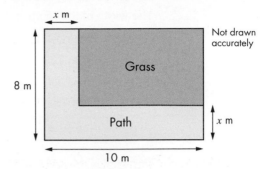

a The area covered by grass is $\frac{3}{5}$ of the area of the garden.

Show that x satisfies the equation

$$x^2 - 18x + 32 = 0 \qquad \text{(3 marks)}$$

b Hence, or otherwise, find the width of the path. *(2 marks)*

AQA, November 2008, Paper 1, Question 20

Worked Examination Questions

FM **1** The area of a rectangular room is 24 m².

The height of the room is 2.4 m

The length of the room is x metres.

The width of the room is 2 m shorter than the length.

    a Show that $x^2 - 2x - 24 = 0$

    b The two long walls and one of the short walls are to be wallpapered.

      A roll of wallpaper is 12 m long and 80 cm wide.

      How many rolls of paper will be needed?

1 **a** $x(x - 2) = 24$

    $x^2 - 2x - 24 = 0$

> Set up an equation using the area and rearrange into a standard quadratic. This gets 1 mark.

  b $(x - 6)(x + 4) = 0$

    $x = 6$ (ignore -4)

> Solve the equation to find x. This gets 1 mark for method and 1 mark for accuracy.

    Total length that needs to be wallpapered = 16 m

    So number of strips = $16 \div 0.8 = 20$

> Work out how much wall needs to be wallpapered. This gets 1 mark for method. Work out how many strips are needed.

    Number of strips in a roll $12 \div 2.4 = 5$

    So number of rolls = $20 \div 5 = 4$ rolls.

> Work out how many strips there are per roll and how many rolls will be needed. This gets 1 mark for method and 1 mark for accuracy.

Total: 6 marks

AU **2** **a** Show that $(a + b)(a - b) \equiv a^2 - b^2$

    b Hence simplify $(3x + 1)^2 - (2x - 1)^2$

2 **a** $(a + b)(a - b) = a^2 + ab - ab - b^2 = a^2 - b^2$

> This is just a lead in to part **b**. Make sure you show all four terms and show that two of them cancel out. This gets 1 mark.

  b Using the identity from part **a**:

    $(3x + 1)^2 - (2x - 1)^2 = (3x + 1 + 2x - 1) \times (3x + 1 - (2x - 1))$

> As this is an identity it is true for all values whether numerical or algebraic so substitute the brackets for **a** and **b**. This gets 1 mark for method.

                  $= 5x(x + 2)$

                  $= 5x^2 + 10x$

> Expand and simplify the brackets. This gets 1 mark for method and 1 mark for accuracy. This is easier than expanding both squared brackets and collecting terms.

Total: 4 marks

Worked Examination Questions

PS **3** The sketch shows four quadratic graphs.

Here are four quadratic equations.

P: $x^2 + 2x + 1 = 0$

Q: $-x^2 + x - 12 = 0$

R: $x^2 + 2x + 6 = 0$

S: $x^2 + 7x + 12 = 0$

Match the graph to the equations.

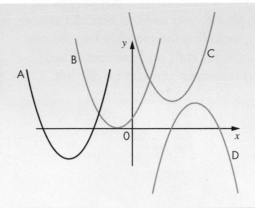

3 Graph D matches equation Q.

> Start with the obvious one.
> This gets 1 mark.

Graph B matches equation P.

> P factorises to $(x + 1)^2 = 0$ so only has one solution.
> This gets 1 mark.

Graph A matches equation S.

> S factorises to $(x + 3)(x + 4) = 0$ which has solutions −3 or −4.
> This gets 1 mark.

Graph C matches equation R.

> This is the only pair left but the equation does not factorise, and if you try to solve by using the quadratic formula, you end up with the root of a negative number. So there are no solutions.

(**Total:** 3 marks)

When you are choosing a pay-as-you-go mobile phone, you need to consider many factors, including the monthly fee, the cost per minute for calls and the cost of texts. Making a comparison can be difficult.

Getting started

Look at the three plans for pay-as-you-go mobile phones.

Plan 1

Monthly rental	Voice calls per minute	Cost of texts
£5.00	15p	6p

Plan 2

Monthly rental	Voice calls per minute	Cost of texts
£8.00	11p	8p

Plan 3

Monthly rental	Voice calls per minute	Cost of texts
£10.00	7p	10p

For each plan, write down an algebraic expression for the cost of the plan for voice calls only (no texts), where x is the number of minutes of calls and y is the total cost.

Your task

1 Compare the three mobile phone plans.

- Find the number of minutes of voice calls after which each plan becomes cheaper.

   Hint: Think about these questions.

   – After how many minutes does plan 2 become cheaper than plan 1?

   – After how many minutes does plan 3 become cheaper than plan 2?

   – After how many minutes does plan 3 become cheaper than plan 1?

- Decide which plan you would choose if you made 3 hours of voice calls per month and sent no texts.

- Write down an algebraic expression for the cost of the plan for 3 hours of voice calls and x texts, where y is the total cost.

- Work out the number of texts after which each plan becomes cheaper.

Using this information, decide which plan you would choose if you made 3 hours of voice calls per month and sent 250 texts.

Top up £10 each month and get unlimited FREE texts for life.

Samsung
Tocco Lite
£88.08

Nokia
6303
£97.87

October offers from T-Mobile

Your task (continued)

2 Ask a few friends or relatives how many minutes of voice calls they make and how many texts they send per month.

Which of these plans would be best value for them? Write a short report for each of them, so that they can understand how you reached your conclusions.

We use proportion and speed as part of our everyday lives to help when dealing with facts or to compare two or more pieces of information.

Proportions are often used to compare sizes, speed is used to compare distances with the time taken to travel them.

Speed

What do you think of as a high speed?

On 16 August 2009 Usain Bolt set a new world record for the 100 m sprint of 9.58 seconds. This is an average speed of 23.3 mph.

The sailfish is the fastest fish and can swim at 68 mph.

The cheetah is the fastest land animal and can run at 75 mph.

The fastest bird is the swift, which can fly at 106 mph.

Ratio and proportion facts

- Russia is the largest country. Vatican City is the smallest country. The area of Russia is nearly 39 million times bigger than the area of Vatican City.
- Monaco has the most people per square mile. Mongolia has the least people per square mile. The ratio of the number of people per square mile in Monaco to the number of people in Mongolia is 10 800 : 1.
- Japan has the highest life expectancy. Sierra Leone has the lowest life expectancy. On average, people in Japan live over twice as long as people in Sierra Leone.
- Taiwan has the most mobile phones per 100 people (106.5). This is approximately four times more than in Thailand (26.04).
- About one-seventh of England is green-belt land.

This chapter is about comparing pieces of information. You can compare the speeds of Usain Bolt, the sailfish, the cheetah and the swift by answering questions such as: How much faster is a sailfish than Usain Bolt?

Number: Proportions

This chapter will show you ...

D how to solve problems involving direct proportion

D how to compare prices of products

to **D** **C** how to calculate speed

B how to calculate density

Visual overview

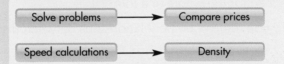

Solve problems → Compare prices

Speed calculations → Density

What you should already know

- Multiplication tables up to 10 × 10 (**KS3 level 4, GCSE grade G**)
- How to simplify fractions (**KS3 level 5, GCSE grade G**)
- How to find a fraction of a quantity (**KS3 level 4, GCSE grade F**)
- How to multiply and divide, with and without a calculator (**KS3 level 5, GCSE grade G**)

Quick check

1 Cancel the following fractions.

a $\frac{6}{10}$ **b** $\frac{4}{20}$ **c** $\frac{4}{12}$ **d** $\frac{32}{50}$ **e** $\frac{36}{90}$ **f** $\frac{18}{24}$ **g** $\frac{16}{48}$

2 Find the following quantities.

a $\frac{2}{5}$ of £30 **b** $\frac{3}{8}$ of £88 **c** $\frac{7}{10}$ of 250 litres **d** $\frac{5}{8}$ of 24 kg

e $\frac{2}{3}$ of 60 m **f** $\frac{5}{6}$ of £42 **g** $\frac{9}{20}$ of 300 g **h** $\frac{3}{10}$ of 3.5 litres

This section will show you how to:
- recognise the relationship between speed, distance and time
- calculate average speed from distance and time
- calculate distance travelled from the speed and the time
- calculate the time taken on a journey from the speed and the distance

Key words

average
distance
speed
time

The relationship between **speed**, **time** and **distance** can be expressed in three ways:

$$speed = \frac{distance}{time} \qquad distance = speed \times time \qquad time = \frac{distance}{speed}$$

In problems relating to speed, you usually mean **average** speed, as it would be unusual to maintain one exact speed for the whole of a journey.

The diagram will help you remember the relationships between distance (D), time (T) and speed (S).

$$D = S \times T \qquad S = \frac{D}{T} \qquad T = \frac{D}{S}$$

EXAMPLE 1

Paula drove a distance of 270 miles in 5 hours. What was her average speed?

Paula's average speed = $\frac{distance\ she\ drove}{time\ she\ took} = \frac{270}{5} = 54$ miles per hour (mph)

EXAMPLE 2

Edith drove from Sheffield to Peebles for $3\frac{1}{2}$ hours at an average speed of 60 mph. How far is it from Sheffield to Peebles?

Since: *distance = speed × time*

the distance from Sheffield to Peebles is given by

60 × 3.5 = 210 miles

Note: You need to change the time to a decimal number and use 3.5 (not 3.30).

EXAMPLE 3

Sean is going to drive from Newcastle upon Tyne to Nottingham, a distance of 190 miles. He estimates that he will drive at an average speed of 50 mph. How long will it take him?

$$\text{Sean's time} = \frac{\text{distance he covers}}{\text{his average speed}} = \frac{190}{50} = 3.8 \text{ hours}$$

Change the 0.8 hour to minutes by multiplying by 60, to give 48 minutes.

So, the time for Sean's journey will be 3 hours 48 minutes.

Remember: When you calculate a time and get a decimal answer, as in Example 3, *do not mistake* the decimal part for minutes. You must either:

● leave the time as a decimal number and give the unit as hours, or

● change the decimal part to minutes by multiplying it by 60 (1 hour = 60 minutes) and give the answer in hours and minutes.

EXERCISE 3A

1 A cyclist travels a distance of 90 miles in 5 hours. What was her average speed?

HINTS AND TIPS

Remember to convert time to a decimal if you are using a calculator, for example, 8 hours 30 minutes is 8.5 hours.

2 How far along a motorway would you travel if you drove at 70 mph for 4 hours?

3 I drive to Bude in Cornwall from Sheffield in about 6 hours. The distance from Sheffield to Bude is 315 miles. What is my average speed?

4 The distance from Leeds to London is 210 miles. The train travels at an average speed of 90 mph. If I catch the 9.30 am train in London, at what time should I expect to arrive in Leeds?

5 How long will an athlete take to run 2000 m at an average speed of 4 metres per second?

6 Copy and complete the following table.

	Distance travelled	Time taken	Average speed
a	150 miles	2 hours	
b	260 miles		40 mph
c		5 hours	35 mph
d		3 hours	80 km/h
e	544 km	8 hours 30 minutes	
f		3 hours 15 minutes	100 km/h
g	215 km		50 km/h

D

7 Eliot drove from Sheffield to Inverness, a distance of 410 miles, in 7 hours 45 minutes.

   a Change the time 7 hours 45 minutes to a decimal.

   b What was the average speed of the journey? Round your answer to 1 decimal place.

8 Colin drives home from his son's house in 2 hours 15 minutes. He says that he drives at an average speed of 44 mph.

   a Change the 2 hours 15 minutes to a decimal.

   b How far is it from Colin's home to his son's house?

9 The distance between Paris and Le Mans is 200 km. The express train between Paris and Le Mans travels at an average speed of 160 km/h.

   a Calculate the time taken for the journey from Paris to Le Mans, giving your answer as a decimal number of hours.

   b Change your answer to part a to hours and minutes.

C

FM 10 The distance between Sheffield and Land's End is 420 miles.

   a What is the average speed of a journey from Sheffield to Land's End that takes 8 hours 45 minutes?

   b If Sam covered the distance at an average speed of 63 mph, how long would it take him?

FM 11 A train travels at 50 km/h for 2 hours, then slows down to do the last 30 minutes of its journey at 40 km/h.

   a What is the total distance of this journey?

   b What is the average speed of the train over the whole journey?

FM 12 Jade runs and walks the 3 miles from home to work each day. She runs the first 2 miles at a speed of 8 mph, then walks the next mile at a steady 4 mph.

   a How long does it take Jade to get to work?

   b What is her average speed?

13 Change the following speeds to metres per second.

   a 36 km/h   **b** 12 km/h   **c** 60 km/h

   d 150 km/h   **e** 75 km/h

14 Change the following speeds to kilometres per hour.

   a 25 m/s **b** 12 m/s **c** 4 m/s **d** 30 m/s **e** 0.5 m/s

AU 15 A train travels at an average speed of 18 m/s.

   a Express its average speed in km/h.

   b Find the approximate time the train would take to travel 500 m.

   c The train set off at 7.30 on a 40 km journey. At approximately what time will it reach its destination?

HINTS AND TIPS

Remember that there are 3600 seconds in an hour and 1000 metres in a kilometre. So to change from km/h to m/s multiply by 1000 and divide by 3600.

HINTS AND TIPS

To change from m/s to km/h multiply by 3600 and divide by 1000.

16 A cyclist is travelling at an average speed of 24 km/h.

    a What is this speed in metres per second?

    b What distance does he travel in 2 hours 45 minutes?

    c How long does it take him to travel 2 km?

    d How far does he travel in 20 seconds?

> **HINTS AND TIPS**
>
> To convert a decimal fraction of an hour to minutes, just multiply by 60.

PS **17** How much longer does it take to travel 100 miles at 65 mph than at 70 mph?

18 It takes me 20 minutes to walk from home to the bus station.

I catch the bus from the bus station to work each morning. My bus journey is 10 miles and usually takes 30 minutes. I can catch a bus at 20 minutes past the hour or 10 minutes to the hour. When I get off the bus it takes me 5 minutes to walk to work.

FM   **a** What is the average speed of my bus?

PS   **b** I have to be at work for 08.30. What time is the latest I can leave home to be at work on time?

3.2 Direct proportion problems

This section will show you how to:
- recognise and solve problems, using direct proportion

Key words
direct proportion
unitary method
unit cost

Suppose you buy 12 items that each cost the same. The total amount you spend is 12 times the cost of one item.

That is, the total cost is said to be in **direct proportion** to the number of items bought. The cost of a single item (the **unit cost**) is the constant factor that links the two quantities.

Direct proportion is not only concerned with costs. Any two related quantities can be in direct proportion to each other.

The best way to solve all problems involving direct proportion is to start by finding the single unit value. This method is called the **unitary method**, because it involves referring to a single *unit* value.

Remember: Before solving a direct proportion problem, think carefully about it to make sure that you know how to find the required single unit value.

EXAMPLE 4

If eight pens cost £2.64, what is the cost of five pens?

First, we need to find the cost of one pen. This is £2.64 ÷ 8 = £0.33

So, the cost of five pens is £0.33 × 5 = £1.65

EXAMPLE 5

Eight loaves of bread will make packed lunches for 18 people. How many packed lunches can be made from 20 loaves?

First, find how many lunches one loaf will make.

One loaf will make 18 ÷ 8 = 2.25 lunches

So, 20 loaves will make 2.25 × 20 = 45 lunches

EXERCISE 3B

1 If 30 matches weigh 45 g, what would 40 matches weigh?

2 Five bars of chocolate cost £2.90. Find the cost of nine bars.

3 Eight men can chop down 18 trees in a day. How many trees can 20 men chop down in a day?

4 Find the cost of 48 eggs when 15 eggs can be bought for £2.10.

5 Seventy maths textbooks cost £875.

   a How much will 25 maths textbooks cost?

   b How many maths textbooks can you buy for £100?

HINTS AND TIPS

Remember to work out the value of one unit each time. Always check that answers are sensible.

FM 6 A lorry uses 80 litres of diesel fuel on a trip of 280 miles.

   a How much diesel would the same lorry use on a trip of 196 miles?

   b How far would the lorry travel on a full tank (100 litres) of diesel?

FM 7 During the winter, I find that 200 kg of coal keeps my open fire burning for 12 weeks.

   a If I want an open fire all through the winter (18 weeks), how much coal will I need?

   b Last year I bought 150 kg of coal. For how many weeks did I have an open fire?

8 It takes a photocopier 16 seconds to produce 12 copies of a document. How long will it take to produce 30 copies?

9 A recipe for 12 biscuits uses:

200 g margarine   400 g sugar   500 g flour   300 g ground rice

a What quantities are needed for:

i 6 biscuits

ii 9 biscuits

iii 15 biscuits?

PS   b What is the maximum number of biscuits I could make if I had just 1 kg of each ingredient?

AU 10 Peter the butcher sells sausages in packs of 6 for £2.30.

Paul the butcher sells sausages in packs of 10 for £3.50.

I have £10 to spend on sausages. If I want to buy as many sausages as possible from one shop, which shop should I use? Show your working.

PS 11 A shredding machine can shred 20 sheets of paper in 14 seconds. The bin has room for 1000 sheets of shredded paper.

How long will it take to fill the bin if the machine has to stop for 3 minutes after every 200 sheets to prevent overheating?

FM 12 Here is a recipe for making Yorkshire pudding.

Adjust this recipe to use it for two people.
Justify any decision you make.

Yorkshire pudding recipe (Serves 8)
125 g plain flour
235 ml whole milk
2 eggs
3 g salt
45 ml beef dripping or lard

FM 13 An aircraft has two fuel tanks, one in each wing.

The tanks each hold 40 litres when full.

The left tank is quarter full. The right tank is half full.

How much fuel is needed so that both tanks are three-quarters full?

Best buys

This section will show you how to:
- find the cost per unit weight
- find the weight per unit cost
- use the above to find which product is the cheaper

Key words
best buy
better value
value for money

When you wander around a supermarket and see all the different prices for the many different-sized packets, it is rarely obvious which are the **best buys**. However, with a calculator you can easily compare **value for money** by finding either:

the cost per unit weight   *or*   the weight per unit cost

To find:
- *cost per unit weight*, divide *cost by weight*
- *weight per unit cost*, divide *weight by cost*.

The next two examples show you how to do this.

EXAMPLE 6

A 300 g tin of cocoa costs £1.20.

First change £1.20 to 120p. Then divide, using a calculator, to get:

cost per unit weight	120p ÷ 300 g = 0.4p per gram
weight per unit cost	300 g ÷ 120p = 2.5 g per penny

EXAMPLE 7

A supermarket sells two different-sized packets of Whito soap powder. The medium size contains 800 g and costs £1.60 and the large size contains 2.5 kg and costs £4.75. Which is the better buy?

Find the weight per unit cost for both packets.

Medium:	800 g ÷ 160p = 5 g per penny
Large:	2500 g ÷ 475p = 5.26 g per penny

From these it is clear that there is more weight per penny with the large size, which means that the large size is the better buy.

Sometimes it is easier to us a scaling method to compare prices to find the **better value**.

EXAMPLE 8

| Small |
| Price £3.40 |

| Large |
| Price £4.95 |

12 is a common factor of 24 and 36 so work out the cost of 12 fish fingers.

For the small box 12 fish fingers cost £3.40 ÷ 2 = £1.70

For the large box 12 fish fingers cost £4.95 ÷ 3 = £1.65

So the large box is better value.

EXAMPLE 9

| Price £1.45 |

| Price £1.20 |

30 is the least common multiple of 5 and 6 so work out the cost of 30 yoghurts.

For the six-pack the cost of 30 yoghurts is £1.45 × 5 = £7.25

For the five-pack the cost of 30 yoghurts is £1.20 × 6 = £7.20

So the five-pack is better value.

EXERCISE 3C

1 Compare the prices of the following pairs of products and state which, if either, is the better buy.

a Chocolate bars: £2.50 for a 5-pack, £4.50 for a 10-pack

b Eggs: £1.08 for 6, £2.25 for 12

c Car shampoo: £4.99 for 2 litres, £2.45 for 1 litre

d Dishwasher tablets: £7.80 for 24, £3.90 for 12

e Carrots: 29p for 250 grams, 95p for 750 grams

f Bread rolls: £1.39 for a pack of 6, £4.90 for a pack of 20

g Juice: £2.98 for 2, £4 for 3

D

FM **AU** **2** Compare the following pairs of product and state which is the better buy, and why.

   a Coffee: a medium jar which is 140 g for £1.10 or a large jar which is 300 g for £2.18

   b Beans: a 125 g tin at 16p or a 600 g tin at 59p

   c Flour: a 3 kg bag at 75p or a 5 kg bag at £1.20

   d Toothpaste: a large tube which is 110 ml for £1.79 or a medium tube which is 75 ml for £1.15

   e Frosted flakes: a large box which is 750 g for £1.64 or a medium box which is 500 g for £1.10

   f Rice Crisps: a medium box which is 440 g for £1.64 or a large box which is 600 g for £2.13

   g Shampoo: a bottle containing 400 ml for £1.15 or a bottle containing 550 ml for £1.60

FM **3** Julie wants to respray her car with yellow paint. In the local shop, she sees the following tins:

   small tin: 350 ml at a cost of £1.79

   medium tin: 500 ml at a cost of £2.40

   large tin: 1.5 litres at a cost of £6.70

   a What is the cost per litre of paint in the small tin?

   b Which tin is offered at the lowest price per litre?

FM **4** Tisco's sells bottled water in three sizes.

   a Work out the cost per litre of the 'handy' size.

   b Which bottle is the best value for money?

Handy size 40 cl   Family size 2 l   Giant size 5 l
£0.38   £0.98   £2.50

PS **5** Two drivers are comparing the petrol consumption of their cars.

   Ahmed says, "I get 320 miles on a tank of 45 litres".

   Bashir says, "I get 230 miles on a tank of 32 litres".

Whose car is more economical?

PS **6** Mary and Jane are arguing about which of them is better at mathematics.

   Mary scored 49 out of 80 on a test.

   Jane scored 60 out of 100 on a test of the same standard.

Who is better at mathematics?

AU **PS** **7** Paula and Kelly are comparing their running times.

   Paula completed a 10-mile run in 65 minutes.

   Kelly completed a 10-km run in 40 minutes.

Given that 8 km are equal to 5 miles, which girl has the greater average speed?

Density

This section will show you how to:
- solve problems involving density

Key words
density
mass
volume

Density is the **mass** of a substance per unit **volume**, usually expressed in grams per cm^3. The relationship between the three quantities is:

$$density = \frac{mass}{volume}$$

You can remember this with a triangle similar to that for distance, speed and time.

mass   = density × volume

density = mass ÷ volume

volume = mass ÷ density

Note: Density is defined in terms of mass. The common metric units for mass are grams and kilograms. Try not to mix up mass with weight. The common metric unit for weight is the Newton. You may have learnt about the difference between mass and weight in science.

EXAMPLE 10

A piece of metal has a mass of 30 g and a volume of 4 cm^3. What is the density of the metal?

$$\text{Density} = \frac{mass}{volume}$$

$$= \frac{30}{4} = 7.5 \ g/cm^3$$

EXAMPLE 11

What is the mass of a piece of rock which has a volume of 34 cm^3 and a density of 2.25 g/cm^3?

Mass = volume × density

$$= 34 × 2.25 = 76.5 \ g$$

EXERCISE 3D

B

1 Find the density of a piece of wood with a mass of 6 g and a volume of 8 cm^3.

2 Calculate the density of a metal if 12 cm^3 of it has a mass of 100 g.

3 Calculate the mass of a piece of plastic, 20 cm^3 in volume, if its density is 1.6 g/cm^3.

4 Calculate the volume of a piece of wood which has a mass of 102 g and a density of 0.85 g/cm^3.

5 Find the mass of a marble model, 56 cm^3 in volume, if the density of marble is 2.8 g/cm^3.

6 Calculate the volume of a liquid with a mass of 4 kg and a density of 1.25 g/cm^3.

7 Find the density of the material of a pebble which has a mass of 34 g and a volume of 12.5 cm^3.

8 It is estimated that the statue of Queen Victoria in Endcliffe Park, Sheffield, has a volume of about 4 m^3.

The density of the material used to make the statue is 9.2 g/cm^3. What is the estimated mass of the statue?

9 I bought a 50 kg bag of coal, and estimated the total volume of coal to be about 28 000 cm^3.

What is the density of coal, in g/cm^3?

10 A 1 kg bag of sugar has a volume of about 625 cm^3. What is the density of sugar in g/cm^3?

PS 11 Two statues look identical and both appear to be made out of gold. One of them is a fake.

The density of gold is 19.3 g/cm^3.

The statues each have a volume of approximately 200 cm^3.

The first statue has a mass of 5.2 kg.

The second statue has a mass of 3.8 kg.

Which one is the fake?

AU 12 A piece of metal has a mass of 345 g and a volume of 15 cm^3.

A different piece of metal has a mass of 400 g and a density of 25 g/cm^3.

Which piece of metal has the bigger volume and by how much?

FM 13 Two pieces of scrap metal are melted down to make a single piece of metal.

The first piece has a mass of 1.5 tonnes and a density of 7000 kg/m^3.

The second piece has a mass of 1 tonne and a density of 8000 kg/m^3.

Work out the total volume of the new piece.

GRADE BOOSTER

D You can calculate average speeds from data

D You can calculate distance from speed and time

D You can calculate time from speed and distance

C You can solve problems involving speed

B You can solve problems involving density

What you should know now

- How to divide any amount into a given ratio
- The relationships between speed, time and distance
- How to do problems involving direct proportion
- How to compare the prices of products
- How to work out the density of materials

1 Two towns, A and B, are connected by a motorway of length 100 miles and a dual carriageway of length 80 miles as shown.

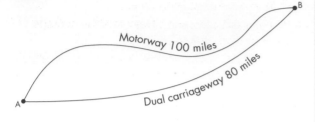

Jack travels from A to B along the motorway at an average speed of 60 mph.

Fred travels from A to B along the dual carriageway at an average speed of 50 mph.

What is the difference in time between the two journeys? Give your answers in minutes.

(4 marks)

AQA, June 2005, Paper 2 Intermediate, Question 8

2 Blushing Pink paint is made by mixing red and white paint.

The ratio of red paint to white paint used is 3 : 1.

a What percentage of Blushing Pink is red paint? *(2 marks)*

b One day 27 000 litres of red paint are used to make Blushing Pink paint. *(3 marks)*

How many litres of Blushing Pink are made?

AQA, November 2008, Module 3 Higher, Question 1

3 Paula goes for a 30-minute run.

For the first 20 minutes she runs at an average speed of 9 miles per hour. In the next 10 minutes she runs a distance of 1 mile.

Work out the average speed for her 30-minute run.

Give your answer in miles per hour. *(4 marks)*

AQA, Question 3, Specification B, Module 3, Section A, November 2008

4 Bill and Ben buy £10 worth of lottery tickets. Ben pays £7 and Bill pays £3. They decide to share any prize in the ratio of the money they each paid.

a They win £350. How much does Bill get?

b What percentage of the £350 does Ben get?

5 A car produces 2.78 kg of carbon dioxide per hour when driven in a city. The car travels 30 miles in a city at an average speed of 20 mph.

How much carbon dioxide does the car produce during its journey? *(3 marks)*

AQA, November 2006, Paper 2, Question 2

6 Susan completes a journey in two stages. In stage 1 of her journey, she drives at an average speed of 80 km/h and takes 1 hour 45 minutes.

a How far does Susan travel in stage 1 of her journey?

b Altogether, Susan drives 190 km and takes a total time of 2 hours 15 minutes. What is her average speed, in km/h, in stage 2 of her journey?

B C D

Worked Examination Questions

1   To be on time, a train must complete a journey of 210 miles in 3 hours.

   a   Calculate the average speed of the train for the whole journey when it is on time.

   b   The train averages a speed of 56 mph over the first 98 miles of the journey. Calculate the average speed for the remainder of the journey so that the train arrives on time.

1   **a**   Average speed = distance ÷ time

$210 \div 3 = 70$ mph

> 1 mark for method. 1 mark for correct answer.

> Note that one question in the examination will ask you to state the units of your answer. This is often done with a speed question.

   b $98 \div 56 = 1.75$ which is
1 hour and 45 minutes.

> First find out how long the train took to do the first 98 miles.

> $98 \div 56$ gets 1 mark for method.
> 1.75 or 1 hour 45 minutes gets 1 mark for accuracy.

$(210 - 98) \div (3 - 1.75) = 112 \div 1.25$
$= 89.6$ mph

> Now work out the distance still to be travelled (112 miles) and the time left (1 hour 15 minutes = 1.25 hours). Divide distance by time to get the average speed.

Total: 6 marks

> $(210 - 98) \div (3 - 1.75)$ gets 1 mark for method even if there is an error in one of the figures.
> 89.6 or an answer following an arithmatic error gets 1 mark for accuracy.

PS   **2**   Jonathan is comparing two ways to travel from his flat in London to his parents' house.

   Tube, train and taxi

   It takes 35 minutes to get to the railway station by tube in London. A train journey from London to Doncaster takes 1 hour 40 minutes. From Doncaster it is 15 miles by taxi at an average speed of 20 mph.

   Car

   The car journey is 160 miles at an average speed of 50 mph. Which is the slower journey, tube, train and taxi or car?

2   Time   = distance ÷ speed = $\frac{15}{20}$

> Work out the time taken by taxi. This gets 1 mark for method.

   = 0.75 hour (or 45 minutes)

> This gets 1 mark for accuracy.

Total time = 35 minutes + 1 hour 40 minutes + 45 minutes

> Work out the **total time** for tube, train and taxi.

   = 3 hours

> This is required to compare with the car. This gets 1 mark.

Time   = distance ÷ speed = $160 \div 50$

> Work out the time taken by car. This gets 1 mark for method and 1 mark for accuracy.

   = 3.2 hours (or 3 hours 12 minutes)

Car is 12 minutes slower.

Total: 6 marks

> State the conclusion following from your results. This gets 1 mark.

To celebrate your birthday, you have decided to hold a large dinner party for your friends and family.

You have invited 15 people in total and so far you have had responses from eight people, all of whom can attend.

As the dinner party will be a big event for you, you want to begin preparing for it straight away. You decide to plan for several different themes, so that you can work out the price of the ingredients for each menu for your dinner and work out how much money you will need to spend.

Chilli pasta   Serves 2

175 g pasta
40 ml olive oil
2 onions
4 cloves garlic
1 red jalapeno pepper
185 g yellow peppers, roasted
Basil

Ragu Bolognese   Serves 16

450 g minced beef
450 g minced pork
14 kg pasta
30 ml olive oil
225 g chicken liver
2 onions
4 garlic cloves
150 g streaky bacon
400 g chopped tomatoes
200 g tomato purée
400 ml red wine
Basil

Wild mushroom tart   Serves 4

275 g puff pastry
25 g butter
300 g wild mushrooms
25 g cheese
1 clove garlic
1 egg

Steak and kidney pudding   Serves 6

450 g diced beef
150 g kidney
30 ml beef dripping
2 onions
40 g plain flour
Thyme
Bay leaves
Parsley
1 pint brown beef stock
175 g self-raising flour
75 g suet

Getting started

- Find the cost of 175 g of pasta, if you can buy 500 g for 70p.
- The butcher sells sausages in packs of eight for £2.50. How much would you pay for three sausages, if he will sell them individually?
- How many 300-g portions will 1.3 kg provide?
- Which is cheaper, 200 g of tomatoes for £1.90 or 350 g for £2.50?

Prices of ingredients	Quantity	Cost
Beef dripping	500 g	55p
Beef stock	12 cubes	98p
Minced beef	500 g	£2.89
Diced beef	1 kg	£5.20
Kidney	400 g	£1.20
Minced pork	500 g	£2.00
Chicken liver	400 g	99p
Streaky bacon	300 g	£2.00
Suet	200 g	65p
Puff pastry	500 g	79p
Butter	250 g	85p
Eggs	6	91p
Pasta	500 g	70p
Onion	1kg	75p
Jalapeno pepper	200 g jar	£1.25
Yellow pepper	each	80p
Plain flour	1.5 kg	43p
Self-raising flour	1.5 kg	43p
Cheese	1 kg	£5.12
Chopped tomatoes	400 g tin	55p
Tomato purée	200 g	33p
Wild mushrooms	125 g	£1.69
Olive oil	500 ml	£188
Garlic (8 cloves per bulb)	3 bulbs	89p
Thyme	16 g	68p
Bay leaves	6 grams	88p
Parsley	180g	79p
Basil	115 g	£2.20
Red wine	750 ml	£3.99

Your task

You have not chosen the main course of your dinner yet. To help you decide, you have chosen four of your favourite recipes.

You now need to look at the lists of ingredients and the price list, then work out what you will need for each one, and how much it will cost.

1 First, work on the assumption that no more than the eight guests, who have already confirmed that they are coming, will be able to attend your party.

   Work out the ingredients you will need for each recipe, and the cost of these ingredients (in total and per portion).

2 To make sure that you are able to cater for more guests, work out the ingredients and costs for each recipe for:
   - 10 guests
   - 15 guests.

3 You decide to set a budget for the ingredients for your main course and you choose £75 as a starting point.

   Evaluate how realistic this budget is, considering the number of guests that could attend and the level of choice you would like to offer, taking account that some will eat meat and some will be vegetarians.

   Remember: you must include yourself when you are working out the ingredients that you must buy and the potential cost.

Extension

Your friends and family will need to travel to get to your dinner party. Your friend Sam will set out at 4.30pm and travel 35 miles to your house; your cousin Charlie will set out at 4.00pm and travel 65 miles. If they both travel at the same speed, who will reach your house first? How fast will they each have to travel for both to reach your house at the same time?

Why this chapter matters

People have always needed to measure areas and volumes.

In everyday life, you will, for instance, need to find the area to work out how much carpet to buy to cover a floor; or you will need to find the volume to see how much water is needed to fill a swimming pool. You can do this quickly using formulae.

Measuring the world

From the earliest times, farmers have needed to know the area of their fields to see how many crops they could grow or animals they could support. One of the oldest units of area used in England was the acre, which was the amount of land that a man could plough in a day. When land is bought and sold, the cost depends on the area. That is true today, too, and a considerable part of the cost of a new house will be the cost of the land it stands on.

Volumes are important too. Volumes tell us how much space there is inside any structure. Whether it is a house, barn, aeroplane, car or office, the volume is important. Did you know, for example, that in England there is a regulation that governs the number of people who can use an office, and this is based on the volume of the room?

Volumes of containers for liquids also need to be measured. Think, for example, of a car fuel tank, the water tank in a building, your local swimming pool or a reservoir. It is important to be able to calculate the capacity of all these things.

So how do we measure areas and volumes? Some shapes and objects are easy. Others take more ingenuity and skill. In this chapter, you will learn formulae that can be used to calculate areas and volumes of different shapes, based on a few measurements. Many of these formulae were first worked out thousands of years ago. We know, for example, that Archimedes, perhaps the greatest mathematician who ever lived, discovered how to find the volume and surface area of a sphere over 2000 years ago. The fact that these formulae are still in use today shows how important they are.

Chapter

Geometry: Shapes

This chapter will show you ...

D how to calculate the area of a trapezium

C how to calculate the volume and surface area of a prism

B how to calculate the volume and surface area of a cylinder

B how to calculate the volume of a pyramid

A how to calculate the length of an arc and the area of a sector

A how to calculate the volume and surface area of a cone and a sphere

Visual overview

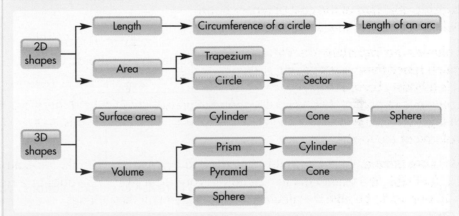

What you should already know

- The area of a rectangle is given by Area = length × width or $A = lw$ (KS3 level 5, GCSE grade F)

- The area of a triangle is given by Area = $\frac{1}{2}$ × base × height or $A = \frac{1}{2}bh$ (KS3 level 6, GCSE grade D)

- The area of a parallelogram is given by Area = base × height or $A = bh$ (KS3 level 6, GCSE grade E)

- The circumference of a circle is given by $C = \pi d$, where d is the diameter of the circle (KS3 level 6, GCSE grade D)

- The area of a circle is given by $A = \pi r^2$, where r is the radius of the circle (KS3 level 6, GCSE grade D)

- The volume of a cuboid is given by Volume = length × width × height or $V = lwh$ (KS3 level 6, GCSE grade E)

continued

● The common metric units to measure area, volume and capacity are shown in this table **(KS3 level 6, GCSE grade E)**

Area	Volume	Capacity
$100 \text{ mm}^2 = 1 \text{ cm}^2$	$1000 \text{ mm}^3 = 1 \text{ cm}^3$	$1000 \text{ cm}^3 = 1$ litre
$10\,000 \text{ cm}^2 = 1 \text{ m}^2$	$1\,000\,000 \text{ cm}^3 = 1 \text{ m}^3$	$1 \text{ m}^3 = 1000$ litres

Quick check

1 Find the areas of the following shapes.

a

15 mm

6 mm

b

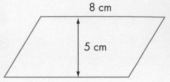

8 cm

5 cm

c

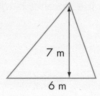

7 m

6 m

2 Find the volume of this cuboid.

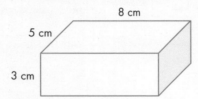

8 cm

5 cm

3 cm

If you need to revise circle calculations, you should work through Exercise 4A.

Circumference and area of a circle

This section will show you how to:

● calculate the circumference and area of a circle

Key words

π

area

circumference

EXAMPLE 1

Calculate the **circumference** of the circle. Give your answer to 3 significant figures.

$C = \pi d$

$= \pi \times 5.6$ cm

$= 17.6$ cm (to 3 significant figures)

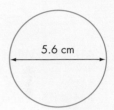

5.6 cm

EXAMPLE 2

Calculate the **area** of the circle. Give your answer in terms of π.

$A = \pi r^2$

$= \pi \times 6^2$ m^2

$= 36\pi$ m^2

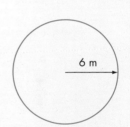

6 m

EXERCISE 4A

1 Copy and complete the following table for each circle. Give your answers to 3 significant figures.

	Radius	Diameter	Circumference	Area
a	4.0 cm			
b	2.6 m			
c		12.0 cm		
d		3.2 m		

2 Find the circumference of each of the following circles. Give your answers in terms of π.

a Diameter 5 cm   **b** Radius 4 cm   **c** Radius 9 m   **d** Diameter 12 cm

3 Find the area of each of the following circles. Give your answers in terms of π.

a Radius 5 cm   **b** Diameter 12 cm   **c** Radius 10 cm   **d** Diameter 1 m

D

D

AU **4** A rope is wrapped eight times around a capstan (a cylindrical post), the diameter of which is 35 cm. How long is the rope?

PS **5** The roller used on a cricket pitch has a radius of 70 cm.

A cricket pitch has a length of 20 m. How many complete revolutions does the roller make when rolling the pitch?

6 The diameter of each of the following coins is as follows.

1p: 2.0 cm,   2p: 2.6 cm,   5p: 1.7 cm,   10p: 2.4 cm

Calculate the area of one face of each coin. Give your answers to 1 decimal place.

7 The distance around the outside of a large pipe is 2.6 m. What is the diameter of the pipe?

C

AU **8** What is the total perimeter of a semicircle of diameter 15 cm?

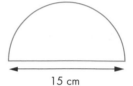

15 cm

FM **9** A restaurant sells two sizes of pizzas. The diameters are 24 cm and 30 cm. The restaurant claims that the larger size is 50% bigger.

Your friend disagrees and wants to complain to the local trading standards officer. What would you advise? Give a reason for your answer.

10 Calculate the area of each of these shapes, giving your answers in terms of π.

a

12 cm

b

4 cm

AU **11** Calculate the area of the shaded part of the diagram, giving your answer in terms of π.

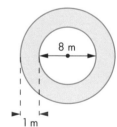

8 m

1 m

12 This is the plan of a large pond with a gravel path all around it. What area needs to be covered with gravel?

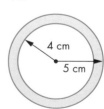

4 cm

5 cm

13 A tree in Sequoia National Park in USA is considered to be the largest in the world. It has a circumference at the base of 31.3 m. Would the base of the tree fit inside your classroom?

AU **14** The wheel of a bicycle has a diameter of 70 cm. The bicycle travels 100 m.

How many complete revolutions does the wheel make?

Area of a trapezium

The area of a **trapezium** is calculated by finding the average of the lengths of its parallel sides and multiplying this by the perpendicular distance between them.

$$A = \frac{1}{2}(a + b)h$$

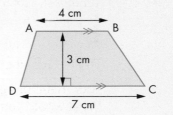

EXAMPLE 3

Find the area of the trapezium ABCD.

$$A = \frac{1}{2}(4 + 7) \times 3 \text{ cm}^2$$
$$= 16.5 \text{ cm}^2$$

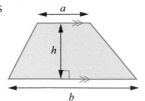

EXERCISE 4B

1 Copy and complete the following table for each trapezium.

	Parallel side 1	Parallel side 2	Vertical height	Area
a	8 cm	4 cm	5 cm	
b	10 cm	12 cm	7 cm	
c	7 cm	5 cm	4 cm	
d	5 cm	9 cm	6 cm	
e	3 m	13 m	5 m	
f	4 cm	10 cm		42 cm²
g	7 cm	8 cm		22.5 cm²
h	6 cm		5 cm	40 cm²

2 Calculate the perimeter and the area of each of these trapeziums.

a

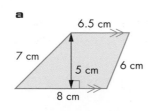

b

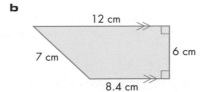

c

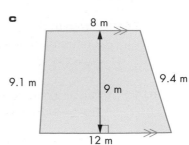

D

AU **3** How does this diagram show that the area of a trapezium is $\frac{1}{2}(a + b)h$?

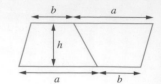

PS **4** Find the area of each part of this picture frame.

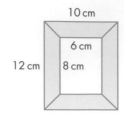

5 Calculate the area of each of these compound shapes.

a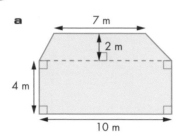

b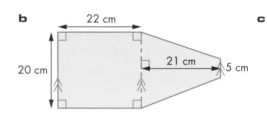

c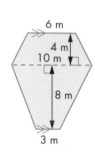

C

AU **6** Calculate the area of the shaded part in this diagram.

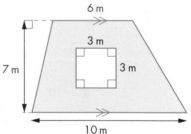

FM **7** This is a sketch of a shed with four walls and a sloping roof.

A one-litre can of wood-protection paint will cover 10 m².

How many one-litre cans do you need to put two coats of preservative on each of the four walls?

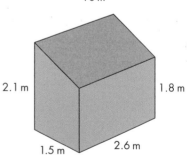

AU **8** What percentage of this shape has been shaded?

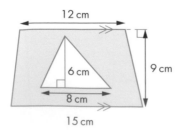

AU 9 The shape of most of Egypt (see map) roughly approximates to a trapezium. The north coast is about 900 km long, the south boundary is about 1100 km long and the distance from north to south is about 1100 km.

What is the approximate area of this part of Egypt?

10 The diagram shows an isosceles trapezium.

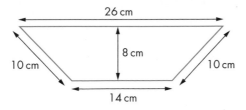

Calculate its area.

4.3 Sector

Sectors

This section will show you how to:	Key words
• calculate the length of an arc and the area of a sector	arc sector subtend

A **sector** is part of a circle, bounded by two radii of the circle and one of the **arcs** formed by the intersections of these radii with the circumference.

The angle **subtended** at the centre of the circle by the arc of a sector is known as the angle of the sector.

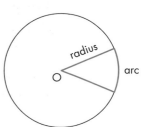

When a circle is divided into only two sectors, the larger one is called the major sector and the smaller one is called the minor sector.

Likewise, their arcs are called the major arc and the minor arc respectively.

Length of an arc and area of a sector

A sector is a fraction of the whole circle, the size of the fraction being determined by the size of angle of the sector. The angle is often written as θ, a Greek letter pronounced *theta*. For example, the sector shown in the diagram represents the fraction $\dfrac{\theta}{360}$.

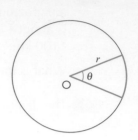

This applies to both its arc length and its area. Therefore,

$$\text{arc length} \;=\; \frac{\theta}{360} \times 2\pi r \quad \text{or} \quad \frac{\theta}{360} \times \pi d$$

$$\text{sector area} \;=\; \frac{\theta}{360} \times \pi r^2$$

EXAMPLE 4

Find the arc length and the area of the sector in the diagram.

The sector angle is 28° and the radius is 5 cm. Therefore,

$$\text{arc length} \;=\; \frac{28}{360} \times \pi \times 2 \times 5 = 2.4 \text{ cm (1 decimal place)}$$

$$\text{sector area} \;=\; \frac{28}{360} \times \pi \times 5^2 = 6.1 \text{ cm}^2 \text{ (1 decimal place)}$$

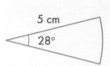

EXERCISE 4C

1 For each of these sectors, calculate: **i** the arc length   **ii** the sector area.

a

40°
8 cm

b
95°
5 cm

c
78°
12 cm

d
130°
7 cm

2 Calculate the arc length and the area of a sector whose arc subtends an angle of 60° at the centre of a circle with a diameter of 12 cm. Give your answer in terms of π.

3 Calculate the total perimeter of each of these sectors.   **a**

11 cm

b
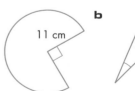
22°
8.5 cm

4 Calculate the area of each of these sectors.

a

110°
7 cm

b

50°
8 cm

5 O is the centre of a circle of radius 12.5 cm.

Calculate the length of the arc ACB.

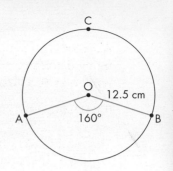

PS **6** **a** Calculate the angle of the minor sector of this circle. Give your answer in terms of π.

b Angles are sometime measured in radians.

The angle you found in part **a** is equal to one radian.

By comparing the sector to an equilateral triangle of side 10 cm, explain why one radian must be a bit less than 60°.

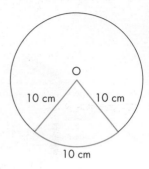

AU **7** The diagram shows a quarter of a circle. Calculate the area of the shaded shape, giving your answer in terms of π.

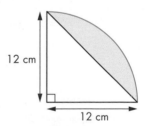

PS **8** ABCD is a square of side length 8 cm. APC and AQC are arcs of the circles with centres D and B. Calculate the area of the shaded part.

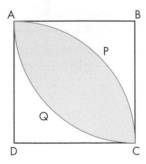

FM **9** Antique clocks are powered by a pendulum which swings from side to side.

The pendulum of an old clock is 90 cm long.

It swings from side to side through an angle of 10°.

How wide must the clock case be made so that the pendulum can swing freely?

10 Find:

a the perimeter

b the area of this shape.

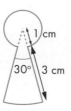

Volume of a prism

This section will show you how to:
● calculate the volume of a prism

Key words
cross-section
prism

A **prism** is a 3D shape which has the same **cross-section** running all the way through it.

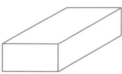

| **Name:** | Cuboid | Triangular prism | Cylinder |
| **Cross-section:** | Rectangle | Isosceles Triangle | Circle |

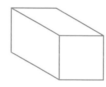
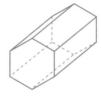

| **Name:** | Cuboid | Hexagonal prism |
| **Cross-section:** | Square | Regular Hexagon |

The volume of a prism is found by multiplying the area of its cross-section by the length of the prism (or height if the prism is stood on end).

That is, volume of prism = area of cross-section × length   **or** $V = Al$

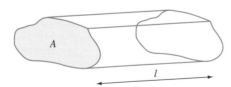

EXAMPLE 5

Find the volume of the triangular prism.

The area of the triangular cross-section $= A = \dfrac{5 \times 7}{2} = 17.5 \text{ cm}^2$

The volume is the area of its cross-section × length $= Al$
$= 17.5 \times 9 = 157.5 \text{ cm}^3$

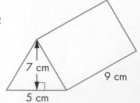

7 cm

5 cm

9 cm

EXERCISE 4D

1 For each prism shown:

    i calculate the area of the cross-section   **ii** calculate the volume.

a

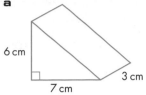

b

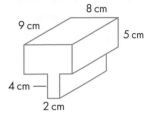

c

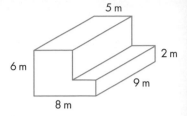

2 Calculate the volume of each of these prisms.

a

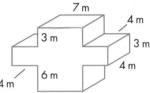

b

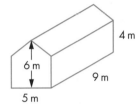

c

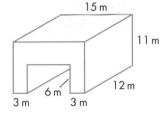

FM 3 A swimming pool is 10 m wide and 25 m long.

It is 1.2 m deep at one end and 2.2 m deep at the other end. The floor slopes uniformly from one end to the other.

    a Explain why the shape of the pool is a prism.

    b The pool is filled with water at a rate of 2 m^3 per minute. How long will it take to fill the pool?

PS 4 A conservatory is in the shape of a prism. Calculate the volume of air inside the conservatory with the dimensions shown in the diagram.

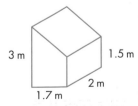

5 Each of these prisms has a uniform cross-section in the shape of a right-angled triangle.

    a Find the volume of each prism.   **b** Find the total surface area of each prism.

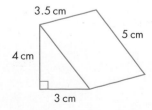

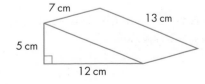

B

AU 6 The top and bottom of the container shown here are the same size, both consisting of a rectangle, 4 cm by 9 cm, with a semicircle at each end. The depth is 3 cm.

Find the volume of the container.

PS 7 In 2009 the sculptor Anish Kapoor exhibited a work called *Svayambh* at the Royal Academy in London. It was a block of red wax in the shape of a prism.

The cross-section was in the shape of an arched entrance.

It was 8 m long and weighed 30 tonnes. It slowly travelled through the galleries on a track.

Calculate the volume of wax used.

4.5 m

2.3 m

AU 8 A horse trough is in the shape of a semicircular prism as shown.

What volume of water will the trough hold when it is filled to the top? Give your answer in litres.

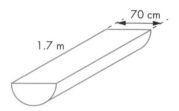

70 cm

1.7 m

FM 9 The dimensions of the cross-section of a girder (in the shape of a prism), 2 m in length, are shown on the diagram. The girder is made of iron. 1 cm^3 of iron weighs 79 g.

What is the mass of the girder?

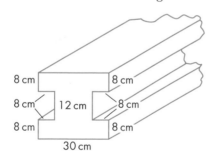

8 cm 8 cm
8 cm 12 cm 8 cm
8 cm 8 cm
30 cm

AU 10 Calculate the volume of this prism.

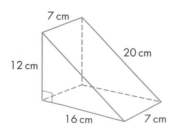

7 cm
20 cm
12 cm
16 cm 7 cm

Cylinders

This section will show you how to:
- calculate the volume and surface area of a cylinder

Key words
cylinder
surface area
volume

Volume

Since a **cylinder** is an example of a prism, its **volume** is found by multiplying the area of one of its circular ends by the height.

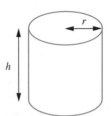

That is, volume = $\pi r^2 h$

where r is the radius of the cylinder and h is its height or length.

EXAMPLE 6

What is the volume of a cylinder having a radius of 5 cm and a height of 12 cm?

Volume = area of circular base × height
$$= \pi r^2 h$$
$$= \pi \times 5^2 \times 12 \text{ cm}^3$$
$$= 942 \text{ cm}^3 \text{ (3 significant figures)}$$

Surface area

The total **surface area** of a cylinder is made up of the area of its curved surface plus the area of its two circular ends.

The curved surface area, when opened out, is a rectangle with length equal to the circumference of the circular end.

curved surface area = circumference of end × height of cylinder
$$= 2\pi rh \quad \textbf{or} \quad \pi dh$$
area of one end $= \pi r^2$

Therefore, total surface area = $2\pi rh + 2\pi r^2$ **or** $\pi dh + 2\pi r^2$

EXAMPLE 7

What is the total surface area of a cylinder with a radius of 15 cm and a height of 2.5 m?

First, you must change the dimensions to a *common unit*. Use centimetres in this case.

Total surface area = $\pi dh + 2\pi r^2$
$$= \pi \times 30 \times 250 + 2 \times \pi \times 15^2 \text{ cm}^2$$
$$= 23\,562 + 1414 \text{ cm}^2$$
$$= 24\,976 \text{ cm}^2$$
$$= 25\,000 \text{ cm}^2 \text{ (3 significant figures)}$$

EXERCISE 4E

1 For the cylinders below find:

   i the volume   **ii** the total surface area.

Give your answers to 3 significant figures.

a 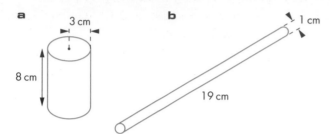 **b**   **c** 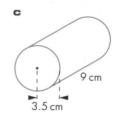 **d**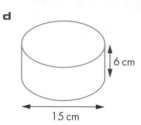

2 For each of these cylinder dimensions find:

   i the volume   **ii** the curved surface area.

Give your answers in terms of π.

   a Base radius 3 cm and height 8 cm   **b** Base diameter 8 cm and height 7 cm

   c Base diameter 12 cm and height 5 cm   **d** Base radius of 10 m and length 6 m

AU 3 The diameter of a marble, cylindrical column is 60 cm and its height is 4.2 m. The cost of making this column is quoted as £67.50 per cubic metre. What is the estimated total cost of making the column?

AU 4 Find the mass of a solid iron cylinder 55 cm high with a base diameter of 60 cm. 1 cm^3 iron has a mass of 7.9 g.

5 A solid cylinder has a diameter of 8.4 cm and a height of 12.0 cm. Calculate the volume of the cylinder.

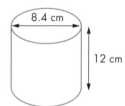

FM 6 A cylindrical food can has a height of 10.5 cm and a diameter of 7.4 cm.

What can you say about the size of the paper label around the can?

7 A cylindrical container is 65 cm in diameter. Water is poured into the container until it is 1 m deep. How much water is in the container? Give your answer in litres.

FM 8 A drinks manufacturer wishes to market a new drink in a can. The quantity in each can must be 330 ml.

Suggest a suitable height and diameter for the can.

You might like to look at the dimensions of a real drinks can.

9 A cylindrical can of soup has a diameter of 7 cm and a height of 9.5 cm. It is full of soup, which weighs 625 g. What is the density of the soup?

AU 10 A metal bar, 1 m long and with a diameter of 6 cm, has a mass of 22 kg. What is the density of the metal from which the bar is made?

PS 11 Wire is commonly made by putting hot metal through a hole in a plate.

What length of wire of diameter 1 mm can be made from a 1 cm cube of metal?

FM 12 The engine size of a car is measured in litres. This tells you the total capacity of the cylinders in which the pistons move up and down. For example, in a 1.6 litre engine with four cylinders, each cylinder will have a capacity of 0.4 litres.

Cylinders of a particular size can be long and thin or short and fat; they will give the engine different running characteristics.

In a racing car, the diameter can be approximately twice the length. This means the engine will run at very high revs.

Suggest possible dimensions for a 0.4 litre racing car cylinder.

4.6 Volume of a pyramid

This section will show you how to:	Key words
• calculate the volume of a pyramid	apex frustum pyramid volume

A **pyramid** is a 3D shape with a base from which triangular faces rise to a common vertex, called the **apex**. The base can be any polygon, but is usually a triangle, a rectangle or a square.

The **volume** of a pyramid is given by:

volume = $\frac{1}{3}$ × base area × vertical height

$V = \frac{1}{3}Ah$

where A is the base area and h is the vertical height.

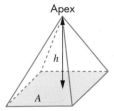

EXAMPLE 8

Calculate the volume of the pyramid on the right.

Base area = 5 × 4 = 20 cm^2

Volume = $\frac{1}{3}$ × 20 × 6 = 40 cm^3

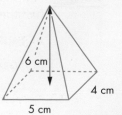

EXAMPLE 9

A pyramid, with a square base of side 8 cm, has a volume of 320 cm³. What is the vertical height of the pyramid?

Let h be the vertical height of the pyramid. Then,

$$\text{volume} = \tfrac{1}{3} \times 64 \times h = 320 \text{ cm}^3$$

$$\frac{64h}{3} = 320 \text{ cm}^3$$

$$h = \frac{960}{64} \text{ cm}$$

$$h = 15 \text{ cm}$$

EXERCISE 4F

B

1 Calculate the volume of each of these pyramids, all with rectangular bases.

a

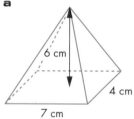

6 cm
4 cm
7 cm

b

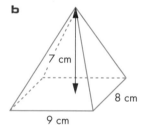

7 cm
8 cm
9 cm

c

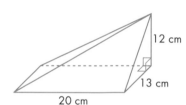

12 cm
13 cm
20 cm

d

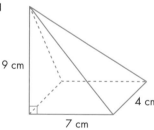

9 cm
4 cm
7 cm

e

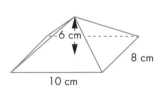

6 cm
8 cm
10 cm

2 Calculate the volume of a pyramid having a square base of side 9 cm and a vertical height of 10 cm.

AU 3 Suppose you have six pyramids which have a height that is half the side of the square base.

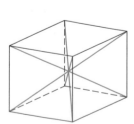

a Explain how they can fit together to make a cube.

b How does this show that the formula for the volume of a pyramid is correct?

4 The glass pyramid outside the Louvre Museum in Paris was built in the 1980s. It is 20.6 m tall and the base is a square of side 35 m. The design was very controversial.

Suppose that instead of a pyramid, the building was a conventional shape with the same square base, a flat roof and the same volume.

How high would it have been?

5 Calculate the volume of each of these shapes.

a

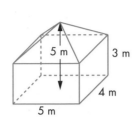

5 m   3 m
4 m
5 m

b

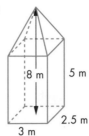

8 m   5 m
3 m   2.5 m

c

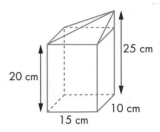

25 cm
20 cm
15 cm   10 cm

AU 6 What is the mass of a solid pyramid having a square base of side 4 cm, a height of 3 cm and a density of 13 g/cm^3? (1 cm^3 has a mass of 13 g.)

PS 7 A crystal is in the form of two square-based pyramids joined at their bases (see diagram). The crystal has a mass of 31.5 g. What is the mass of 1 cm^3 of the substance?

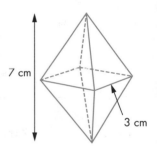

7 cm   3 cm

8 A pyramid has a square base of side 6.4 cm. Its volume is 81.3 cm^3.

Calculate the height of the pyramid.

PS 9 A pyramid has the same volume as a cube of side 10.0 cm.

The height of the pyramid is the same as the side of the square base.

Calculate the height of the pyramid.

10 The pyramid in the diagram has its top 5 cm cut off as shown. The shape which is left is called a **frustum**.

Calculate the volume of the frustum.

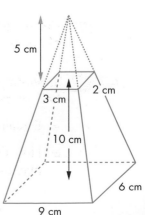

5 cm
3 cm   2 cm
10 cm
9 cm   6 cm

Cones

This section will show you how to:

- calculate the volume and surface area of a cone

Key words

slant height
surface area
vertical height
volume

A cone can be treated as a pyramid with a circular base. Therefore, the formula for the **volume** of a cone is the same as that for a pyramid.

volume = $\frac{1}{3}$ × base area × vertical height

$$V = \frac{1}{3}\pi r^2 h$$

where r is the radius of the base and h is the **vertical height** of the cone.

The curved **surface area** of a cone is given by:

curved surface area = π × radius × slant height

$$S = \pi r l$$

where l is the **slant height** of the cone.

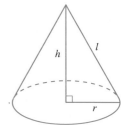

So the total surface area of a cone is given by the curved surface area plus the area of its circular base.

$$A = \pi r l + \pi r^2$$

EXAMPLE 10

For the cone in the diagram, calculate:

i   its volume

ii its total surface area.

Give your answers in terms of π.

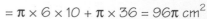

i   The volume is given by $V = \frac{1}{3}\pi r^2 h$

$$= \frac{1}{3} \times \pi \times 36 \times 8 = 96\pi \text{ cm}^3$$

ii The total surface area is given by $A = \pi r l + \pi r^2$

$$= \pi \times 6 \times 10 + \pi \times 36 = 96\pi \text{ cm}^2$$

EXERCISE 4G

1 For each cone, calculate:

i its volume

ii its total surface area.

Give your answers to 3 significant figures.

a

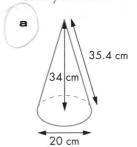

35.4 cm

34 cm

20 cm

b

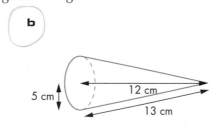

5 cm

12 cm

13 cm

c

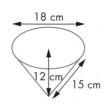

18 cm

12 cm

15 cm

2 A solid cone, base radius 6 cm and vertical height 8 cm, is made of metal whose density is 3.1 g/cm^3. Find the mass of the cone.

3 Find the total surface area of a cone whose base radius is 3 cm and slant height is 5 cm. Give your answer in terms of π.

4 Calculate the volume of each of these shapes. Give your answers in terms of π.

a

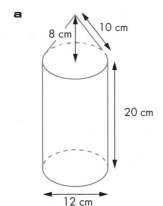

8 cm

10 cm

20 cm

12 cm

b

8 mm

40 mm

15 mm

5 You could work with a partner on this question.

A sector of a circle, as in the diagram, can be made into a cone (without a base) by sticking the two straight edges together.

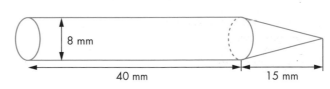

6 cm   6 cm

120°

a What would be the diameter of the base of the cone in this case?

b What is the diameter if the angle is changed to 180°?

c Investigate other angles.

6 A cone has the dimensions shown in the diagram.

Calculate the total surface area, leaving your answer in terms of π.

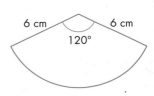

5 cm

4 cm

6 cm

PS 7 If the slant height of a cone is equal to the base diameter, show that the area of the curved surface is twice the area of the base.

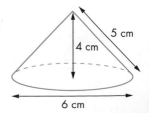

A*

8 The model shown on the right is made from aluminium. What is the mass of the model, given that the density of aluminium is 2.7 g/cm³?

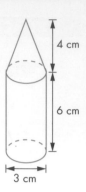

4 cm

6 cm

3 cm

PS 9 A container in the shape of a cone, base radius 10 cm and vertical height 19 cm, is full of water. The water is poured into an empty cylinder of radius 15 cm. How high is the water in the cylinder?

4.8 Spheres

This section will show you how to:
• calculate the volume and surface area of a sphere

Key words
sphere
surface area
volume

The **volume** of a **sphere**, radius r, is given by:

$$V = \tfrac{4}{3}\pi r^3$$

Its **surface area** is given by:

$$A = 4\pi r^2$$

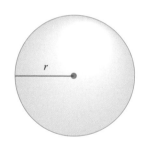

r

EXAMPLE 11

For a sphere of radius of 8 cm, calculate **i** its volume and **ii** its surface area.

i The volume is given by:

$$V = \tfrac{4}{3}\pi r^3$$

$$= \tfrac{4}{3} \times \pi \times 8^3 = \tfrac{2048}{3} \times \pi = 2140 \text{ cm}^3 \quad \text{(3 significant figures)}$$

ii The surface area is given by:

$$A = 4\pi r^2$$

$$= 4 \times \pi \times 8^2 = 256 \times \pi = 804 \text{ cm}^2 \quad \text{(3 significant figures)}$$

EXERCISE 4H

1 Calculate the volume of each of these spheres. Give your answers in terms of π.

    a Radius 3 cm   **b** Radius 6 cm   **c** Diameter 20 cm

2 Calculate the surface area of each of these spheres. Give your answers in terms of π.

    a Radius 3 cm   **b** Radius 5 cm   **c** Diameter 14 cm

3 Calculate the volume and the surface area of a sphere with a diameter of 50 cm.

4 A sphere fits exactly into an open cubical box of side 25 cm. Calculate the following.

    a The surface area of the sphere   **b** The volume of the sphere

AU 5 A metal sphere of radius 15 cm is melted down and recast into a solid cylinder of radius 6 cm. Calculate the height of the cylinder.

PS 6 Lead has a density of 11.35 g/cm^3. (This means that 1 cm^3 of lead has a mass of 11.35 g.) Calculate the maximum number of shot (spherical lead pellets) of radius 1.5 mm which can be made from 1 kg of lead.

FM 7 The standard (size 5) football must be between 68 cm and 70 cm in circumference and weigh between 410 g and 450 g. They are usually made from 32 panels: 12 regular pentagons and 20 regular hexagons.

    a Will a maker of footballs be more interested in the surface area or the volume of the ball? Why?

    b What variation in the surface area of a football is allowed?

AU 8 A sphere has a radius of 5.0 cm.

A cone has a base radius of 8.0 cm.

The sphere and the cone have the same volume.

Calculate the height of the cone.

PS 9 A sphere of diameter 10 cm is carved out of a wooden block in the shape of a cube of side 10 cm.

What percentage of the wood is wasted?

AU 10 A manufacturer is making cylindrical packaging for a sphere as shown. The curved surface of the cylinder is made from card.

Show that the area of the card is the same as the surface area of the sphere.

GRADE BOOSTER

D You can calculate the circumference and area of a circle

D You can calculate the area of a trapezium

C You can calculate the volume of prisms and cylinders

B You can calculate the length of an arc and the area of a sector

B You can calculate the surface area of cylinders, cones and spheres

B You can calculate the volume of pyramids, cones and spheres

A You can calculate volume and surface area of compound 3D shapes

What you should know now

- For a sector of radius r and angle θ:

$$\text{Arc length} = \frac{\theta}{360} \times 2\pi r \text{ or } \frac{\theta}{360} \times \pi d$$

$$\text{Area of a sector} = \frac{\theta}{360} \times \pi r^2$$

- The area of a trapezium is given by:

$$A = \tfrac{1}{2}(a + b)h$$

where h is the vertical height, and a and b are the lengths of the two parallel sides

- The volume of a prism is given by $V = Al$, where A is the cross-section area and l is the length of the prism

- The volume of a cylinder is given by $V = \pi r^2 h$, where r is the radius and h is the height or length of the cylinder

- The curved surface area of a cylinder is given by $S = 2\pi rh$, where r is the radius and h is the height or length of the cylinder

- The volume of a pyramid is given by $V = \tfrac{1}{3}Ah$, where A is the area of the base and h is the vertical height of the pyramid

- The volume of a cone is given by $V = \tfrac{1}{3}\pi r^2 h$, where r is the base radius and h is the vertical height of the cone

- The curved surface area of a cone is given by $S = \pi rl$, where r is the base radius and l is the slant height of the cone

- The volume of a sphere is given by $V = \tfrac{1}{3}\pi r^3$, where r is its radius

- The surface area of a sphere is given by $A = 4\pi r^2$, where r is its radius

1

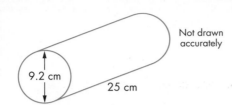

Not drawn accurately

9.2 cm

25 cm

a Calculate the area of one end of the cylinder. *(2 marks)*

b Calculate the **total** surface area of the cylinder. You **must** show your working. *(3 marks)*

AQA, June 2007, Module 5, Paper 2 Higher, Question 3

2 a Cylinder A has a height of 5 cm and a diameter of 16 cm.

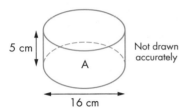

Calculate the volume of the cylinder A.

5 cm

A

Not drawn accurately

16 cm

Give your answer in terms of π.

State the units of your answer. *(4 marks)*

b Cylinder B has a height of 20 cm and a radius of *r* cm. *(3 marks)*

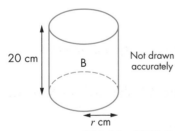

Cylinder B has the same volume as cylinder A.

20 cm

B

Not drawn accurately

r cm

Calculate the value of *r*. *(3 marks)*

AQA, May 2008, Paper 1 Higher, Question 14

3 A solid cube of side 25 cm has a circular hole cut through vertically.

The circle has a diameter of 14 cm.

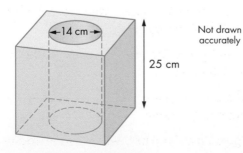

←14 cm→

Not drawn accurately

25 cm

Calculate the volume remaining. *(4 marks)*

AQA, November 2008, Paper 2 Higher, Question 17

4 AB is a minor arc of a circle of radius 5.2 m.

Angle AOB = 100°

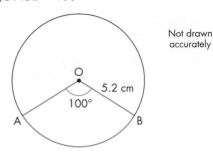

Not drawn accurately

5.2 cm

100°

A   B

Calculate the length of the minor arc AB. *(3 marks)*

AQA, June 2007, Module 5, Paper 2 Higher, Question 11

5 The diagram shows a prism.

The cross-section of the prism is a sector of a circle of radius 12 cm.

The angle of the sector is 60°.

The prism is 20 cm long.

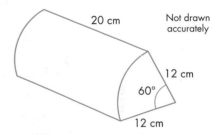

20 cm

Not drawn accurately

12 cm

60°

12 cm

Calculate the volume of the prism.

Give your answer in terms of π. *(4 marks)*

AQA, November 2008, Paper 1 Higher, Question 21

6 A solid sphere of radius 3 cm just fits inside a hollow cone of radius 6 cm and height 8 cm.

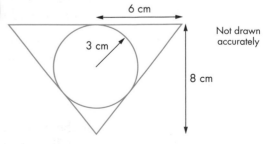

6 cm

3 cm

Not drawn accurately

8 cm

Calculate the fraction of the volume of the cone taken up by the sphere.

You **must** show your working. *(3 marks)*

AQA, November 2007, Paper 2 Higher, Question 18

Worked Examination Questions

AU **1** The diagram shows a pepper pot. The pot consists of a cylinder and a hemisphere. The cylinder has a diameter of 5 cm and a height of 7 cm.

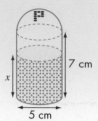

7 cm

x

5 cm

The pepper takes up half the total volume of the pot. Find the depth of pepper in the pot marked x in the diagram.

1 Volume of pepper pot

$= \pi r^2 h + \frac{2}{3} \pi r^3$ ────────────────

> This gets 1 method mark for setting up equation.

$= \pi \times 2.5^2 \times 7 + \frac{2}{3} \times \pi \times 2.5^3$ cm^3 ────────

> This gets 1 method mark for correct substitutions.

$= 170.2$ cm^3 ────────────────────

> This gets 1 accuracy mark for correct answers.

So volume of pepper $= 85.1$ cm^3

Therefore,

$\pi r^2 x = 85.1$ cm^3 ────────────────

> This gets 1 method mark for setting up equation.

and $x = \dfrac{85.1}{\pi \times 2.5^2} = 4.3$ cm (1 decimal place) ──────

> This gets 1 method mark for correct rearrangement and 1 accuracy mark for correct answer.

Total: 6 marks

Worked Examination Questions

FM **2** Aluminium craft wire is available in different diameters. One manufacturer sells a 5 metre coil of wire with a diameter of 1.6 mm for £5.00.

What volume of aluminium is that?

2   Volume = π × r^2 × h = π × 0.82 × 5000

= 10 000 mm^3 to 2 sf

> Find the volume of a cylinder with a length of 5 m and a diameter of 1.6 mm. This gets 1 mark for method.
> The units need to be the same. In millimetres, the length is 5000mm. This gets 1 mark for method.
> This gets 1 mark for accuracy for correct substitution.

> This gets 1 mark for accuracy and rounding answer to 2 sf. The answer could also be given in cm^3 (10 or 10.1). Rounding off to 3 sf would also be acceptable (10 100).

PS **3** Three balls of diameter 8.2 cm just fit inside a cylindrical container.

What is the internal volume of the container?

3   The diameter of the cylinder is 8.2 cm and the height is 24.6 cm. — > This gets 1 mark for method.

The internal volume = π × 4.12 × 24.6

= 1299.13…

= 1300 cm^3 to 2 sf

> This gets 1 mark for method, 1 mark for accuracy and 1 mark for sensible rounding.

Farmers have to do mathematical calculations almost every day. For example, an arable farmer may need to know how much seed to buy, how much water is required to irrigate the field each day, how much wheat they expect to grow and how much storage space they need to store wheat once it is harvested.

Farming can be filled with uncertainties, including changes in weather, crop disease and changes in consumption. It is therefore important that farmers correctly calculate variables that are within their control, to minimise the impact of changes that are outside their control.

Grain storage
Wheat is stored in large containers called silos. These are usually big cylinders but can also be various other shapes.

Important information about wheat crops (yield data)

- A 1 kg bag of seeds holds 26 500 seeds

- A 1 kg bag of seeds costs 50p

- I want to plant 60 bags of seed

- I need to plant 100 seeds in each square metre (m²) of field

- I need to irrigate each square metre of the field with 5 litres of water each day

- I expect to harvest 0.7 kg of wheat from each square metre of the field

- Every cubic metre (m³) of storage will hold 800 kg of wheat

Your task

Rufus, a crop farmer, is going to grow his first field of wheat next summer. Using all the information that he has gathered, help him to plan for his wheat crop. You should consider:

- the size of the field that he will require
- how much seed he will need
- how much water he will need to irrigate the crops, per day, and how it will be stored
- how he will store the seeds and wheat
- how much profit he could make if grain is sold at £92.25 per tonne.

Getting started

Think about these points to help you create your plan.

- What different shapes and sizes of field could the crops be grown in?
- If Rufus needs a reservoir to hold one day's irrigation water, what size cylinder would he need? How would this change if he chose a cuboid? What other shapes and sizes of reservoir could he use?
- What shapes and sizes could the silos be?

Handy hints

Remember: 1000 litres = 1 m^3

1000 kg = 1 tonne

Why this chapter matters

Looking at the angles and sides of triangles and the connections between them has led to the development of a whole branch of mathematics called trigonometry.

How do you find the height of a mountain?

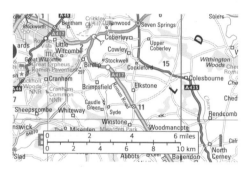

Why do modern builders use a rule that was used by the Egyptians when they built the pyramids?

How do you draw an accurate map?

How can computers take an image and make it rotate so that you can view it from different directions?

How were sailors able to navigate before GPS?

And how does GPS work?

How can music be produced electronically?

The mathematics behind all these things is called trigonometry. It has a huge range of applications in science, engineering, electronics and everyday life. This chapter gives a brief introduction to the subject and introduces some important new mathematical tools. The topic has its origins thousands of years ago but new applications are still being found.

Geometry: Pythagoras and trigonometry

This chapter will show you ...

C how to use Pythagoras' theorem in right-angled triangles

C how to solve problems using Pythagoras' theorem

B how to use Pythagoras' theorem in three dimensions

B how to use trigonometric ratios in right-angled triangles

A how to use trigonometry to solve problems

Visual overview

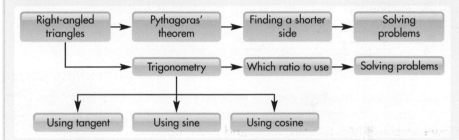

What you should already know

- how to find the square and square root of a number (**KS3 level 5, GCSE grade F**)
- how to round numbers to a suitable degree of accuracy (**KS3 level 6, GCSE grade E**)

Quick check

Use your calculator to evaluate the following, giving your answers to one decimal place.

1 2.3^2

2 15.7^2

3 0.78^2

4 $\sqrt{8}$

5 $\sqrt{260}$

6 $\sqrt{0.5}$

This section will show you how to:	Key words
● calculate the length of the hypotenuse in a right-angled triangle	hypotenuse Pythagoras' theorem

Pythagoras, who was a philosopher as well as a mathematician, was born in 580BC, on the island of Samos in Greece. He later moved to Crotona (Italy), where he established the Pythagorean Brotherhood, which was a secret society devoted to politics, mathematics and astronomy. It is said that when he discovered his famous theorem, he was so full of joy that he showed his gratitude to the gods by sacrificing a hundred oxen.

Consider squares being drawn on each side of a right-angled triangle, with sides 3 cm, 4 cm and 5 cm.

The longest side is called the **hypotenuse** and is always opposite the right angle.

Pythagoras' theorem can then be stated as follows:

For any right-angled triangle, the area of the square drawn on the hypotenuse is equal to the sum of the areas of the squares drawn on the other two sides.

The form in which most of your parents would have learnt the theorem when they were at school – and which is still in use today – is as follows:

In any right-angled triangle, the square of the hypotenuse is equal to the sum of the squares of the other two sides.

Pythagoras' theorem is more usually written as a formula:

$$c^2 = a^2 + b^2$$

Remember that Pythagoras' theorem can only be used in right-angled triangles.

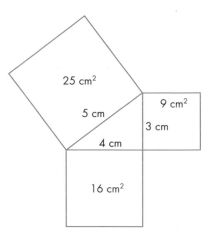

Finding the hypotenuse

EXAMPLE 1

Find the length of the hypotenuse, marked x on the diagram.

Using Pythagoras' theorem gives:
$$x^2 = 8^2 + 5.2^2 \text{ cm}^2$$
$$= 64 + 27.04 \text{ cm}^2$$
$$= 91.04 \text{ cm}^2$$

So $x = \sqrt{91.04} = 9.5$ cm (1 decimal place)

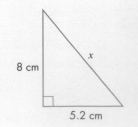

EXERCISE 5A

For each of the following triangles, calculate the length of the hypotenuse, x, giving your answers to 1 decimal place.

1
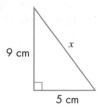
9 cm
x
5 cm

2
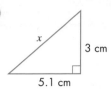
x
3 cm
5.1 cm

3
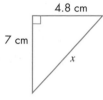
4.8 cm
7 cm
x

4
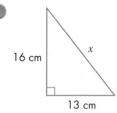
16 cm
x
13 cm

5
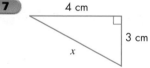
x
11 cm
15 cm

6
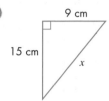
9 cm
15 cm
x

7
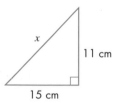
4 cm
3 cm
x

8
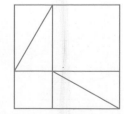
12 cm
x
5 cm

9
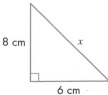
8 cm
x
6 cm

PS 10 How does this diagram show that Pythagoras' theorem is true?

5.2 Finding a shorter side

This section will show you how to:
● calculate the length of a shorter side in a right-angled triangle

Key words
Pythagoras' theorem

By rearranging the formula for **Pythagoras' theorem**, the length of one of the shorter sides can easily be calculated.

$$c^2 = a^2 + b^2$$

So, $a^2 = c^2 - b^2$ or $b^2 = c^2 - a^2$

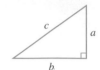

EXAMPLE 2

Find the length x.

x is one of the shorter sides.

So using Pythagoras' theorem gives:
$$x^2 = 15^2 - 11^2 \text{ cm}^2$$
$$= 225 - 121 \text{ cm}^2$$
$$= 104 \text{ cm}^2$$

So $x = \sqrt{104} = 10.2$ cm (1 decimal place)

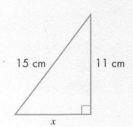

EXERCISE 5B

1 For each of the following triangles, calculate the length x, giving your answers to 1 decimal place.

HINTS AND TIPS

In these examples you are finding a short side. The square of the other short side is subtracted from the square of the hypotenuse in every case.

a

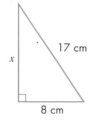
17 cm
x
8 cm

b

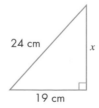
24 cm
x
19 cm

c

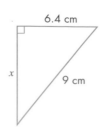
6.4 cm
x
9 cm

d

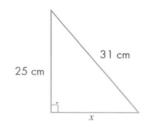
31 cm
25 cm
x

2 For each of the following triangles, calculate the length x, giving your answers to 1 decimal place.

a
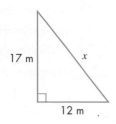
17 m, x, 12 m

b
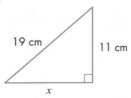
19 cm, 11 cm, x

c

17 m, x, 23 m

d
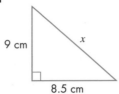
9 cm, x, 8.5 cm

3 For each of the following triangles, find the length marked x.

a
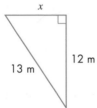
x, 12 m, 13 m

b
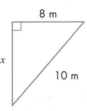
8 m, x, 10 m

c
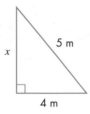
5 m, x, 4 m

d
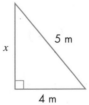
5 m, x, 4 m

PS 4 In question **3** you found sets of three whole numbers which satisfy $a^2 + b^2 = c^2$.

Can you find any more?

5 Calculate the value of x.

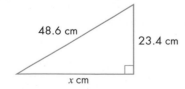
48.6 cm, 23.4 cm, x cm

This section will show you how to:
- solve problems using Pythagoras' theorem

Key words
isosceles triangle
Pythagoras' theorem

Pythagoras' theorem can be used to solve certain practical problems. When a problem involves two lengths only, follow these steps.

- Draw a diagram for the problem that includes a right-angled triangle.

- Look at the diagram and decide which side has to be found: the hypotenuse or one of the shorter sides. Label the unknown side x.

- If it is the hypotenuse, square both numbers, add the squares and take the square root of the sum.

- If it is one of the shorter sides, square both numbers, subtract the squares and take the square root of the difference.

- Finally, round the answer to a suitable degree of accuracy.

EXAMPLE 3

A plane leaves Manchester airport heading due east. It flies 160 km before turning due north. It then flies a further 280 km and lands. What is the distance of the return flight if the plane flies straight back to Manchester airport?

First, sketch the situation.

Using Pythagoras' theorem gives:

$$x^2 = 160^2 + 280^2 \text{ km}^2$$
$$= 25\,600 + 78\,400 \text{ km}^2$$
$$= 104\,000 \text{ km}^2$$

So $x = \sqrt{104\,104\,000} = 322$ km
(3 significant figures)

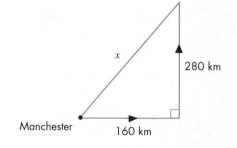

Manchester   160 km   280 km x

Remember the following tips when solving problems.

- Always sketch the right-angled triangle you need. Sometimes, the triangle is already drawn for you but some problems involve other lines and triangles that may confuse you. So identify which right-angled triangle you need and sketch it separately.

- Label the triangle with necessary information, such as the length of its sides, taken from the question. Label the unknown side x.

- Set out your solution as in Example 3. Avoid short cuts, since they often cause errors. You gain marks in your examination for clearly showing how you are applying Pythagoras' theorem to the problem.

- Round your answer to a suitable degree of accuracy.

EXERCISE 5C

FM 1 A ladder, 12 m long, leans against a wall. The ladder reaches 10 m up the wall. The ladder is safe if the foot of the ladder is about 2.5 m away from the wall. Is this ladder safe?

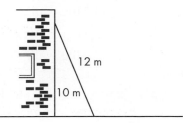

2 A model football pitch is 2 m long and 0.5-m wide. How long is the diagonal?

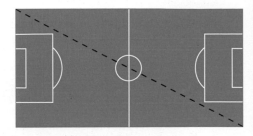

PS 3 How long is the diagonal of a square with a side of 8 m?

AU 4 A ship going from a port to a lighthouse steams 15 km east and 12 km north. The journey takes 1 hour. How much time would be saved by travelling directly to the lighthouse in a straight line?

FM 5 Some pedestrians want to get from point X on one road to point Y on another. The two roads meet at right angles.

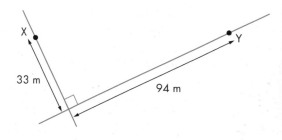

Instead of following the roads, they decide to follow a footpath which goes directly from X to Y.

How much shorter is this route?

6 A mast on a sailboat is strengthened by a wire (called a stay), as shown on the diagram. The mast is 10 m tall and the stay is 11 m long. How far from the base of the mast does the stay reach?

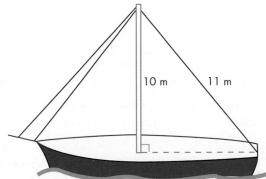

FM 7 A ladder, 4 m long, is put up against a wall.

   a How far up the wall will it reach when the foot of the ladder is 1 m away from the wall?

   b When it reaches 3.6 m up the wall, how far is the foot of the ladder away from the wall?

AU 8 A pole, 8 m high, is supported by metal wires, each 8.6 m long, attached to the top of the pole. How far from the foot of the pole are the wires fixed to the ground?

AU 9 A and B are two points on a coordinate grid. They have coordinates (13, 6) and (1, 1). How long is the line that joins them?

FM 10 The regulation for safe use of ladders states that: *the foot of a 5.00 m ladder must be placed between 1.20 m and 1.30 m from the foot of the wall.*

   a What is the maximum height the ladder can safely reach up the wall?

   b What is the minimum height the ladder can safely reach up the wall?

AU 11 Is the triangle with sides 7 cm, 24 cm and 25 cm a right-angled triangle? Give a reason for your answer.

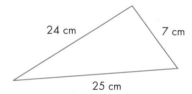

PS 12 A 4 m long ladder is leaning against a wall. The foot of the ladder is 1 m from the wall. The foot of the ladder is not securely held and slips 20 cm further away from the wall.

How far does the top of the ladder move down the wall?

PS 13 The diagonal of a rectangle is 10 cm. What can you say about the perimeter of the rectangle?

Pythagoras' theorem and isosceles triangles

This section shows you how to to use Pythagoras' theorem in isosceles triangles.

Every **isosceles triangle** has a line of symmetry that divides the triangle into two congruent right-angled triangles. So when you are faced with a problem involving an isosceles triangle, be aware that you are quite likely to have to split that triangle down the middle to create a right-angled triangle which will help you to solve the problem.

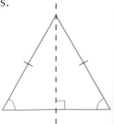

EXAMPLE 4

Calculate the area of this triangle.

It is an isosceles triangle and you need to calculate its height to find its area.

First split the triangle into two right-angled triangles to find its height.

Let the height be x.

Then, using Pythagoras' theorem,

$$x^2 = 7.5^2 - 3^2 \text{ cm}^2$$
$$= 56.25 - 9 \text{ cm}^2$$
$$= 47.25 \text{ cm}^2$$

So $x = \sqrt{47.25}$ cm

$x = 6.87$ cm

Keep the accurate figure in the calculator memory.

The area of the triangle is $\frac{1}{2} \times 6 \times 6.87$ cm^2 (from the calculator memory), which is 20.6 cm^2 (1 decimal place).

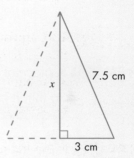

EXERCISE 5D

1 Calculate the areas of these isosceles triangles.

a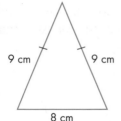

b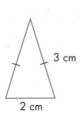

c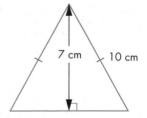

2 Calculate the area of an isosceles triangle whose sides are 8 cm, 8 cm and 6 cm.

PS 3 Calculate the area of an equilateral triangle of side 6 cm.

PS 4 An isosceles triangle has sides of 5 cm and 6 cm.

    a Sketch the two different isosceles triangles that fit this data.

    b Which of the two triangles has the greater area?

5 **a** Sketch a regular hexagon, showing all its lines of symmetry.

    b Calculate the area of the hexagon if its side is 8 cm.

PS 6 Calculate the area of a hexagon of side 10 cm.

PS 7 These isosceles triangles have the same perimeter.

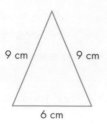 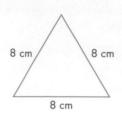 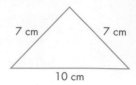

9 cm   9 cm   8 cm   8 cm   7 cm   7 cm

6 cm   8 cm   10 cm

    a   Do the three triangles have the same area?

    b   Can you find an isosceles triangle with the same perimeter but a larger area?

    c   Can you generalise your findings?

FM 8 A piece of land is in the shape of an isosceles triangle with sides 6.5 m, 6.5 m and 7.4 m.

So that it can be sown with the correct quantity of grass seed to make a lawn, you have been asked to calculate the area.

What is the area of the land?

9 The diagram shows an isosceles triangle ABC.

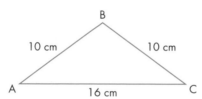

B

10 cm   10 cm

A   16 cm   C

Calculate the area of triangle ABC.

State the units of your answer.

10 Calculate the lengths marked x in these isosceles triangles.

    a   **b**   **AU c**

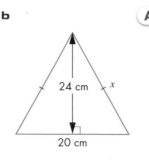 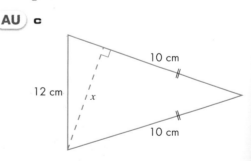

12 cm   13 cm

x

24 cm x

20 cm

12 cm x 10 cm

10 cm

HINTS AND TIPS

Find the area first.

Pythagoras' theorem in three dimensions

This section will show you how to:
- use Pythagoras' theorem in problems involving three dimensions

Key words
3D
Pythagoras' theorem

This section shows you how to solve problems in **3D** using **Pythagoras' theorem**.

In your GCSE examinations, there may be questions which involve applying Pythagoras' theorem in 3D situations. Such questions are usually accompanied by clearly-labelled diagrams, which will help you to identify the lengths needed for your solutions.

You deal with these 3D problems in exactly the same way as 2D problems.

- Identify the right-angled triangle you need.

- Redraw this triangle and label it with the given lengths and the length to be found, usually x or y.

- From your diagram, decide whether it is the hypotenuse or one of the shorter sides which has to be found.

- Solve the problem, rounding to a suitable degree of accuracy.

EXAMPLE 5

What is the longest piece of straight wire that can be stored in this box measuring 30 cm by 15 cm by 20 cm?

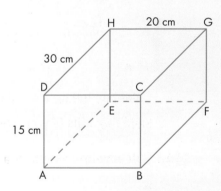

The longest distance across this box is any one of the diagonals AG, DF, CE or HB.

Let us take AG.

First, identify a right-angled triangle containing AG and draw it.

 This gives a triangle AFG, which contains two lengths you do not know, AG and AF.

Let AG = x and AF = y

 Next identify a right-angled triangle that contains the side AF and draw it.

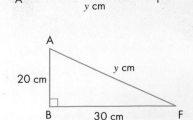

This gives a triangle ABF. You can now find AF.

By Pythagoras' theorem,
$$y^2 = 30^2 + 20^2 \text{ cm}^2$$
$$y^2 = 1300 \text{ cm}^2 \text{ (there is no need to find } y)$$

EXAMPLE 5 (continued)

Now find AG using triangle AFG.

By Pythagoras' theorem,
$$x^2 = y^2 + 15^2 \text{ cm}^2$$
$$x^2 = 1300 + 225 = 1525 \text{ cm}^2$$

So $x = 39.1$ cm (1 decimal place)

So, the longest straight wire that can be stored in the box is 39.1 cm.

Note that in any cuboid with sides a, b and c; the length of a diagonal is given by:

$$\sqrt{(a^2 + b^2 + c^2)}$$

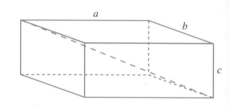

EXERCISE 5E

1 A box measures 8 cm by 12 cm by 5 cm.

   a Calculate the lengths of the following.

   i AC   **ii** BG   **iii** BE

   b Calculate the diagonal distance BH.

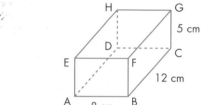

AU 2 A garage is 5 m long, 3 m wide and 3 m high. Can a 7 m long pole be stored in it?

AU 3 Spike, a spider, is at the corner S of the wedge shown in the diagram. Fred, a fly, is at the corner F of the same wedge.

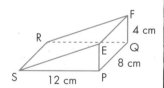

   a Calculate the shortest distance Spike would have to travel to get to Fred if she used the edges of the wedge.

   b Calculate the distance Spike would have to travel across the face of the wedge to get directly to Fred.

AU 4 Fred is now at the top of a baked-beans can and Spike is directly below him on the base of the can. To catch Fred by surprise, Spike takes a diagonal route round the can. How far does Spike travel?

HINTS AND TIPS

Imagine the can opened out flat.

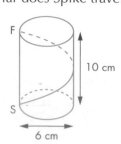

FM **5** A corridor is 3 m wide and turns through a right angle, as in the diagram.

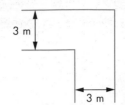

    a What is the longest pole that can be carried along the corridor horizontally?

    b If the corridor is 3 m high, what is the longest pole that can be carried along in any direction?

PS **6** If each side of a cube is 10 cm long, how far will it be from one corner of the cube to the opposite one?

AU **7** A pyramid has a square base of side 20 cm and each sloping edge is 25 cm long.

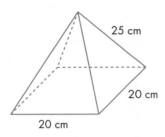

How high is the pyramid?

AU **8** The diagram shows a square-based pyramid with base length 8 cm and sloping edges 9 cm. M is the midpoint of the side AB, X is the midpoint of the base, and E is directly above X.

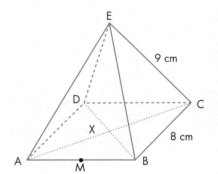

    a Calculate the length of the diagonal AC.

    b Calculate EX, the height of the pyramid.

    c Using triangle ABE, calculate the length EM.

9 The diagram shows a cuboid with sides of 40 cm, 30 cm and 22.5 cm. M is the midpoint of the side FG. Calculate (or write down) these lengths, giving your answers to 3 significant figures if necessary.

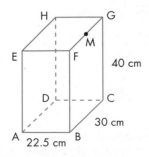

    a AH   **b** AG   **c** AM   **d** HM

Trigonometric ratios

This section will show you how to:
- use the three trigonometric ratios

Key words
adjacent side
cosine
hypotenuse
opposite side
sine
tangent
trigonometry

Trigonometry is concerned with the calculation of sides and angles in triangles, and involves the use of three important ratios: **sine**, **cosine** and **tangent**. These ratios are defined in terms of the sides of a right-angled triangle and an angle. The angle is often written as θ.

In a right-angled triangle:

- the side opposite the right angle is called the **hypotenuse** and is the longest side
- the side opposite the angle θ is called the **opposite side**
- the other side next to both the right angle and the angle θ is called the **adjacent side**.

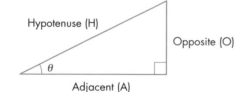

The sine, cosine and tangent ratios for *θ* are defined as:

$$\text{sine } \theta = \frac{\text{Opposite}}{\text{Hypotenuse}} \qquad \text{cosine } \theta = \frac{\text{Adjacent}}{\text{Hypotenuse}} \qquad \text{tangent } \theta = \frac{\text{Opposite}}{\text{Adjacent}}$$

These ratios are usually abbreviated as:

$$\sin \theta = \frac{O}{H} \qquad \cos \theta = \frac{A}{H} \qquad \tan \theta = \frac{O}{A}$$

These abbreviated forms are also used on calculator keys.

Memorising these formulae may be helped by a mnemonic such as,

Silly **O**ld **H**itler **C**ouldn't **A**dvance **H**is **T**roops **O**ver **A**frica

in which the first letter of each word is taken in order to give:

$$S = \frac{O}{H} \qquad C = \frac{A}{H} \qquad T = \frac{O}{A}$$

Using your calculator

You will need to use a calculator to find trigonometric ratios.

Different calculators work in different ways, so make sure you know how to use your model.

Angles are not always measured in degrees. Sometimes radians or grads are used instead. You do not need to learn about those in your GCSE course. Calculators can be set to operate in any of these three units, so make sure your calculator is operating in degrees.

Use your calculator to find the sine of 60 degrees.

You will probably press the keys `sin` `6` `0` `=` in that order, but it might be different on your calculator.

The answer should be 0.8660... or $\frac{\sqrt{3}}{2}$. If it is the latter, make sure you can convert that to the decimal form.

3 cos 57° is a shorthand way of writing 3 × cos 57°.

On most calculators you do not need to use the × button and you can just press the keys in the way it is written: `3` `cos` `5` `7` `=`

Check to see whether your calculator works this way.

The answer should be 1.63.

EXAMPLE 6

Find 5.6 sin 30°.

This means 5.6 × sine of 30 degrees.

Remember that you may not need to press the × button.

5.6 sin 30° = 2.8

EXERCISE 5F

1 Find these values, rounding off your answers to 3 significant figures.

a sin 43°　　　b sin 56°　　　c sin 67.2°　　　d sin 90°

e sin 45°　　　f sin 20°　　　g sin 22°　　　h sin 0°

2 Find these values, rounding off your answers to 3 significant figures.

a cos 43°　　　b cos 56°　　　c cos 67.2°　　　d cos 90°

e cos 45°　　　f cos 20°　　　g cos 22°　　　h cos 0°

3 From your answers to questions **1** and **2**, what angle has the same value for sine and cosine?

4
  a **i** What is sin 35°? **ii** What is cos 55°?

  b **i** What is sin 12°? **ii** What is cos 78°?

  c **i** What is cos 67°? **ii** What is sin 23°?

  d What connects the values in parts **a**, **b** and **c**?

  e Copy and complete these sentences.

  i sin 15° is the same as cos …

  ii cos 82° is the same as sin …

  iii sin x is the same as cos …

5 Use your calculator to work out the values of the following.

  a tan 43°   **b** tan 56°   **c** tan 67.2°   **d** tan 90°

  e tan 45°   **f** tan 20°   **g** tan 22°   **h** tan 0°

6 Use your calculator to work out the values of the following.

  a sin 73°   **b** cos 26°   **c** tan 65.2°   **d** sin 88°

  e cos 35°   **f** tan 30°   **g** sin 28°   **h** cos 5°

7 What is so different about tan compared with both sin and cos?

8 Use your calculator to work out the values of the following.

  a 5 sin 65°   **b** 6 cos 42°   **c** 6 sin 90°   **d** 5 sin 0°

9 Use your calculator to work out the values of the following.

  a 5 tan 65°   **b** 6 tan 42°   **c** 6 tan 90°   **d** 5 tan 0°

10 Use your calculator to work out the values of the following.

  a 4 sin 63°   **b** 7 tan 52°   **c** 5 tan 80°   **d** 9 cos 8°

11 Use your calculator to work out the values of the following.

  a $\dfrac{5}{\sin 63°}$ **b** $\dfrac{6}{\sin 32°}$ **c** $\dfrac{6}{\sin 90°}$ **d** $\dfrac{5}{\sin 30°}$

12 Use your calculator to work out the values of the following.

  a $\dfrac{3}{\tan 64°}$ **b** $\dfrac{7}{\tan 42°}$ **c** $\dfrac{5}{\tan 89°}$ **d** $\dfrac{6}{\tan 40°}$

13 Use your calculator to work out the values of the following.

  a 8 sin 75°   **b** $\dfrac{19}{\sin 23°}$ **c** 7 cos 71°   **d** $\dfrac{15}{\sin 81°}$

14 Use your calculator to work out the values of the following.

  a 8 tan 75°   **b** $\dfrac{19}{\tan 23°}$ **c** 7 tan 71°   **d** $\dfrac{15}{\tan 81°}$

15 Using the following triangles calculate sin x, cos x, and tan x. Leave your answers as fractions.

a

b

c

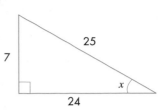

5.6 Calculating angles

This section will show you how to:
- use the trigonometric ratios to calculate an angle

Key words

inverse

What angle has a cosine of 0.6? We can use a calculator to find out.

'The angle with a cosine of 0.6' is written as $\cos^{-1} 0.6$ and is called the 'inverse cosine of 0.6'.

Find out where $\cos^{-1}$ is on your calculator.

You will probably find it on the same key as cos, but you will need to press SHIFT or INV or 2ndF first.

Look to see if $\cos^{-1}$ is written above the cos key.

Check that $\cos^{-1} 0.6 = 53.1301\ldots = 53.1°$ (1 decimal place)

Check that $\cos 53.1° = 0.600$ (3 decimal places)

Check that you can find the inverse sine and the inverse tangent in the same way.

EXAMPLE 7

What angle has a sine of $\frac{3}{8}$?

You need to find $\sin^{-1} \frac{3}{8}$.

You could use the fraction button on your calculator or you could calculate $\sin^{-1} (3 \div 8)$.

If you use the fraction key you may not need a bracket, or your calculator may put one in automatically.

Try to do it in both of these ways and then use whichever you prefer.

The answer should be 22.0°.

EXAMPLE 8

Find the angle with a tangent of 0.75.

$\tan^{-1} 0.75 = 36.86989765 = 36.9°$ (1 decimal place)

EXERCISE 5G

Use your calculator to find the answers to the following. Give your answers to 1 decimal place.

1 What angles have the following sines?

     a 0.5   **b** 0.785   **c** 0.64   **d** 0.877   **e** 0.999   **f** 0.707

2 What angles have the following cosines?

     a 0.5   **b** 0.64   **c** 0.999   **d** 0.707   **e** 0.2   **f** 0.7

3 What angles have the following tangents?

     a 0.6   **b** 0.38   **c** 0.895   **d** 1.05   **e** 2.67   **f** 4.38

4 What angles have the following sines?

     a $4 \div 5$ **b** $2 \div 3$ **c** $7 \div 10$ **d** $5 \div 6$ **e** $1 \div 24$ **f** $5 \div 13$

5 What angles have the following cosines?

     a $4 \div 5$ **b** $2 \div 3$ **c** $7 \div 10$ **d** $5 \div 6$ **e** $1 \div 24$ **f** $5 \div 13$

6 What angles have the following tangents?

     a $3 \div 5$ **b** $7 \div 9$ **c** $2 \div 7$ **d** $9 \div 5$ **e** $11 \div 7$ **f** $6 \div 5$

7 What happens when you try to find the angle with a sine of 1.2? What is the largest value of sine you can put into your calculator without getting an error when you ask for the inverse sine? What is the smallest?

PS **8** **a** **i** What angle has a sine of 0.3? (Keep the answer in your calculator memory.)

     ii What angle has a cosine of 0.3?

     iii Add the two accurate answers of parts **i** and **ii** together.

     b Will you always get the same answer to the above no matter what number you start with?

Using the sine and cosine functions

This section will show you how to:
- find lengths of sides and angles in right-angled triangles using the sine and cosine functions

Key words
cosine
sine

Sine function

Remember sine $\theta = \dfrac{\text{Opposite}}{\text{Hypotenuse}}$

We can use the **sine** ratio to calculate the lengths of sides and angles in right-angled triangles.

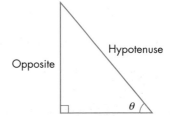

EXAMPLE 9

Find the angle θ, given that the opposite side is 7 cm and the hypotenuse is 10 cm.

Draw a diagram. (This is an essential step.)

From the information given, use sine.

$$\sin \theta = \frac{O}{H} = \frac{7}{10} = 0.7$$

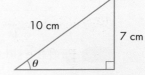

What angle has a sine of 0.7? To find out, use the inverse sine function on your calculator.

$$\sin^{-1} 0.7 = 44.4° \text{ (1 decimal place)}$$

EXAMPLE 10

Find the length of the side marked a in this triangle.

Side a is the opposite side, with 12 cm as the hypotenuse, so use sine.

$$\sin \theta = \frac{O}{H}$$

$$\sin 35° = \frac{a}{12}$$

So $a = 12 \sin 35° = 6.88$ cm (3 significant figures)

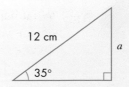

EXAMPLE 11

Find the length of the hypotenuse, h, in this triangle.

Note that although the angle is in the other corner, the opposite side is again given. So use sine.

$$\sin \theta = \frac{O}{H}$$

$$\sin 52° = \frac{8}{h}$$

So $h = \dfrac{8}{\sin 52°} = 10.2$ cm (3 significant figures)

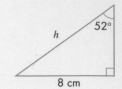

EXERCISE 5H

1 Find the angle marked x in each of these triangles.

a

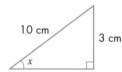

b

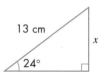

c

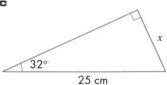

2 Find the side marked x in each of these triangles.

a

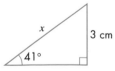

b

c

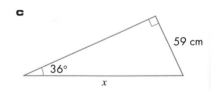

3 Find the side marked x in each of these triangles.

a

b

c

4 Find the side marked x in each of these triangles.

a

b

c

d

5 Find the value of x in each of these triangles.

a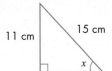

b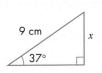

c

d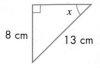

6 Angle θ has a sine of $\frac{3}{5}$. Calculate the missing lengths in these triangles.

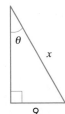

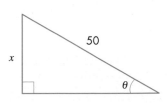

Cosine function

Remember cosine $\theta = \dfrac{\text{Adjacent}}{\text{Hypotenuse}}$

We can use the **cosine** ratio to calculate the lengths of sides and angles in right-angled triangles.

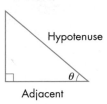

EXAMPLE 12

Find the angle θ, given that the adjacent side is 5 cm and the hypotenuse is 12 cm.

Draw a diagram. (This is an essential step.)

From the information given, use cosine.

$$\cos \theta = \frac{A}{H} = \frac{5}{12}$$

What angle has a cosine of $\frac{5}{12}$? To find out, use the inverse cosine function on your calculator.

$$\cos^{-1} = 65.4° \text{ (1 decimal place)}$$

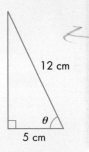

EXAMPLE 13

Find the length of the side marked a in this triangle.

Side a is the adjacent side, with 9 cm as the hypotenuse, so use cosine.

$$\cos \theta = \frac{A}{H}$$

0.68

$$\cos 47° = \frac{a}{9}$$

So $a = 9 \cos 47° = 6.14$ cm (3 significant figures)

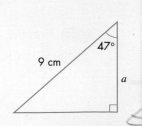

EXAMPLE 14

Find the length of the hypotenuse, *h*, in this triangle.

The adjacent side is given. So use cosine.

$$\cos \theta = \frac{A}{H}$$

$$\cos 40° = \frac{20}{h}$$

So $h = \dfrac{20}{\cos 40°} = 26.1$ cm (3 significant figures)

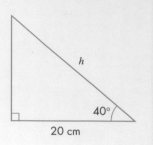

EXERCISE 5I

1 Find the angle marked *x* in each of these triangles.

a

8 cm
5 cm
x

b
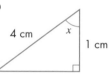
4 cm
x
1 cm

c
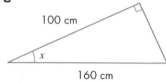
100 cm
x
160 cm

2 Find the side marked *x* in each of these triangles.

a

9 cm
44°
x

b

42 cm
39°
x

c
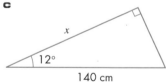
x
12°
140 cm

3 Find the side marked *x* in each of these triangles.

a

x
35°
6 cm

b
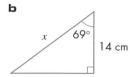
x
69°
14 cm

c
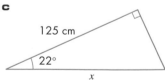
125 cm
22°
x

4 Find the side marked *x* in each of these triangles.

a
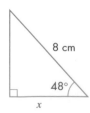
8 cm
48°
x

b
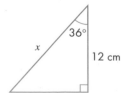
36°
x
12 cm

c
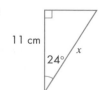
11 cm
24°
x

d

52° 14 cm
x

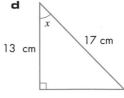

5 Find the value of x in each of these triangles.

a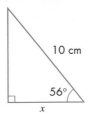

b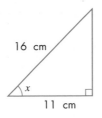

c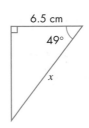

d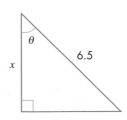

6 Angle θ has a cosine of $\frac{5}{13}$. Calculate the missing lengths in these triangles.

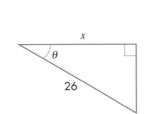

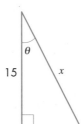

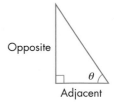

5.8 Using the tangent function

This section will show you how to:	Key words
• find lengths of sides and angles in right-angled triangles using the tangent function	tangent

Remember tangent $\theta = \dfrac{\text{Opposite}}{\text{Adjacent}}$

We can use the **tangent** ratio to calculate the lengths of sides and angles in right-angled triangles.

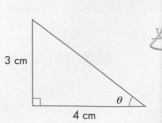

Opposite

Adjacent

EXAMPLE 15

Find the angle θ, given that the opposite side is 3 cm and the adjacent side is 4 cm.

Draw a diagram. (This is an essential step.)

From the information given, use tangent.

$$\tan \theta = \frac{O}{A} = \frac{3}{4} = 0.75$$

What angle has a tangent of 0.75? To find out, use the inverse tangent function on your calculator.

$$\tan^{-1} 0.75 = 36.9° \text{ (1 decimal place)}$$

3 cm

4 cm

EXAMPLE 16

Find the length of the side marked x in this triangle.

Side x is the opposite side, with 9 cm as the adjacent side, so use tangent.

$$\tan \theta = \frac{O}{A}$$

$$\tan 62° = \frac{x}{9}$$

So $x = 9 \tan 62° = 16.9$ cm (3 significant figures)

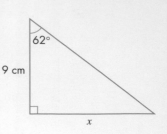

EXAMPLE 17

Find the length of the side marked a in this triangle.

Side a is the adjacent side and the opposite side is given. So use tangent.

$$\tan \theta = \frac{O}{A}$$

$$\tan 35° = \frac{6}{a}$$

So $a = \dfrac{6}{\tan 35°} = 8.57$ cm (3 significant figures)

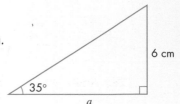

EXERCISE 5J

1 Find the angle marked x in each of these triangles.

a

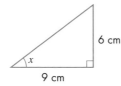

b

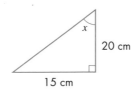

c

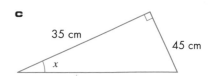

2 Find the side marked x in each of these triangles.

a

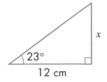

b

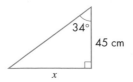

c

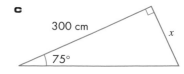

3 Find the side marked x in each of these triangles.

a

b

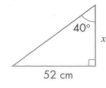

c

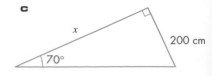

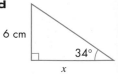

4 Find the side marked x in each of these triangles.

a
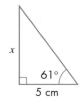
61°
5 cm
x

b
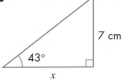
7 cm
43°
x

c
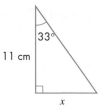
33°
11 cm
x

d
6 cm
34°
x

5 Find the value x in each of these triangles.

a
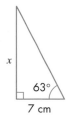
x
63°
7 cm

b
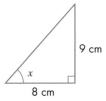
9 cm
x
8 cm

c
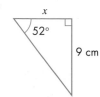
x
52°
9 cm

d
x
4 cm
3.5 cm

6 Angle θ has a tangent of $\frac{4}{3}$. Calculate the missing lengths in these triangles.

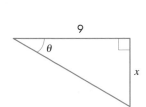
9
θ
x

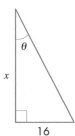
θ
x
16

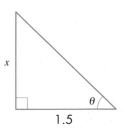
x
θ
1.5

5.9 **Which ratio to use**

This section will show you how to:	Key words
• decide which trigonometric ratio to use in a right-angled triangle	cosine sine tangent

The difficulty with any trigonometric problem is knowing which ratio to use to solve it.

The following examples show you how to determine which ratio you need in any given situation.

EXAMPLE 18

Find the length of the side marked x in this triangle.

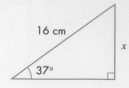

Step 1 Identify what information is given and what needs to be found. Namely, x is opposite the angle and 16 cm is the hypotenuse.

Step 2 Decide which ratio to use. Only one ratio uses opposite and hypotenuse: **sine**.

Step 3 Remember $\sin\theta = \dfrac{O}{H}$

Step 4 Put in the numbers and letters: $\sin 37° = \dfrac{x}{16}$

Step 5 Rearrange the equation and work out the answer:
$x = 16\sin 37° = 9.629\,040\,371$ cm

Step 6 Give the answer to an appropriate degree of accuracy: $x = 9.63$ cm (3 significant figures)

In reality, you do not write down every step as in Example 18. Step 1 can be done by marking the triangle. Steps 2 and 3 can be done in your head. Steps 4 to 6 are what you write down.

Remember that examiners will want to see evidence of working. Any reasonable attempt at identifying the sides and using a ratio will probably get you some method marks, but only if the fraction is the right way round.

The next examples are set out in a way that requires the *minimum* amount of working but gets *maximum* marks.

EXAMPLE 19

Find the length of the side marked x in this triangle.

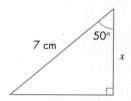

Mark on the triangle the side you know (H) and the side you want to find (A).

Recognise it is a **cosine** problem because you have A and H.

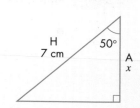

So $\cos 50° = \dfrac{x}{7}$

$x = 7\cos 50° = 4.50$ cm (3 significant figures)

EXAMPLE 20

Find the angle marked x in this triangle.

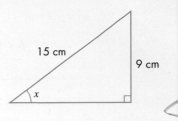

Mark on the triangle the sides you know.

Recognise it is a sine problem because you have O and H.

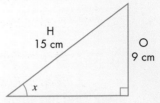

So $\sin x = \dfrac{9}{15} = 0.6$

$x = \sin^{-1} 0.6 = 36.9°$ (1 decimal place)

EXAMPLE 21

Find the angle marked x in this triangle.

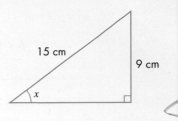

Mark on the triangle the sides you know.

Recognise it is a **tangent** problem because you have O and A.

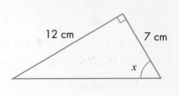

So $\tan x = \dfrac{12}{7}$

$x = \tan^{-1} \dfrac{12}{7} = 59.7°$ (1 decimal place)

EXERCISE 5K

1 Find the length marked x in each of these triangles.

a

20
x
39°

b

40°
x
50

c

x
48°
50

d

20
37°
x

e

x
40°
52

f

x
76°
5

5K

2 Find the angle marked x in each of these triangles.

a
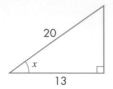
20
14
x

b
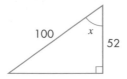
x
60
50

c
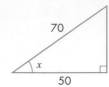
70
x
50

d
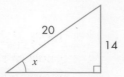
20
x
13

e
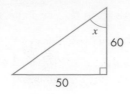
100
x
52

f
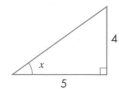
4
x
5

3 Find the angle or length marked x in each of these triangles.

a
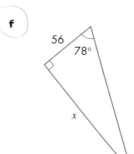
5
x
12

b
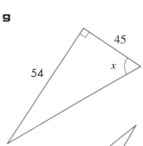
x
10
62°

c
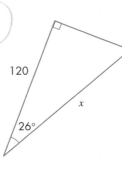
120
x
26°

d

34
x
16

e
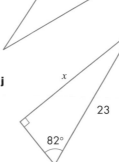
x
39°
25

f
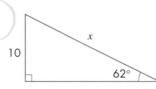
56
78°
x

g
45
x
54

h
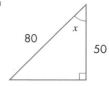
80
x
50

i
x
230
59°

j
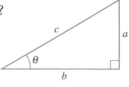
x
23
82°

PS **4** **a** How does this diagram show that $\tan \theta = \dfrac{\sin \theta}{\cos \theta}$?

b How does the diagram show that
$(\sin \theta)^2 + (\cos \theta)^2 = 1$?

c Choose a value for θ and check the two results
in parts **a** and **b** are true.

c a $\xrightarrow{\div c}$ 1 $\dfrac{a}{c}$
θ θ
b $\dfrac{b}{c}$

This section will show you how to:
- solve practical problems using trigonometry
- solve problems using an angle of elevation or an angle of depression

Key words
angle of depression
angle of elevation
trigonometry

Many **trigonometry** problems in GCSE examination papers do not come as straightforward triangles. Sometimes, solving a triangle is part of solving a practical problem. You should follow these steps when solving a practical problem using trigonometry.

- Draw the triangle required.
- Put on the information given (angles and sides).
- Put on x for the unknown angle or side.
- Mark on two of O, A or H as appropriate.
- Choose which ratio to use.
- Write out the equation with the numbers in.
- Rearrange the equation if necessary, then work out the answer.
- Give your answer to a sensible degree of accuracy. Answers given to 3 significant figures or to the nearest degree are acceptable in exams.

EXAMPLE 22

A window cleaner has a ladder which is 7 m long. The window cleaner leans it against a wall so that the foot of the ladder is 3 m from the wall. What angle does the ladder make with the wall?

Draw the situation as a right-angled triangle.

Then mark the sides and angle.

Recognise it is a sine problem because you have O and H.

So $\sin x = \dfrac{3}{7}$

$x = \sin^{-1} \dfrac{3}{7} = 25°$ (to the nearest degree)

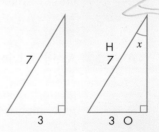

EXERCISE 5L

In these questions, give answers involving angles to the nearest degree.

1 A ladder, 6 m long, rests against a wall. The foot of the ladder is 2.5 m from the base of the wall. What angle does the ladder make with the ground?

FM 2 The ladder in question **1** has a 'safe angle' with the ground of between 70° and 80°. What are the safe limits for the distance of the foot of this ladder from the wall? How high up the wall does the ladder reach?

B

FM 3 A ladder, of length 10 m, is placed so that it reaches 7 m up the wall. What angle does it make with the ground?

FM 4 A ladder is placed so that it makes an angle of 76° with the ground. The foot of the ladder is 1.7 m from the foot of the wall. How high up the wall does the ladder reach?

PS 5 Calculate the angle that the diagonal makes with the long side of a rectangle which measures 10 cm by 6 cm.

FM 6 This diagram shows a frame for a bookcase.

a What angle does the diagonal strut make with the long side?

b Use Pythagoras' theorem to calculate the length of the strut.

c Why might your answers be inaccurate in this case?

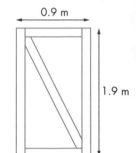

FM 7 This diagram shows a roof truss.

a What angle will the roof make with the horizontal?

b Calculate the length of the sloping strut.

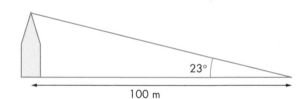

FM 8 Alicia paces out 100 m from the base of a church. She then measures the angle to the top of the spire as 23°. How would Alicia find the height of the church spire?

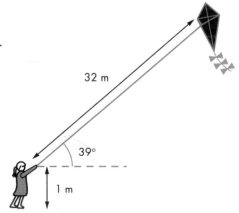

AU 9 A girl is flying a kite on a string 32 m long. The string, which is being held at 1 m above the ground, makes an angle of 39° with the horizontal. How high is the kite above the ground?

32 m

39°

1 m

FM 10 Helena is standing on one bank of a wide river. She wants to find the width of the river. She cannot get to the other side.
She asks if you can use trigonometry to find the width of the river.

What can you suggest?

Angles of elevation and depression

When you look *up* at an aircraft in the sky, the angle through which your line of sight turns from looking straight ahead (the horizontal) is called the **angle of elevation**.

When you are standing on a high point and look *down* at a boat, the angle through which your line of sight turns from looking straight ahead (the horizontal) is called the **angle of depression**.

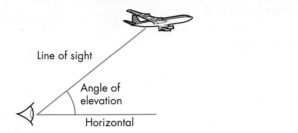

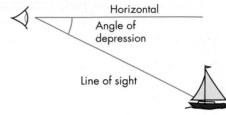

EXAMPLE 23

From the top of a vertical cliff, 100 m high, Andrew sees a boat out at sea. The angle of depression from Andrew to the boat is 42°. How far from the base of the cliff is the boat?

The diagram of the situation is shown in figure **i**.

From this, you get the triangle shown in figure **ii**.

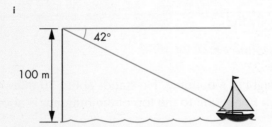   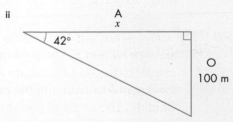

From figure **ii**, you see that this is a tangent problem.

So $\tan 42° = \dfrac{100}{x}$

$x = \dfrac{100}{\tan 42°} = 111$ m (3 significant figures)

EXERCISE 5M

In these questions, give any answers involving angles to the nearest degree.

1   Eric sees an aircraft in the sky. The aircraft is at a horizontal distance of 25 km from Eric. The angle of elevation is 22°. How high is the aircraft?

2   An aircraft is flying at an altitude of 4000 m and is 10 km from the airport. If a passenger can see the airport, what is the angle of depression?

B

3 A man standing 200 m from the base of a television transmitter looks at the top of it and notices that the angle of elevation of the top is 65°. How high is the tower?

AU 4 **a** From the top of a vertical cliff, 200 m high, a boat has an angle of depression of 52°. How far from the base of the cliff is the boat?

b The boat now sails away from the cliff so that the distance is doubled. Does that mean that the angle of depression is halved? Give a reason for your answer.

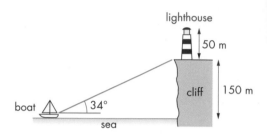

FM 5 From a boat, the angle of elevation of the foot a boathas an angle of depression of 52°. of a lighthouse on the edge of a cliff is 34°.

a If the cliff is 150 m high, how far from the base of the cliff is the boat?

b If the lighthouse is 50 m high, what would be the angle of elevation of the top of the lighthouse from the boat?

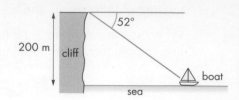

AU 6 A bird flies from the top of a 12 m tall tree, at an angle of depression of 34°, to catch a worm on the ground.

a How far does the bird actually fly?

b How far was the worm from the base of the tree?

FM 7 Sunil wants to work out the height of a building. He stands about 50 m away from a building. The angle of elevation from Sunil to the top of the building is about 15°. How tall is the building?

8 The top of a ski run is 100 m above the finishing line. The run is 300 m long. What is the angle of depression of the ski run?

PS 9 Nessie and Cara are standing on opposite sides of a tree.

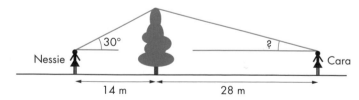

Nessie is 14 m away and the angle of elevation of the top of the tree is 30°.

Cara is 28 m away. She says the angle of elevation for her must be 15° because she is twice as far away.

Is she correct?

What do you think the angle of elevation is?

This section will show you how to:
- solve bearing problems using trigonometry
- use trigonometry to solve problems involving isosceles triangles

Key words

bearing
isosceles triangle
three-figure bearing
trigonometry

Trigonometry and bearings

A **bearing** is the direction to one place from another. The usual way of giving a bearing is as an angle measured from north in a clockwise direction. This is how a navigational compass and a surveyor's compass measure bearings.

A bearing is always written as a three-digit number, known as a **three-figure bearing**.

The diagram shows how this works, using the main compass points as examples.

When working with bearings, follow these three rules.

- Always start from *north*.

- Always measure *clockwise*.

- Always give a bearing in degrees and as a *three-figure bearing*.

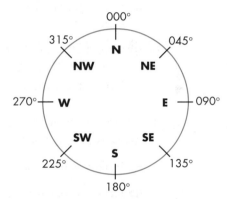

The difficulty with trigonometric problems involving bearings is dealing with those angles greater than 90° whose trigonometric ratios have negative values. To avoid this, we have to find a right-angled triangle that we can readily use. Example 24 shows you how to deal with such a situation.

EXAMPLE 24

A ship sails on a bearing of 120° for 50 km. How far east has it travelled?

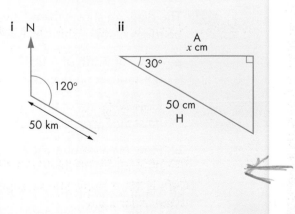

The diagram of the situation is shown in figure **i**. From this, you can get the acute-angled triangle shown in figure **ii**.

From figure **ii**, you see that this is a cosine problem.

So $\cos 30° = \dfrac{x}{50}$

$x = 50 \cos 30° = 43.301$

Distance east = 43.3 km (to 3 significant figures)

B

EXERCISE 5N

1 A ship sails for 75 km on a bearing of 078°.

a How far east has it travelled?   b How far north has it travelled?

2 Lopham is 17 miles from Wath on a bearing of 210°.

a How far south of Wath is Lopham?   b How far east of Lopham is Wath?

FM 3 A plane sets off from an airport and flies due east for 120 km, then turns to fly due south for 70 km before landing at Seddeth. Another pilot decides to fly the direct route from the airport to Seddeth. On what bearing should he fly?

PS 4 A helicopter leaves an army base and flies 60 km on a bearing of 278°.

a How far west has the helicopter flown?   b How far north has the helicopter flown?

5 A ship sails from a port on a bearing of 117° for 35 km before heading due north for 40 km and docking at Angle Bay.

a How far south had the ship sailed before turning?

b How far north had the ship sailed from the port to Angle Bay?

c How far east is Angle Bay from the port?

d What is the bearing from the port to Angle Bay?

AU 6 Mountain A is due west of a walker. Mountain B is due north of the walker. The guidebook says that mountain B is 4.3 km from mountain A, on a bearing of 058°. How far is the walker from mountain B?

PS 7 The shopping mall is 5.5 km east of my house and the supermarket is 3.8 km south. What is the bearing of the supermarket from the shopping mall?

8 The diagram shows the relative distances and bearings of three ships A, B and C.

a How far north of A is B? (Distance x on diagram.)

b How far north of B is C? (Distance y on diagram.)

c How far west of A is C? (Distance z on diagram.)

d What is the bearing of A from C? (Angle $w°$ on diagram.)

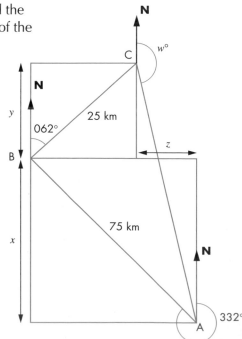

A ship sails from port A for 42 km on a bearing of 130° to point B. It then changes course and sails for 24 km on a bearing of 040° to point C, where it breaks down and anchors. What distance and on what bearing will a helicopter have to fly from port A to go directly to the ship at C?

Trigonometry and isosceles triangles

Isosceles triangles often feature in **trigonometry** problems because such a triangle can be split into two right-angled triangles that are congruent.

EXAMPLE 25

a Find the length x in this isosceles triangle.

b Calculate the area of the triangle.

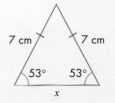

Draw a perpendicular from the apex of the triangle to its base, splitting the triangle into two congruent, right-angled triangles.

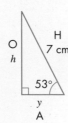

a To find the length y, which is $\frac{1}{2}$ of x, use cosine.

So, $\cos 53° = \dfrac{y}{7}$

$y = 7 \cos 53° = 4.2127051$ cm

So the length $x = 2y = 8.43$ cm (3 significant figures)

b To calculate the area of the original triangle, you first need to find its vertical height, h.

You have two choices, both of which involve the right-angled triangle of part **a**. We can use either Pythagoras' theorem ($h^2 + y^2 = 7^2$) or trigonometry. It is safer to use trigonometry again, since we are then still using known information.

This is a sine problem.

So, $\sin 53° = \dfrac{h}{7}$

$h = 7 \sin 53° = 5.5904486$ cm
(Keep the accurate figure in the calculator.)

The area of the triangle $= \frac{1}{2} \times$ base $\times$ height. (We should use the most accurate figures we have for this calculation.)

$A = \frac{1}{2} \times 8.4254103 \times 5.5904486 = 23.6$ cm^2 (3 significant figures)

You are not expected to write down these eight-figure numbers, just to use them.

EXERCISE 5P

1 Find the side or angle marked x.

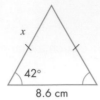
a

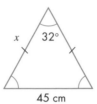
b

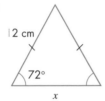
c

d

AU 2 This diagram below shows a roof truss. How wide is the roof?

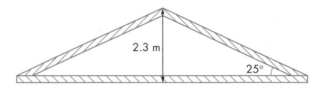

3 Calculate the area of each of these triangles.

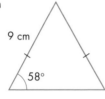
a

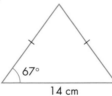
b

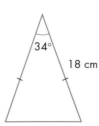
c

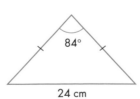
d

PS 4 An equilateral triangle has sides of length 10 cm.

A square is drawn on each side.

The corners of the squares are joined as shown.

What is the area of the resulting hexagon?

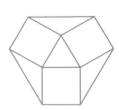

GRADE BOOSTER

C You can use Pythagoras' theorem in right-angled triangles

C You can solve problems in 2D using Pythagoras' theorem

B You can solve problems in 3D using Pythagoras' theorem

B You can use trigonometry to find lengths of sides and angles in right-angled triangles

B You can use trigonometry to solve problems

What you should know now

- How to use Pythagoras' theorem
- How to solve problems using Pythagoras' theorem
- How to use the trigonometric ratios for sine, cosine and tangent in right-angled triangles
- How to solve problems using trigonometry
- How to solve problems using angles of elevation, angles of depression and bearings

1 Calculate the length, x cm, in the triangle below.

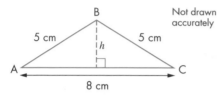

Not drawn accurately

13 cm

x

73°

(3 marks)

AQA, June 2008, Paper 2 Higher, Question 17

2 The diagram shows an isosceles triangle ABC.

Not drawn accurately

B

5 cm   5 cm

h

A

8 cm

C

Calculate the area of the triangle ABC.

Show your working.

State the units of your answer.   *(6 marks)*

AQA, June 2007, Module 5, Paper 1 Higher, Question 3

3 In triangle LMN, angle M = 90°

LN = 32 cm and MN = 14 cm.

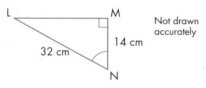

L   M

Not drawn accurately

14 cm

32 cm

N

Calculate the size of angle N.   *(3 marks)*

AQA, June 2007, Module 5, Paper 2 Higher, Question 7

4 **a** Calculate the length x.

Not drawn accurately

32 cm

21 cm

x

b Calculate the length y.

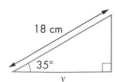

Not drawn accurately

18 cm

35°

y

5 TG is a vertical wireless mast standing on level ground.

P is a point on the ground 50 metres due west of the mast.

The angle of elevation of t from p is 29°.

Q is a point on the ground 75 metres due south of the mast.

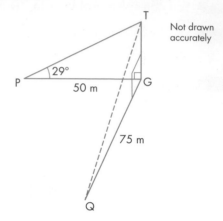

T

Not drawn accurately

29°

P

50 m

G

75 m

Q

Calculate the angle of elevation of T from Q.   *(4 marks)*

AQA, June 2007, Module 5, Paper 2 Higher, Question 16

6 A prism ABCDEF with a right-angled triangular cross-section has dimensions as shown.

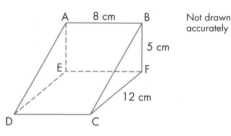

A   8 cm   B

Not drawn accurately

5 cm

E   F

D   C

12 cm

a Calculate the length BD.   *(3 marks)*

b Hence, or otherwise, calculate the angle BDF.   *(2 marks)*

AQA, June 2008, Paper 2 Higher, Question 24

A   B

Worked Examination Questions

1 a ABC is a right-angled triangle. AC = 19 cm and AB = 9 cm.

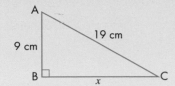

Calculate the length of BC.

b PQR is a right-angled triangle. PQ = 11 cm and QR = 24 cm.

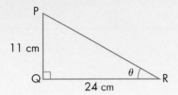

Calculate the size of angle PRQ.

c ABC and ACD are right-angled triangles. AD is parallel to BC.

AB = 12 cm, BC = 5 cm and AD = 33.8 cm.

Calculate the size of angle ADC.

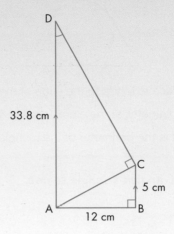

---

1 a Let BC = x

By Pythagoras' theorem

$x^2 = 19^2 - 9^2$ cm^2 — This gets 1 mark for method.

$= 280$ cm^2 — This gets 1 mark for method.

So $x = \sqrt{280}$

$= 16.7$ cm (3 sf) — This gets 1 mark for accuracy.

b Let $\angle PRQ = \theta$

So $\tan \theta = \dfrac{11}{24}$ — This gets 1 mark for method.

$\theta = \tan^{-1} \dfrac{11}{24} = 24.6°$ (1 dp) — This gets 1 mark for accuracy.

c In triangle ABC, let AC = y

By Pythagoras' theorem

$y^2 = 5^2 + 12^2$ cm^2 — This gets 1 mark for method.

$= 169$ cm^2

$y = \sqrt{169} = 13$ cm — This gets 1 mark for accuracy.

In triangle ACD, let $\angle ADC = z$

So, $\sin z = \dfrac{13}{33.8} = 0.3846$ — This gets 1 mark for method.

$z = \sin^{-1} 0.3846 = 22.6°$ (1 dp) — This gets 1 mark for accuracy.

Total: 9 marks

Worked Examination Questions

FM **2** A clock is designed to have circular face on a triangular surround. The triangle is equilateral.

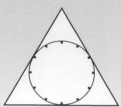

The face extends to the edge of the triangle.

The diameter of the clock face is 18.0 cm.

What is the perimeter of the triangle?

2 Find a right-angled triangle to use.

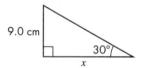

The radius is 9 cm. The angle is 30° because it is half the angle of an equilateral triangle.

Drawing the triangle scores 1 mark for method.

$$\frac{9}{x} = \tan 30°$$

This gets 1 mark for method.

$$x = \frac{9}{\tan 30°} = 15.58\ldots$$

This gets 1 mark for method and 1 mark for accuracy.

Perimeter of triangle = 15.88... × 6 = 93.5 cm or 94 cm

This gets 1 mark for accuracy.

Total: 5 marks

Worked Examination Questions

PS **3** Find the area of a regular hexagon of side 6 cm.

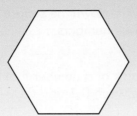

3 Divide the hexagon into smaller parts and add the separate areas together.
One way is to divide it into six equilateral triangles.

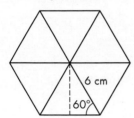

This gets 1 mark for method.

Use Pythagoras' theorem (or trigonometry) to find
the height of the triangle.

For example, height = $\sqrt{(6^2 - 3^2)}$ = 5.19...

This gets 1 mark for method.

Area of one triangle = 3 × 5.19... = 15.58...

Area of hexagon = 6 × area of triangle = 94 cm^2

This gets 1 mark for method and
1 mark for accuracy. Remember not
to round your answer until the end.

Total: 5 marks

When you are out walking on the hills it can be very useful to be able to estimate various distances that you have to cover. Of course, you can just use the scale on the map, but another way is by using Pythagoras' theorem with small right-angled triangles.

Getting started

- You know that the **square** of 2 is $2^2 = 4$. Write down the **square** of each of these numbers.

    5   0.1   0.4   0.03

    Think of a number that has a square between 0.1 and 0.001.

- You know that the **square root** of 4 is $\sqrt{4} = 2$. Now write down the **square root** of each of these numbers.

    16   81   0.01   0.025

    Think of a number that has a square root between 50 and 60.

- On a set of coordinate axes, draw the points A(1, 2) and B(4, 6).

    What is the distance from point A to point B?

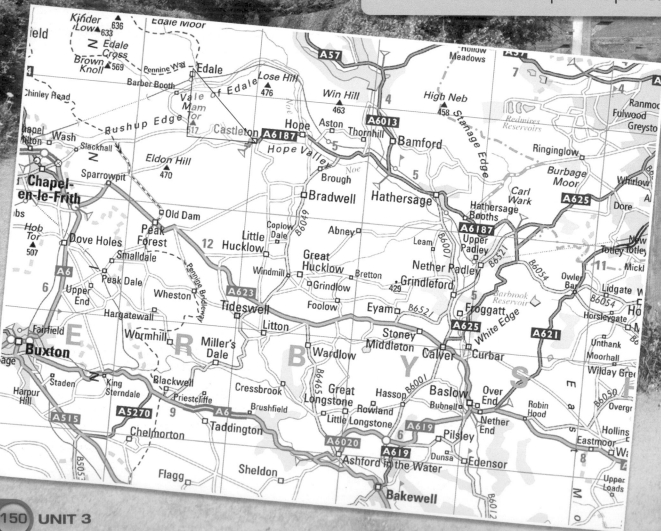

Your task

Freya and Chris often go out walking in the Peak District. On the left is a copy of the map they use. Use this map extract to complete these tasks.

1 Write five questions similar to the examples given on the right. Swap them with the person next to you.

 Answer each other's questions, making sure you show your working clearly.

 Now swap again and mark each other's answers. Give constructive feedback.

2 Plan a walk with a circular route that is between 20 and 35 km long.

 If the average person walks at approximately 4.5 miles per hour, estimate the time it would take to complete your route.

Example

Freya and Chris were at Edale. They wanted to know the rough distance to Castleton. Freya decided to set herself a maths problem, using Pythagoras' theorem.

She looked at the map and imagined the yellow right-angled triangle.

Using the fact that each square on the map represents an area 5 km by 5 km, she estimated each small side of the triangle to be 3 km.

Then she applied Pythagoras' theorem.

$$3^2 + 3^2 = 9 + 9 = 18$$

On the hillside, without a calculator, she estimated the square root of 18 to be just over 4, giving a distance of 4 km.

Another day, Freya and Chris were at Hucklow and wanted to know the distance to Hathersage.

Use Freya's method to estimate the distance from Hucklow to Hathersage.

Additional information

When working in distances, you need to work in either miles and other imperial units or kilometres and other metric units.

To change between these units there are some key conversion facts. Either use a textbook or the internet to find these.

Why this chapter matters

It is essential to understand angles. They help us to construct everything, from a building to a table. So angles literally shape our world.

Ancient civilisations used **right angles** in surveying and in constructing buildings. The ancient Greeks used the right angle to describe relationships between other angles. However, not everything can be measured in right angles. There is a need for a smaller, more useful unit. The ancient Babylonians chose a unit angle that led to the development of the **degree**, which is what we still use today.

Most historians think that the ancient Babylonians thought of the 'circle' of the year as consisting of 360 days. This is not a bad approximation, given the crudeness of the ancient astronomical tools and often having to measure small angles with the naked eye. Mathematics historians believe that the ancient Babylonians knew that the side of a **regular hexagon** inscribed in a circle is equal to the **radius** of the circle. This may have led to the division of the full circle (360 days) into six equal parts, each part consisting of 60 days. They divided one angle of an **equilateral triangle** into 60 equal parts, now called degrees, then further subdivided a degree into 60 equal parts, called **minutes**, and a minute into 60 equal parts, called **seconds**.

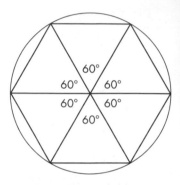

Although many historians believe this is why 60 was the base of the Babylonian system of angle measurement, others think there was a different reason. The number 60 has many **factors**. Work with fractional parts of the whole (60) is greatly simplified, because 2, 3, 4, 5, 6, 10, 12, 15, 20 and 30 are all factors of 60.

Modern measurement of angles

Modern surveyors use theodolites for measuring angles.

A theodolite can be used for measuring both horizontal and vertical angles. It is a key tool in surveying and engineering work, particularly on inaccessible ground, but theodolites have been adapted for other specialised purposes in fields such as meteorology and rocket-launching technology. A modern theodolite comprises a movable telescope mounted within two perpendicular axes – the horizontal and the vertical axis. When the telescope is pointed at a desired object, the angle of each of these axes can be measured with great precision, typically on the scale of arcseconds. (There are 3600 **arcseconds** in 1°.)

Modern theodolite

Chapter

Geometry: Angles and properties of circles

This chapter will show you ...

to **E D** how to find angles in triangles and quadrilaterals

to **D C** how to find interior and exterior angles in polygons

to **B A** how to find angles using circle theorems

Visual overview

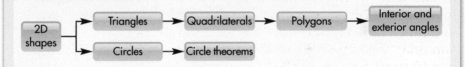

What you should already know

- The three interior angles of a triangle add up to 180°. So, $a + b + c = 180°$

  (KS3 level 5, GCSE grade E)

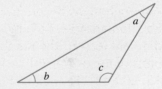

- The four interior angles of a quadrilateral quadrilateral add up to 360°.

  So, $a + b + c + d = 360°$

  (KS3 level 5, GCSE grade E)

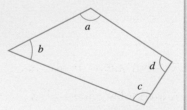

- Angles in parallel lines

a and b are equal
a and b are alternate angles

a and b are equal
a and b are corresponding angles

$a + b = 180°$
a and b are allied angles

(KS3 level 6, GCSE grade D)

continued

● Circle terms

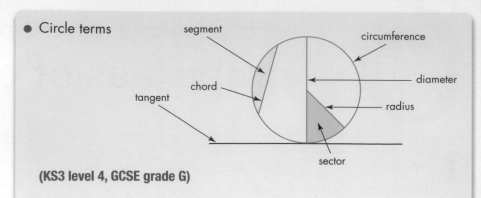

(KS3 level 4, GCSE grade G)

Quick check

Find the sizes of the lettered angles in these diagrams.

1

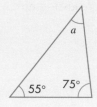

2

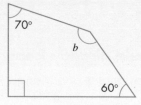

3

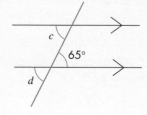

Special triangles and quadrilaterals

This section will show you how to:
- work out the sizes of angles in triangles and quadrilaterals

Key words
equilateral triangle
isosceles triangle
kite
parallelogram
rhombus
trapezium

Special triangles

An **equilateral triangle** is a triangle with all its sides equal.

Therefore, all three interior angles are 60°.

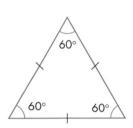

An **isosceles triangle** is a triangle with two equal sides, and therefore with two equal angles.

Notice how to mark the equal sides and equal angles.

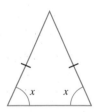

EXAMPLE 1

Find the size of the angle marked *a* in the triangle.

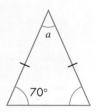

The triangle is isosceles, so both base angles are 70°.

So $a = 180° - (70° + 70°) = 180° - 140° = 40°$

Special quadrilaterals

A **parallelogram** has opposite sides that are parallel.

Its opposite sides are equal. Its diagonals bisect each other. Its opposite angles are equal: that is, $\angle A = \angle C$ and $\angle B = \angle D$

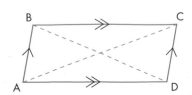

A **rhombus** is a parallelogram with all its sides equal.

Its diagonals bisect each other at right angles. Its diagonals also bisect the angles at the vertices.

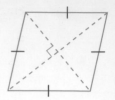

A **kite** is a quadrilateral with two pairs of equal adjacent sides.

Its longer diagonal bisects its shorter diagonal at right angles. The opposite angles between the sides of different lengths are equal.

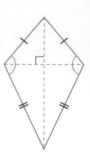

A **trapezium** has two parallel sides.

The sum of the interior angles at the ends of each non-parallel side is 180°: that is, ∠A + ∠D = 180° and ∠B + ∠C = 180°

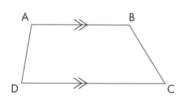

EXAMPLE 2

Find the size of the angles marked x and y in this parallelogram.

$x = 55°$ (opposite angles are equal) and $y = 125°$ ($x + y = 180°$)

EXERCISE 6A

1 Calculate the sizes of the lettered angles in each triangle.

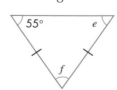

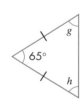

PS 2 An isosceles triangle has an angle of 50°. Sketch the two different possible triangles that match this description, showing what each angle is.

3 Find the sizes of the missing angles in these quadrilaterals.

a
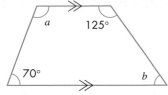

b
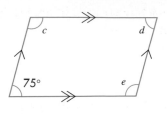

c
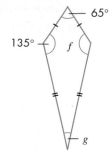

d
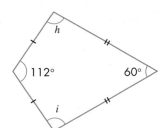

e

f
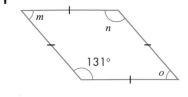

AU 4 The three angles of an isosceles triangle are $2x$, $x - 10$ and $x - 10$. What is the actual size of each angle?

5 Calculate the sizes of the lettered angles in these diagrams.

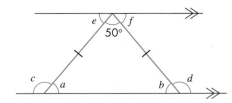

6 Calculate the values of x and y in each of these quadrilaterals.

a
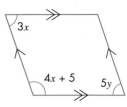

b
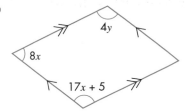

c
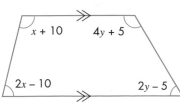

PS 7 Find the value of x in each of these quadrilaterals and hence state what type of quadrilateral it could be.

a A quadrilateral with angles $x + 10$, $x + 20$, $2x + 20$, $2x + 10$

b A quadrilateral with angles $x - 10$, $2x + 10$, $x - 10$, $2x + 10$

c A quadrilateral with angles $x - 10$, $2x$, $5x - 10$, $5x - 10$

d A quadrilateral with angles $4x + 10$, $5x - 10$, $3x + 30$, $2x + 50$

8 The diagram shows a parallelogram ABCD.

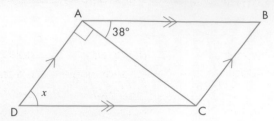

Work out the size of angle x, marked on the diagram.

9 Dani is making a kite and wants Angle C to be half of angle A.

Work out the size of angles B and D.

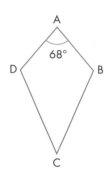

PS 10 This quadrilateral is made from two isosceles triangles. They are both the same size.

Find the value of y in terms of x.

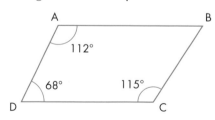

AU 11 The diagram shows a quadrilateral ABCD.

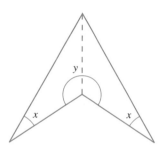

a Calculate the size of angle B.

b What special name is given to the quadrilateral ABCD?

Explain your answer.

Angles in polygons

This section will show you how to:
- work out the sizes of interior angles and exterior angles in a polygon

Key words

decagon	nonagon
exterior angle	octagon
heptagon	pentagon
hexagon	polygon
interior angle	regular polygon

A **polygon** has two kinds of angles.

- **Interior angles** are angles made by adjacent sides of the polygon and lying inside the polygon.

- **Exterior angles** are angles lying on the outside of the polygon, so that the interior angle + the exterior angle = 180°.

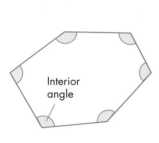

Interior angle

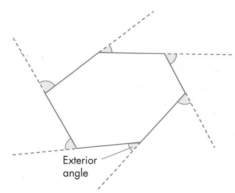

Exterior angle

The *exterior* angles of *any* polygon add up to 360°.

Interior angles

You can find the sum of the interior angles of any polygon by splitting it into triangles.

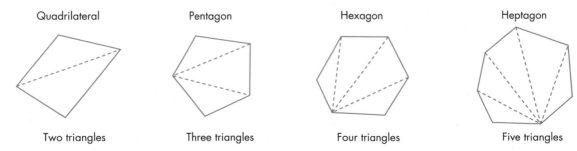

Quadrilateral	Pentagon	Hexagon	Heptagon
Two triangles	Three triangles	Four triangles	Five triangles

Since you already know that the angles in a triangle add up to 180°, you find the sum of the interior angles in a polygon by multiplying the number of triangles in the polygon by 180°, as shown in this table.

Shape	Name	Sum of interior angles
4-sided	Quadrilateral	$2 \times 180° = 360°$
5-sided	**Pentagon**	$3 \times 180° = 540°$
6-sided	**Hexagon**	$4 \times 180° = 720°$
7-sided	**Heptagon**	$5 \times 180° = 900°$
8-sided	**Octagon**	$6 \times 180° = 1080°$
9-sided	**Nonagon**	$7 \times 180° = 1260°$
10-sided	**Decagon**	$8 \times 180° = 1440°$

As you can see from the table, for an n-sided polygon, the sum of the interior angles, S, is given by the formula:

$$S = 180(n - 2)°$$

Exterior angles

As you can see from the diagram, the sum of an exterior angle and its adjacent interior angle is 180°.

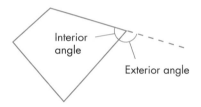

Interior angle

Exterior angle

Regular polygons

A polygon is regular if all its interior angles are equal and all its sides have the same length. This means that all the exterior angles are also equal.

Here are two simple formulae for calculating the interior and the exterior angles of **regular polygons**.

The exterior angle, E, of a regular n-sided polygon is $E = \dfrac{360°}{n}$

The interior angle, I, of a regular n-sided polygon is $I = 180° - E = 180° - \dfrac{360°}{n}$

This can be summarised in the following table.

Regular polygon	Number of sides	Size of each exterior angle	Size of each interior angle
Square	4	90°	90°
Pentagon	5	72°	108°
Hexagon	6	60°	120°
Heptagon	7	$51\frac{3}{7}°$	$128\frac{4}{7}°$
Octagon	8	45°	135°
Nonagon	9	40°	140°
Decagon	10	36°	144°
n-sided	n	$\dfrac{360°}{n}$	$180° - \dfrac{360°}{n}$

EXAMPLE 3

Find the exterior angle, x, and the interior angle, y, for this regular octagon.

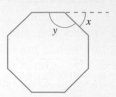

$x = \dfrac{360°}{8} = 45°$ and $y = 180° - 45° = 135°$

EXERCISE 6B

1 Calculate the sum of the interior angles of polygons with these numbers of sides.

   a 10 sides   **b** 15 sides   **c** 100 sides   **d** 45 sides

2 Calculate the size of the interior angle of regular polygons with these numbers of sides.

   a 12 sides   **b** 20 sides   **c** 9 sides   **d** 60 sides

3 Find the number of sides of polygons with these interior angle sums.

   a 1260°   **b** 2340°   **c** 18 000°   **d** 8640°

4 Find the number of sides of regular polygons with these exterior angles.

   a 24°   **b** 10°   **c** 15°   **d** 5°

5 Find the number of sides of regular polygons with these interior angles.

   a 150°   **b** 140°   **c** 162°   **d** 171°

6 Calculate the size of the unknown angle in each of these polygons.

   a   **b**   **c**

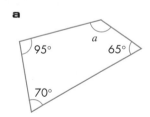 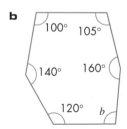 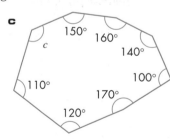

7 Find the value of x in each of these polygons.

   a   **b**   **c**

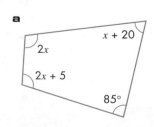 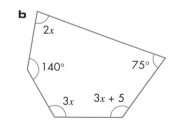 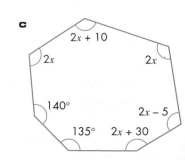

AU **8** What is the name of the regular polygon in which the interior angles are twice its exterior angles?

PS **9** Wesley measured all the interior angles in a polygon. He added them up to make 991°, but he had missed out one angle.

    a What type of polygon did Wesley measure?   **b** What is the size of the missing angle?

10 **a** In the triangle ABC, angle A is 42° and angle B is 67°.

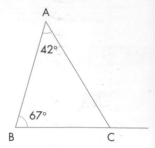

    i Calculate the value of angle C.

    ii What is the value of the exterior angle at C?

    iii What connects the exterior angle at C with the sum of the angles at A and B?

  b Prove that any exterior angle of a triangle is equal to the sum of the two opposite interior angles.

AU **11** Two regular pentagons are placed together.

Work out the value of a.

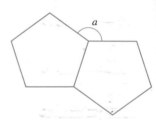

12 A joiner is making tables so that the shape of each one is half a regular hexagon, as shown in the diagram. He needs to know the size of each angle on the table top. What are the sizes of the angles?

PS **13** This star shape has 10 sides that are equal in length.

Each reflex interior angle is 200°.

Work out the size of each acute interior angle.

14 The diagram shows part of a regular polygon.

144°

Each interior angle is 144°.

  a What is the size of each exterior angle of the polygon?

  b How many sides does the polygon have?

Circle theorems

This section will show you how to:
- work out the sizes of angles in circles

Key words

arc	segment
circle	semicircle
circumference	subtended
diameter	

Here are three **circle** theorems you need to know.

- ### Circle theorem 1

  The angle at the centre of a circle is twice the angle at the **circumference** that is **subtended** by the same **arc**.

  $\angle AOB = 2 \times \angle ACB$

  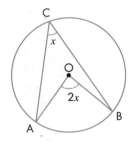

- ### Circle theorem 2

  Every angle at the circumference of a **semicircle** that is subtended by the **diameter** of the semicircle is a right angle.

  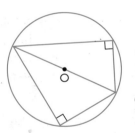

- ### Circle theorem 3

  Angles subtended at the circumference in the same **segment** of a circle are equal.

  Points C_1, C_2, C_3 and C_4 on the circumference are subtended by the same arc AB.

  So $\angle AC_1B = \angle AC_2B = \angle AC_3B = \angle AC_4B$

  Follow through Examples 4–6 to see how these theorems are applied.

  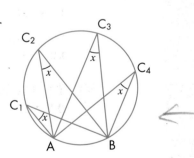

EXAMPLE 4

O is the centre of each circle. Find the angles marked *a* and *b* in each circle.

i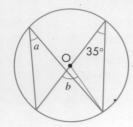

ii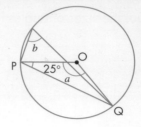

i $a = 35°$ (angles in same segment)

$b = 2 \times 35°$ (angle at centre = twice angle at circumference)

$\quad = 70°$

ii With OP = OQ, triangle OPQ is isosceles and the sum of the angles in this triangle = 180°.

So $a + (2 \times 25°) = 180°$

$\qquad a = 180° - (2 \times 25°)$

$\qquad\quad = 130°$

$\qquad b = 130° \div 2$ (angle at centre = twice angle at circumference)

$\qquad\quad = 65°$

EXAMPLE 5

O is the centre of the circle. PQR is a straight line.

Find the angle labelled *a*.

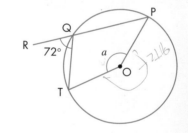

$\angle PQT = 180° - 72° = 108°$ (angles on straight line)

The reflex angle $\angle POT = 2 \times 108°$
(angle at centre = twice angle at circumference)

$\qquad\qquad = 216°$

$a + 216° = 360°$ (sum of angles around a point)

$\qquad a = 360° - 216°$

$\qquad a = 144°$

EXAMPLE 6

O is the centre of the circle. POQ is parallel to TR.

Find the angles labelled *a* and *b*.

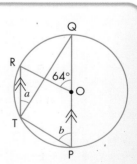

$a = 64° \div 2$ (angle at centre = twice angle at circumference)

$a = 32°$

$\angle TQP = a$ (alternate angles)

$\quad = 32°$

$\angle PTQ = 90°$ (angle in a semicircle)

$b + 90° + 32° = 180°$ (sum of angles in $\triangle PQT$)

$\qquad b = 180° - 122°$

$\qquad b = 58°$

EXERCISE 6C

B

1 Find the angle marked *x* in each of these circles with centre O.

a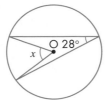

b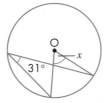

c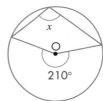

d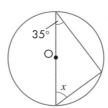

e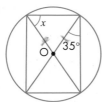

f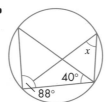

g

h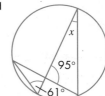

2 Find the angle marked *x* in each of these circles with centre O.

a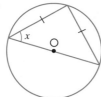

b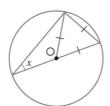

c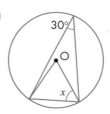

d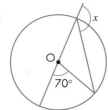

e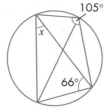

f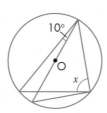

g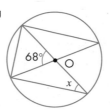

h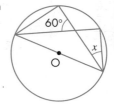

3 In the diagram, O is the centre of the circle. Find these angles.

a ∠ADB

b ∠DBA

c ∠CAD

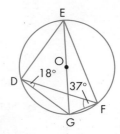

4 In the diagram, O is the centre of the circle. Find these angles.

a ∠EDF

b ∠DEG

c ∠EGF

B

AU **5** In the diagram XY is a diameter of the circle and ∠AZX is *a*.

Ben says that the value of *a* is 55°.

Give reasons to explain why he is wrong.

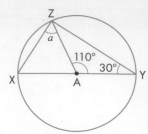

A

6 Find the angles marked *x* and *y* in each of these circles. O is the centre where shown.

a

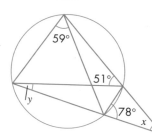

b

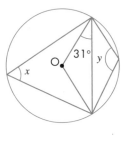

c

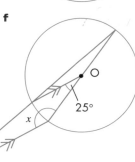

d

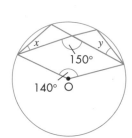

e

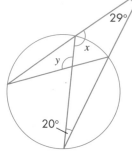

f

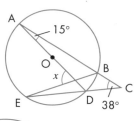

7 In the diagram, O is the centre and AD a diameter of the circle.
Find *x*.

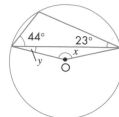

PS **8** In the diagram, O is the centre of the circle and ∠CBD is *x*.

Show that the reflex ∠AOC is 2*x*, giving reasons to explain your answer.

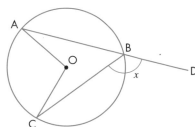

A*

9 A, B, C and D are points on the circumference of a circle with centre O.
Angle ABO is *x*° and angle CBO is *y*°.

a State the value of angle BAO.

b State the value of angle AOD.

c Prove that the angle subtended by the chord AC at the centre of a circle is twice the angle subtended at the circumference.

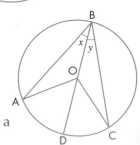

Cyclic quadrilaterals

This section will show you how to:
- find the sizes of angles in cyclic quadrilaterals

Key words
cyclic quadrilateral

A quadrilateral whose four vertices lie on the circumference of a circle is called a **cyclic quadrilateral**.

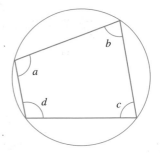

- **Circle theorem 4**

  The sum of the opposite angles of a cyclic quadrilateral is 180°.

  $a + c = 180°$ and $b + d = 180°$

EXAMPLE 7

Find the angles marked x and y in the diagram.

$x + 85° = 180°$ (angles in a cyclic quadrilateral)

So, $x = 95°$

$y + 108° = 180°$ (angles in a cyclic quadrilateral)

So, $y = 72°$

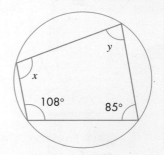

EXERCISE 6D

1 Find the sizes of the lettered angles in each of these circles.

a
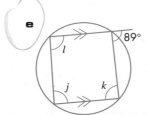
85° 130° a b

b
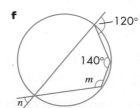
x c 88° x

c
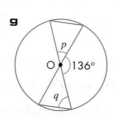
d e f 70°

d
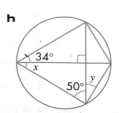
81° g h 105°

e
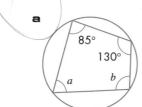
89° l j k

f
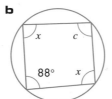
120° 140° m n

g
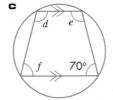
p O 136° q

h
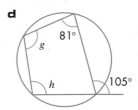
34° x 50° y

B

2 Find the values of *x* and *y* in each of these circles. Where shown, O marks the centre of the circle.

a
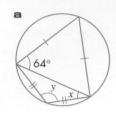

b
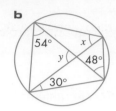

c
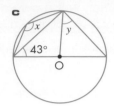

d
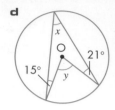

e
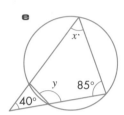

f
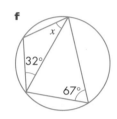

g
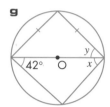

h
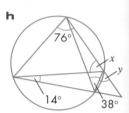

3 Find the values of *x* and *y* in each of these circles. Where shown, O marks the centre of the circle.

a
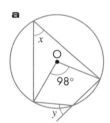

b
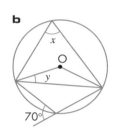

c
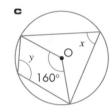

d
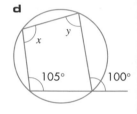

4 Find the values of *x* and *y* in each of these circles.

a
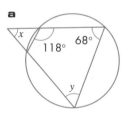

b
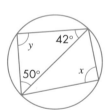

c
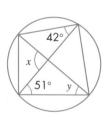

d
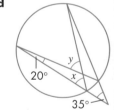

5 Find the values of *x* and *y* in each of these circles with centre O.

a

b
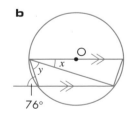

c

d
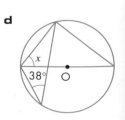

PS 6 The cyclic quadrilateral PQRT has ∠ROQ equal to 38° where O is the centre of the circle. POT is a diameter and parallel to QR. Calculate these angles.

   a ∠ROT   **b** ∠QRT   **c** ∠QPT

AU 7 In the diagram, O is the centre of the circle.

   a Explain why $3x - 30° = 180°$.

   b Work out the size of ∠CDO, marked y on the diagram.

   Give reasons in your working.

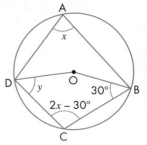

8 ABCD is a cyclic quadrilateral within a circle centre O and ∠AOC is $2x°$.

   a Write down the value of ∠ABC.

   b Write down the value of the reflex angle AOC.

   c Prove that the sum of a pair of opposite angles of a cyclic quadrilateral is 180°.

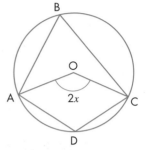

PS 9 In the diagram, ABCE is a parallelogram.

   Prove ∠AED = ∠ADE.

   Give reasons in your working.

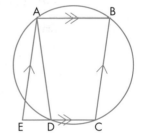

6.5 Tangents and chords

This section will show you how to:

- use tangents and chords to find the sizes of angles in circles

Key words

chord
point of contact
radius
tangent

A **tangent** is a straight line that touches a circle at one point only. This point is called the **point of contact**. A **chord** is a line that joins two points on the circumference.

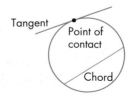

● **Circle theorem 5**

A tangent to a circle is perpendicular to the **radius** drawn to the point of contact.

The radius OX is perpendicular to the tangent AB.

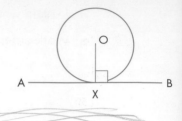

● **Circle theorem 6**

Tangents to a circle from an external point to the points of contact are equal in length.

AX = AY

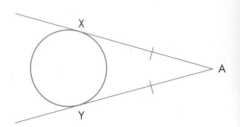

● **Circle theorem 7**

The line joining an external point to the centre of the circle bisects the angle between the tangents.

∠OAX = ∠OAY

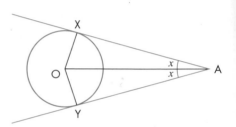

● **Circle theorem 8**

A radius bisects a chord at 90°.

If O is the centre of the circle,

∠BMO = 90° and BM = CM

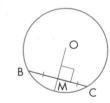

EXAMPLE 8

OA is the radius of the circle and AB is a tangent.

OA = 5 cm and AB = 12 cm

Calculate the length OB.

∠OAB = 90° (radius is perpendicular to a tangent)

Let OB = x

By Pythagoras' theorem,

$x^2 = 5^2 + 12^2$ cm^2

$x^2 = 169$ cm^2

So $x = \sqrt{169} = 13$ cm

EXERCISE 6E

1 In each diagram, TP and TQ are tangents to a circle with centre O. Find each value of x.

a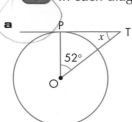

b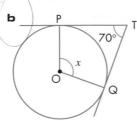

c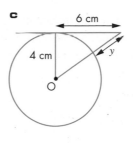

d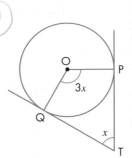

2 Each diagram shows tangents to a circle with centre O. Find each value of y.

a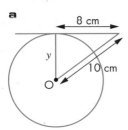

b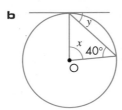

c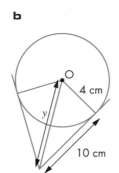

d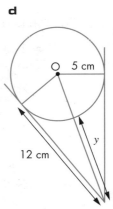

3 Each diagram shows a tangent to a circle with centre O. Find x and y in each case.

a

b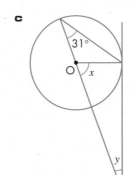

c

d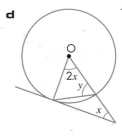

4 In each of the diagrams, TP and TQ are tangents to the circle with centre O. Find each value of x.

a

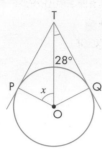

b

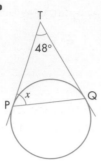

c

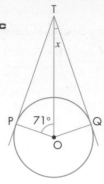

d

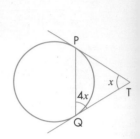

PS 5 Two circles with the same centre have radii of 7 cm and 12 cm respectively. A tangent to the inner circle cuts the outer circle at A and B. Find the length of AB.

PS 6 The diagram shows a circle with centre O.
The circle fits exactly inside an equilateral triangle XYZ.
The lengths of the sides of the triangle are 20 cm.

Work out the radius of the circle.

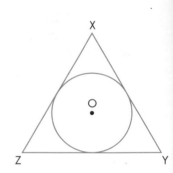

HINTS AND TIPS

Remember you can use Pythagoras' theorem and trigonometry to solve problems.

AU 7 In the diagram, O is the centre of the circle and AB is a tangent to the circle at C.

Explain why triangle BCD is isosceles.

Give reasons to justify your answer.

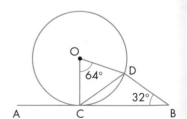

8 AB and CB are tangents from B to the circle with centre O. OA and OC are radii.

a Prove that angles AOB and COB are equal.

b Prove that OB bisects the angle ABC.

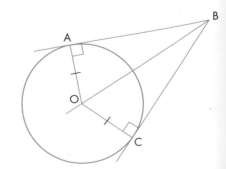

This section will show you how to:
- use the alternate segment theorem to find the sizes of angles in circles

Key words
alternate segment
chord
tangent

PTQ is the **tangent** to a circle at T. The segment containing ∠TBA is known as the **alternate segment** of ∠PTA, because it is on the other side of the **chord** AT from ∠PTA.

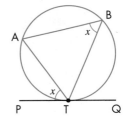

- **Circle theorem 9**

  The angle between a tangent and a chord through the point of contact is equal to the angle in the alternate segment.

  ∠PTA = ∠TBA

EXAMPLE 9

In the diagram, find **a** ∠ATS and **b** ∠TSR.

a ∠ATS = 80° (angle in alternate segment)

b ∠TSR = 70° (angle in alternate segment)

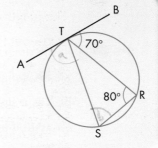

EXERCISE 6F

1 Find the size of each lettered angle.

a

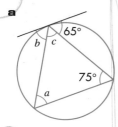

b

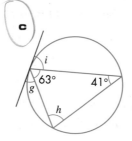

c

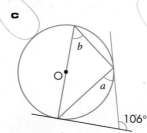

d

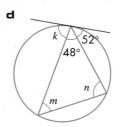

2 In each diagram, find the size of each lettered angle.

a

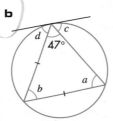

b

c

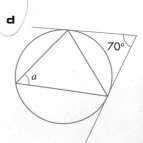

d

A

3 In each diagram, find the value of x.

a

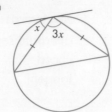

b

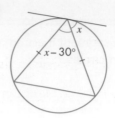

4 ATB is a tangent to each circle with centre O.

Find the size of each lettered angle.

a

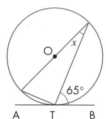

b

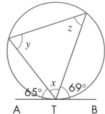

c

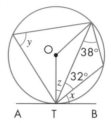

d

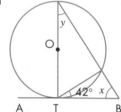

PS 5 In the diagram, O is the centre of the circle.

XY is a tangent to the circle at A.

BCX is a straight line.

Show that triangle ACX is isosceles.

Give reasons to justify your answer.

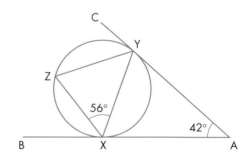

AU 6 AB and AC are tangents to the circle at X and Y.

Work out the size of ∠XYZ.

Give reasons to justify your answer.

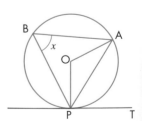

A*

7 PT is a tangent to a circle with centre O.
AB are points on the circumference. Angle PBA is $x°$.

  a Write down the value of angle AOP.

  b Calculate the angle OPA in terms of x.

  c Prove that the angle APT is equal to the angle PBA.

GRADE BOOSTER

D You can find angles in triangles and quadrilaterals

C You can find interior angles and exterior angles in polygons

B You can find angles in circles

A You can find angles in circles, using the alternate segment theorem

A* You can use circle theorems to prove geometrical results

What you should know now

- How to find angles in any triangle or in any quadrilateral
- How to calculate interior and exterior angles in polygons
- How to use circle theorems to find angles

1 a Explain why the sum of the angles in any quadrilateral is 360°. *(2 marks)*

Not drawn accurately

b A quadrilateral has one right angle.

The other angles are $2x$, $3x - 12$ and $x - 6$.

Not drawn accurately

i Write down an equation in terms of x. *(1 mark)*

ii Solve your equation and find the size of the largest angle in the quadrilateral. *(3 marks)*

AQA, June 2007, Paper 1 Higher, Question 3

2 a The diagram shows a regular pentagon.

One side has been extended.

Not drawn accurately

Which **one** of these statements is true?

A The exterior angle of a regular pentagon is equal to 360° ÷ 5 = 72°.

B The interior angle of a regular pentagon is equal to 360° ÷ 5 = 72°.

C The exterior angle of a regular pentagon is equal to 360° − 72° = 288°.

D The interior angle of a regular pentagon is equal to 360° − 72° = 288°.

(1 mark)

b The diagram shows two identical regular pentagons, touching, inside a rectangle.

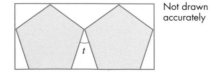

Not drawn accurately

Work out the value of t. *(2 marks)*

AQA, May 2009, Module 5, Paper 1 Higher, Question 8(a)

3 a In the diagram, O is the centre of the circle.

Not drawn accurately

Write down the value of a. *(1 mark)*

b Write down the value of b.

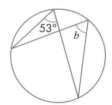

Not drawn accurately

(1 mark)

c In the diagram, O is the centre of the circle.

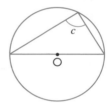

Not drawn accurately

Write down the value of c. *(1 mark)*

d Write down the value of d.

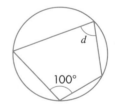

Not drawn accurately

(1 mark)

AQA, June 2005, Module 5, Paper 1 Higher, Question 7

4 A, B and C are points on the circumference of a circle with centre O.

BD and CD are tangents.

Angle BDC = 40°.

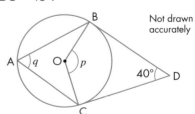

Not drawn accurately

a Work out the value of p. *(2 marks)*

b Hence write down the value of q. *(1 mark)*

AQA, June 2005, Paper 1 Higher, Question 12(a)

A* A B C D

5 On the diagram, TD is a tangent at A.

The line AO is a radius.

Angle TBA = 62°.

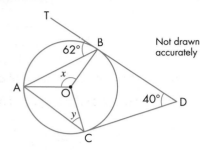

Not drawn accurately

a Work out the value of x. *(2 marks)*

b Work out the value of y. *(2 marks)*

AQA, June 2005, Paper 1 Higher, Question 12(b)

6 ABCD is a cyclic quadrilateral.

PAQ is a tangent to the circle at A.

BC = CD.

Angle QAB = 38° and angle BAD = 76°.

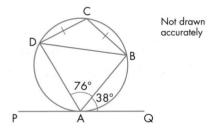

Not drawn accurately

Show that AD is parallel to BC.

Give reasons to justify any values you write down or calculate. *(4 marks)*

AQA, June 2006, Paper 2 Higher, Question 18

7 In the diagram, ABCD is a cyclic quadrilateral and PAQ is a tangent to the circle at A. Angle BCD = 105° and angle DAQ = 63°.

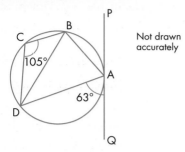

Not drawn accurately

a Work out the size of angle BAD.

Give a reason for your answer. *(1 mark)*

b Work out the size of angle ADB.

You **must** show your working. *(1 mark)*

AQA, May 2008, Paper 1 Higher, Question 18

8 A, B, C and D are points on the circumference of a circle.

The line CD is extended to E.

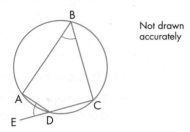

Not drawn accurately

Prove that ∠ABC = ∠ADE. *(3 marks)*

AQA, June 2009, Paper 2 Higher, Question 27

Worked Examination Questions

1 Naomi has a collection of tiles that are all **regular polygons**.

The sides of all the tiles are the same length.

She says that a **regular hexagon** will fit exactly between **a square** and a **regular octagon**.

Explain why she is wrong.

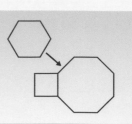

1 Interior angle of the square = 90°

Interior angle of the regular octagon = 135°

Interior angle of the regular hexagon = 120°

> This gets 1 mark for all three correct.

90° + 135° + 120° = 345°

> This gets 1 method mark for finding the total.

So the regular hexagon does not fit exactly as the three angles do not add up to 360°.

> This gets 1 accuracy mark for the reason.

(**Total:** 3 marks)

2 a

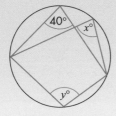

i Write down the value of x.

ii Calculate the value of y.

b A and C are points on the circumference of a circle centre B. AD and CD are tangents and ∠ADB = 40°.

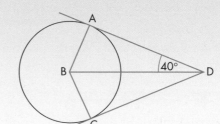

Explain why ABC is 100°. Give **reasons** for your answers.

2 a i $x = 40°$ (angle in same segment)

> This gets 1 mark.

ii $x = 140°$ (opposite angles in cyclic quadrilateral = 180°)

> This gets 1 mark.

b BAD = 90° (radius is perpendicular to tangent)

> This gets 1 mark.

∠ABD = 50° (angles in a triangle)

> This gets 1 mark.

Similarly:

> This gets 1 mark for method.

∠BCD = 90° (radius is perpendicular to tangent)

∠CBD = 50° (angles in a triangle)

So ∠ABC = 2 × 50° = 100°

> This gets 1 mark for accuracy.

(**Total:** 5 marks)

Worked Examination Questions

PS **3** The diagrams show a trapezium and a parallelogram.

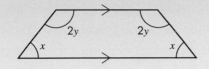 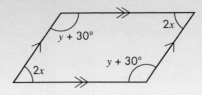

   a Use the trapezium to explain why $x + 2y = 180°$.

   b Use the parallelogram to form another equation in terms of x and y.

   c Work out the values of x and y.

3 a The interior angles at either end of the trapezium add up to 180° ⸺ This gets 1 mark.

   or you could say the two angles are allied angles ⸺ This gets 1 mark.

 b $2x + y + 30° = 180°$ (allied angles)

   This simplifies to $2x + y = 150°$

 c You now have two equations to solve simultaneously.

$$x + 2y = 180° \quad (1)$$
$$2x + y = 150° \quad (2)$$
$$2x + 4y = 360° \quad (3) = (1) \times 2$$
$$(3) - (2)$$

   This gets 1 method mark for attempt to solve equations.

$3y = 210°$ so $y = 70°$ ⸺ This gets 1 accuracy mark for one correct angle.

Substitute into (1) $x + 140° = 180°$, so $x = 40°$ ⸺ This gets 1 accuracy mark for the other angle.

Total: 3 marks

4 In the diagram, XY is a tangent to the circle at A.

BCY is a straight line.

Work out the size of $\angle ABC$.

Give reasons to justify your answer.

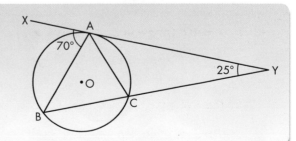

4 $\angle ACB = 70°$ (angle in alternate segment) ⸺ This gets 1 mark.

$\angle ACY = 110°$ (angles on a line $= 180°$)

$\angle CAY = 45°$ (angles in a triangle $= 180°$) ⸺ This gets 1 method mark for using angles in a triangle.

so $\angle ABC = 45°$ (angle in alternate segment) ⸺ This gets 1 accuracy mark.

Total: 3 marks

Circular shapes form the basis of many of the objects that we see and use every day. For example, we see circular shapes in DVDs, wheels, coins and jewellery. Where else do you see circles?

Given how frequently circles appear in our lives, it is important that we understand them mathematically.

In this task you will investigate the properties of circles, using mathematical theory and proof to help you understand this shape more fully.

Getting started

- List the mathematical vocabulary that you know, that is related to circles. Explain each of the words you think of to a classmate.

- Select one fact that you know, that is related to circles. Explain your fact to a partner.

- Select a real-life object that is in the shape of a circle.

  What mathematical questions could you ask about this object?

  How would you use mathematics to find the answers to your questions?

Your task

1   With a partner, develop a statement about the properties of circles. For example, "A radius that is perpendicular to a chord bisects that chord."

    Think carefully about your statement: it will be the hypothesis that forms the basis of a mathematical investigation.

    Alternatively, create a question to form the basis of your investigation. For example, "What is the relationship between an angle subtended at the centre of a circle and the angle subtended by the same two points at the circumference, opposite and on the same arc?"

2   Swap your hypothesis or question with that of another pair.

    Now, use your problem-solving skills to investigate the hypothesis or question. You should create a presentation, using slides or an interactive whiteboard, to explain the mathematical process that you go through in your investigation, the mathematics that you used and the conclusion that you reach.

    In your presentation you must:

    –   explain the overall approach you took in your investigation

    –   summarise each step taken during your investigation

    –   advance a solution to the hypothesis or problem with which you were presented

    –   find the most effective way of representing your solution

    –   give examples to support your conclusions

    –   show what you have now learnt about circles

    –   or any other aspect of geometry.

Why this chapter matters

How many sides does a strip of paper have? Two or one?

Take a strip of paper about 20 cm by 2 cm.

How many sides does it have? Easy! You can see that this has two sides, a topside and an underside. If you were to draw a line along one side of the strip, you would have one side with a line 20 cm long on it and one side blank.

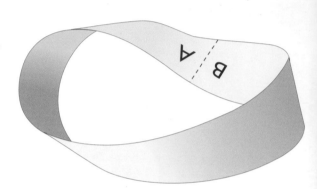

Now mark the ends A and B, put a single twist in the strip of paper and tape (or glue) the two ends together, as shown.

How many sides does this strip of paper have now?

Take a pen and draw a line on the paper, starting at any point you like. Continue the line along the length of the paper – you will eventually come back to your starting point. Your strip has only one side now! There is no blank side.

You have transformed a two-sided piece of paper into a one-sided piece of paper.

This curious shape is called a Möbius strip. It is named after August Ferdinand Möbius, a 19th-century German mathematician and astronomer. Möbius, along with others, caused a revolution in geometry.

Möbius strips have a number of surprising applications that exploit its remarkable property of one-sidedness, including conveyor belts in industry as well as in domestic vacuum cleaners. Have a look at the belt that turns the rotor in the vacuum cleaner at home.

The Möbius strip has become the universal symbol of recycling. The symbol was created in 1970 by Gary Anderson, who was a senior at the University of Southern California, as part of a contest sponsored by a paper company.

The Möbius strip is a form of transformation. In this chapter, you will look at some other transformations of shapes.

Geometry: Transformation geometry

This chapter will show you ...

- **D** what is meant by a transformation
- to **D** **B** how to translate, reflect, rotate and enlarge 2D shapes
- to **B** **A** how to show that two triangles are congruent

Visual overview

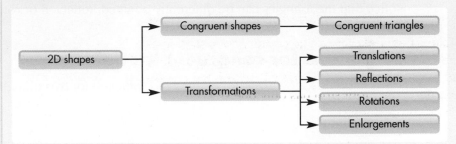

What you should already know

- How to recognise congruent shapes (KS3 level 4, GCSE grade G)
- How to find the lines of symmetry of a 2D shape (KS3 level 4, GCSE grade F)
- How to find the order of rotational symmetry of a 2D shape (KS3 level 4, GCSE grade F)
- How to draw the lines with equations $x = \pm a$, $y = \pm b$, $y = x$ and $y = -x$ (KS3 level 5, GCSE grade E)

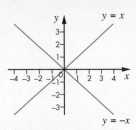

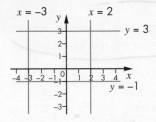

Quick check

Which of these shapes is not congruent to the others?

a   **b**   **c**   **d**

This section will show you how to:
- show that two triangles are congruent

Key words
congruent

Two shapes are **congruent** if they are exactly the same size and shape.

For example, these triangles are all congruent.

 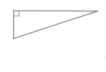 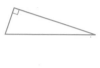

Notice that the triangles can be differently oriented (reflected or rotated).

Conditions for congruent triangles

Any one of the following four conditions is sufficient for two triangles to be congruent.

- **Condition 1**

  All three sides of one triangle are equal to the corresponding sides of the other triangle.

  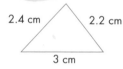 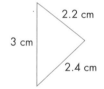

  2.4 cm   2.2 cm   3 cm   2.2 cm   3 cm   2.4 cm

  This condition is known as SSS (side, side, side).

- **Condition 2**

  Two sides and the angle between them of one triangle are equal to the corresponding sides and angle of the other triangle.

  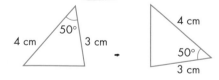

  50°   4 cm   3 cm   4 cm   50°   3 cm

  This condition is known as SAS (side, angle, side).

FM Functional Maths   **AU** (AO2) Assessing Understanding   **PS** (AO3) Problem Solving

- **Condition 3**

  Two angles and a side of one triangle are equal to the corresponding angles and side of the other triangle.

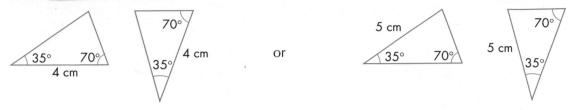

or

  This condition is known as ASA (angle, side, angle) or AAS (angle, angle, side).

- **Condition 4**

  Both triangles have a right angle, an equal hypotenuse and another equal side.

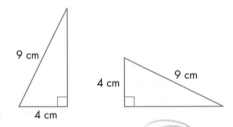

  This condition is known as RHS (right angle, hypotenuse, side).

Notation

Once you have shown that triangle ABC is congruent to triangle PQR by one of the above conditions, it means that:

$\angle A = \angle P$ $AB = PQ$

$\angle B = \angle Q$ $BC = QR$

$\angle C = \angle R$ $AC = PR$

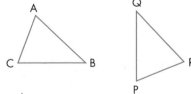

In other words, the points ABC correspond exactly to the points PQR in that order. Triangle ABC is congruent to triangle PQR can be written as $\triangle ABC \equiv \triangle PQR$.

EXAMPLE 1

ABCD is a kite. Show that triangle ABC is congruent to triangle ADC.

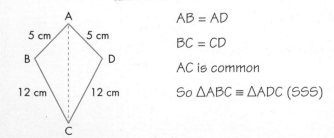

$AB = AD$

$BC = CD$

AC is common

So $\triangle ABC \equiv \triangle ADC$ (SSS)

EXERCISE 7A

1 The triangles in each pair are congruent. State the condition that shows that the triangles are congruent.

a

b

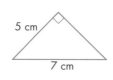
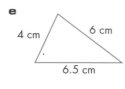

c

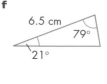

d

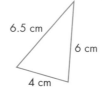

e

f

2 The triangles in each pair are congruent. State the condition that shows that the triangles are congruent and say which points correspond to which.

  a ABC where AB = 8 cm, BC = 9 cm, AC = 7.4 cm
  PQR where PQ = 9 cm, QR = 7.4 cm, PR = 8 cm

  b ABC where AB = 5 cm, BC = 6 cm, angle B = 35°
  PQR where PQ = 6 cm, QR = 50 mm, angle Q = 35°

3 Triangle ABC is congruent to triangle PQR, ∠A = 60°, ∠B = 80° and AB = 5 cm. Find these.

  a ∠P   **b** ∠Q   **c** ∠R   **d** PQ

4 ABCD is congruent to PQRS, ∠A= 110°, ∠B = 55°, ∠C = 85° and RS = 4 cm. Find these.

  a ∠P   **b** ∠Q   **c** ∠R   **d** ∠S   **e** CD

5 Draw a rectangle EFGH. Draw in the diagonal EG. Prove that triangle EFG is congruent to triangle EHG.

6 Draw an isosceles triangle ABC where AB = AC. Draw the line from A to X, the midpoint of BC. Prove that triangle ABX is congruent to triangle ACX.

PS 7 In the diagram ABCD and DEFG are squares.

Use congruent triangles to prove that AE = CG.

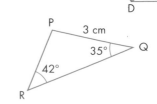

AU 8 Jez says that these two triangles are congruent because two angles and a side are the same.

Explain why he is wrong.

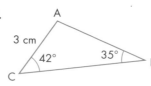

Translations

This section will show you how to:
- translate a 2D shape

Key words
transformation
translation
vector

A **transformation** changes the position or the size of a shape.

There are four basic ways of changing the position and size of 2D shapes: a **translation**, a reflection, a rotation or an enlargement. All of these transformations, except enlargement, keep shapes congruent.

A translation is the 'movement' of a shape from one place to another without reflecting it or rotating it. It is sometimes called a glide, since the shape appears to glide from one place to another. Every point in the shape moves in the same direction and through the same distance.

We describe translations by using **vectors**. A vector is represented by the combination of a horizontal shift and a vertical shift.

EXAMPLE 2

Use vectors to describe the translations of the following triangles.

a A to B

b B to C

c C to D

d D to A

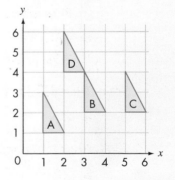

a The vector describing the translation from A to B is $\begin{pmatrix} 2 \\ 1 \end{pmatrix}$.

b The vector describing the translation from B to C is $\begin{pmatrix} 2 \\ 0 \end{pmatrix}$.

c The vector describing the translation from C to D is $\begin{pmatrix} -3 \\ 2 \end{pmatrix}$.

d The vector describing the translation from D to A is $\begin{pmatrix} -1 \\ 3 \end{pmatrix}$.

Note:
- The top number in the vector describes the horizontal movement. To the right +, to the left −.
- The bottom number in the vector describes the vertical movement. Upwards +, downwards −.
- These vectors are also called *direction vectors*.

EXERCISE 7B

1 Use vectors to describe the following translations of the shapes on the grid below.

a **i** A to B **ii** A to C **iii** A to D
   iv A to E **v** A to F **vi** A to G

b **i** B to A **ii** B to C **iii** B to D
   iv B to E **v** B to F **vi** B to G

c **i** C to A **ii** C to B **iii** C to D
   iv C to E **v** C to F **vi** C to G

d **i** D to E **ii** E to B **iii** F to C
   iv G to D **v** F to G **vi** G to E

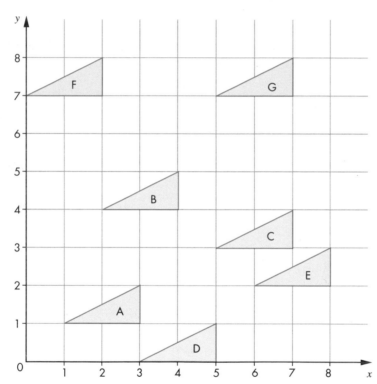

2 **a** Draw a set of coordinate axes and on it the triangle with coordinates A(1, 1), B(2, 1) and C(1, 3).

   b Draw the image of ABC after a translation with vector $\begin{pmatrix} 2 \\ 3 \end{pmatrix}$. Label this triangle P.

   c Draw the image of ABC after a translation with vector $\begin{pmatrix} -1 \\ 2 \end{pmatrix}$. Label this triangle Q.

   d Draw the image of ABC after a translation with vector $\begin{pmatrix} 3 \\ -2 \end{pmatrix}$. Label this triangle R.

   e Draw the image of ABC after a translation with vector $\begin{pmatrix} -2 \\ -4 \end{pmatrix}$. Label this triangle S.

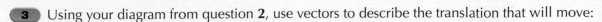

3 Using your diagram from question **2**, use vectors to describe the translation that will move:

a P to Q   **b** Q to R   **c** R to S   **d** S to P

e R to P   **f** S to Q   **g** R to Q   **h** P to S

PS 4 Draw a 10 × 10 coordinate grid and on it the triangle A(0, 0), B(1, 0) and C(0, 1). How many different translations are there that use integer values only and will move the triangle ABC to somewhere in the grid?

PS 5 In a game of *Snakes and ladders*, each of the snakes and ladders can be described by a translation.

Use the following vectors.

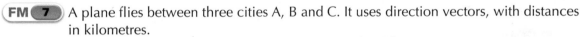

Ladders $\begin{pmatrix} 1 \\ 2 \end{pmatrix}$, $\begin{pmatrix} 2 \\ 5 \end{pmatrix}$, $\begin{pmatrix} -3 \\ 4 \end{pmatrix}$, $\begin{pmatrix} -2 \\ 3 \end{pmatrix}$, $\begin{pmatrix} 3 \\ 2 \end{pmatrix}$

Snakes $\begin{pmatrix} 1 \\ -3 \end{pmatrix}$, $\begin{pmatrix} 3 \\ -4 \end{pmatrix}$, $\begin{pmatrix} -2 \\ -2 \end{pmatrix}$, $\begin{pmatrix} -1 \\ -3 \end{pmatrix}$, $\begin{pmatrix} 2 \\ -5 \end{pmatrix}$

Put all five ladders and all five snakes onto a 10 × 10 coordinate grid in order to design a *Snakes and ladders* game board.

AU 6 If a translation is given by:

$$\begin{pmatrix} x \\ y \end{pmatrix}$$

describe the translation that would take the image back to the original position.

FM 7 A plane flies between three cities A, B and C. It uses direction vectors, with distances in kilometres.

The direction vector for the flight from A to B is $\begin{pmatrix} 500 \\ 200 \end{pmatrix}$ and the direction vector for the flight from B to C is $\begin{pmatrix} -200 \\ 300 \end{pmatrix}$.

Using centimetre-squared paper, draw a diagram to show the three flights. Use a scale of 1 cm represents 100 km.

Work out the direction vector for the flight from C to A.

FM 8 A pleasure cruise travels between three jetties X, Y and Z on a lake. It uses direction vectors, with distance in kilometres.

The direction vector from X to Y is $\begin{pmatrix} 3 \\ -1 \end{pmatrix}$ and the direction vector from Y to Z is $\begin{pmatrix} -2 \\ -3 \end{pmatrix}$.

Using centimetre-squared paper, draw a diagram to show journeys between X, Y and Z. Use a scale of 1 cm represents 1 km. Work out the direction vector for the journey from Z to X.

This section will show you how to:

● reflect a 2D shape in a mirror line

Key words
image
mirror line
object
reflection

A **reflection** transforms a shape so that it becomes a mirror image of itself.

EXAMPLE 3

Object

Mirror line ————————————

Image

Notice the reflection of each point in the original shape, called the **object**, is perpendicular to the mirror line. So if you 'fold' the whole diagram along the **mirror line**, the object will coincide with its reflection, called its **image**.

EXERCISE 7C

D

1 Copy the diagram below and draw the reflection of the given triangle in the following lines.

   a $x = 2$ **b** $x = -1$ **c** $x = 3$

   d $y = 2$ **e** $y = -1$ **f** y-axis

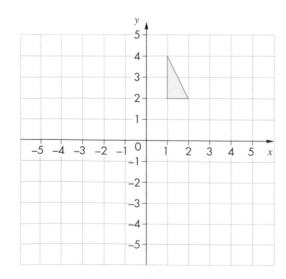

2 **a** Draw a pair of axes. Label the x-axis from –5 to 5 and the y-axis from –5 to 5.

  b Draw the triangle with coordinates A(1, 1), B(3, 1), C(4, 5).

  c Reflect the triangle ABC in the x-axis. Label the image P.

  d Reflect triangle P in the y-axis. Label the image Q.

  e Reflect triangle Q in the x-axis. Label the image R.

  f Describe the reflection that will move triangle ABC to triangle R.

AU 3 **a** Draw a pair of axes. Label the x-axis from –5 to +5 and the y-axis from –5 to +5.

  b Reflect the points A(2, 1), B(5, 0), C(–3, 3), D(3, –2) in the x-axis.

  c What do you notice about the values of the coordinates of the reflected points?

  d What would the coordinates of the reflected point be if the point (a, b) were reflected in the x-axis?

AU 4 **a** Draw a pair of axes. Label the x-axis from –5 to +5 and the y-axis from –5 to +5.

  b Reflect the points A(2, 1), B(0, 5), C(3, –2), D(–4, –3) in the y-axis.

  c What do you notice about the values of the coordinates of the reflected points?

  d What would the coordinates of the reflected point be if the point (a, b) were reflected in the y-axis?

PS 5 By using the middle square as a starting square ABCD, describe how to keep reflecting the square to obtain the final shape in the diagram.

AU 6 Triangle A is drawn on a grid.

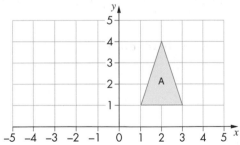

Triangle A is reflected to form a new triangle B.
The coordinates of B are (–4, 4), (–3, 1) and (–5, 1).

Work out the equation of the mirror line.

7 A designer used the following instructions to create a design.

  ● Start with any rectangle ABCD.

  ● Reflect the rectangle ABCD in the line AC.

  ● Reflect the rectangle ABCD in the line BD.

Draw a rectangle and use the above to create a design.

8 Draw each of these triangles on squared paper, leaving plenty of space on the opposite side of the given mirror line. Then draw the reflection of each triangle.

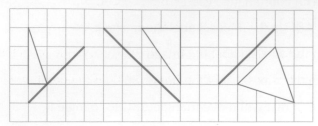

HINTS AND TIPS

Turn the page around so that the mirror lines are vertical or horizontal.

9 **a** Draw a pair of axes and the lines $y = x$ and $y = -x$, as shown.

b Draw the triangle with coordinates A(2, 1), B(5, 1), C(5, 3).

c Draw the reflection of triangle ABC in the x-axis and label the image P.

d Draw the reflection of triangle P in the line $y = -x$ and label the image Q.

e Draw the reflection of triangle Q in the y-axis and label the image R.

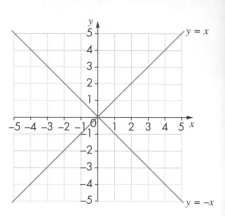

f Draw the reflection of triangle R in the line $y = x$ and label the image S.

g Draw the reflection of triangle S in the x-axis and label the image T.

h Draw the reflection of triangle T in the line $y = -x$ and label the image U.

i Draw the reflection of triangle U in the y-axis and label the image W.

j What single reflection will move triangle W to triangle ABC?

10 Copy the diagram and reflect the triangle in these lines.

a $y = x$ **b** $x = 1$

c $y = -x$ **d** $y = -1$

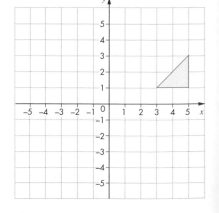

PS **11** **a** Draw a pair of axes. Label the x-axis from -5 to $+5$ and the y-axis from -5 to $+5$.

b Draw the line $y = x$.

c Reflect the points A(2, 1), B(5, 0), C(−3, 2), D(−2, −4) in the line $y = x$.

d What do you notice about the values of the coordinates of the reflected points?

e What would the coordinates of the reflected point be if the point (a, b) were reflected in the line $y = x$?

PS **12** **a** Draw a pair of axes. Label the x-axis from -5 to $+5$ and the y-axis from -5 to $+5$.

b Draw the line $y = -x$.

c Reflect the points A(2, 1), B(0, 5), C(3, −2), D(−4, −3) in the line $y = -x$.

d What do you notice about the values of the coordinates of the reflected points?

e What would the coordinates of the reflected point be if the point (a, b) were reflected in the line $y = -x$?

7.4 Rotations

This section will show you how to:
● rotate a 2D shape about a point

Key words
angle of rotation
anticlockwise
centre of rotation
clockwise
rotation

A **rotation** transforms a shape to a new position by turning it about a fixed point called the **centre of rotation**.

EXAMPLE 4

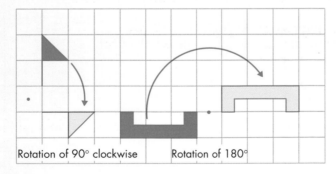

Rotation of 90° clockwise   Rotation of 180°

Note:

● The direction of turn or the **angle of rotation** is expressed as **clockwise** or **anticlockwise**.

● The position of the centre of rotation is always specified.

● The rotations 180° clockwise and 180° anticlockwise are the same.

The rotations that most often appear in examination questions are 90° and 180°.

EXERCISE 7D

1 On squared paper, draw each of these shapes and its centre of rotation, leaving plenty of space all round the shape.

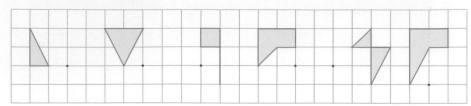

a Rotate each shape about its centre of rotation:

  i first by 90° clockwise (call the image A)

  ii then by 90° anticlockwise (call the image B).

b Describe, in each case, the rotation that would take:

  i A back to its original position   **ii** A to B.

2 A graphics designer came up with the following routine for creating a design.

● Start with a triangle ABC.

● Reflect the triangle in the line AB.

● Rotate the whole shape about point C clockwise 90°, then a further clockwise 90°, then a further clockwise 90°.

From any triangle of your choice, create a design using the above routine.

PS 3 By using the middle square as a starting square ABCD, describe how to keep rotating the square to obtain the final shape in the diagram.

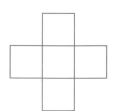

4 Copy the diagram and rotate the given triangle by the following.

a 90° clockwise about (0, 0)

b 180° about (3, 3)

c 90° anticlockwise about (0, 2)

d 180° about (−1, 0)

e 90° clockwise about (−1, −1)

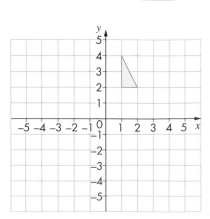

5 What other rotations are equivalent to these rotations?

   a 270° clockwise   **b** 90° clockwise

   c 60° anticlockwise   **d** 100° anticlockwise

6 **a** Draw a pair of axes where both the *x*-values and *y*-values are from –5 to 5.

   b Draw the triangle ABC, where A = (1, 2), B = (2, 4) and C = (4, 1).

   c **i** Rotate triangle ABC 90° clockwise about the origin (0, 0) and label the image A′, B′, C′, where A′ is the image of A, etc.

      ii Write down the coordinates of A′, B′, C′.

     iii What connection is there between A, B, C and A′, B′, C′?

     iv Will this connection always be so for a 90° clockwise rotation about the origin?

7 Repeat question **6**, but rotate triangle ABC through 180°.

8 Repeat question **6**, but rotate triangle ABC 90° anticlockwise.

PS 9 Show that a reflection in the *x*-axis followed by a reflection in the *y*-axis is equivalent to a rotation of 180° about the origin.

PS 10 Show that a reflection in the line $y = x$ followed by a reflection in the line $y = -x$ is equivalent to a rotation of 180° about the origin.

11 **a** Draw a regular hexagon ABCDEF with centre O.

   b Using O as the centre of rotation, describe a transformation that will result in the following movements.

     i Triangle AOB to triangle BOC   **ii** Triangle AOB to triangle COD

    iii Triangle AOB to triangle DOE   **iv** Triangle AOB to triangle EOF

   c Describe the transformations that will move the rhombus ABCO to these positions.

     i Rhombus BCDO   **ii** Rhombus DEFO

AU 12 Triangle A, as shown on the grid, is rotated to form a new triangle B.

The coordinates of the vertices of B are (0, –2), (–3, –2) and (–3, –4).

Describe fully the rotation that maps triangle A onto triangle B.

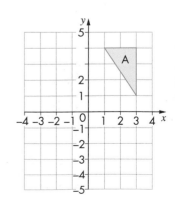

Enlargements

This section will show you how to:
- enlarge a 2D shape by a scale factor

Key words
centre of enlargement
enlargement
scale factor

An **enlargement** changes the size of a shape to give a similar image. It always has a **centre of enlargement** and a **scale factor**. Every length of the enlarged shape will be:

original length × scale factor

The distance of each image point on the enlargement from the centre of enlargement will be:

distance of original point from centre of enlargement × scale factor

EXAMPLE 5

The diagram shows the enlargement of triangle ABC by scale factor 3 about the centre of enlargement X.

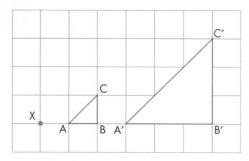

Note:

● Each length on the enlargement A'B'C' is three times the corresponding length on the original shape.

This means that the corresponding sides are in the same ratio:

AB : A'B' = AC : A'C' = BC : B'C' = 1 : 3

● The distance of any point on the enlargement from the centre of enlargement is three times the distance from the corresponding point on the original shape to the centre of enlargement.

There are two distinct ways to enlarge a shape: the ray method and the coordinate, or counting squares, method.

Ray method

This is the *only* way to construct an enlargement when the diagram is not on a grid.

EXAMPLE 6

Enlarge triangle ABC by scale factor 3 about the centre of enlargement X.

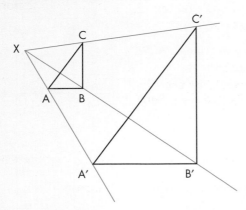

Notice that the rays have been drawn from the centre of enlargement to each vertex and beyond.

The distance from X to each vertex on triangle ABC is measured and multiplied by 3 to give the distance from X to each vertex A′, B′ and C′ for the enlarged triangle A′B′C′.

Once each image vertex has been found, the whole enlarged shape can then be drawn.

Check the measurements and see for yourself how the calculations have been done.

Notice again that the length of each side on the enlarged triangle is three times the length of the corresponding side on the original triangle.

Counting squares method

In this method, you use the coordinates of the vertices to 'count squares'.

EXAMPLE 7

Enlarge the triangle ABC by scale factor 3 from the centre of enlargement (1, 2).

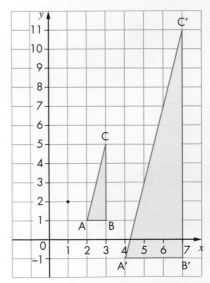

To find the coordinates of each image vertex, first work out the horizontal and vertical distances from each original vertex to the centre of enlargement.

Then multiply each of these distances by 3 to find the position of each image vertex.

For example, to find the coordinates of C′ work out the distance from the centre of enlargement (1, 2) to the point C(3, 5).

   horizontal distance = 2

   vertical distance = 3

Make these 3 times longer to give:

   new horizontal distance = 6

   new vertical distance = 9

So the coordinates of C′ are:

   (1 + 6, 2 + 9) = (7, 11)

Notice again that the length of each side is three times as long in the enlargement.

Negative enlargement

A negative enlargement produces an image shape on the opposite side of the centre of enlargement to the original shape.

EXAMPLE 8

Triangle ABC has been enlarged by scale factor −2, with the centre of enlargement at (1, 0).

You can enlarge triangle ABC to give triangle A′B′C′ by either the ray method or the coordinate method. You calculate the new lengths on the opposite side of the centre of enlargement to the original shape.

Notice how a negative scale factor also inverts the original shape.

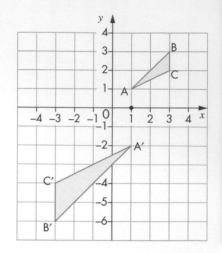

Fractional enlargement

Strange but true – you can have an enlargement in mathematics that is actually smaller than the original shape!

EXAMPLE 9

Triangle ABC has been enlarged by a scale factor of $\frac{1}{2}$ about the centre of enlargement O to give triangle A′B′C′.

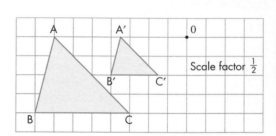

Scale factor $\frac{1}{2}$

EXERCISE 7E

1 Copy each of these figures with its centre of enlargement. Then enlarge it by the given scale factor, using the ray method.

a

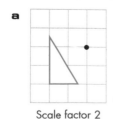

Scale factor 2

b

Scale factor 3

c

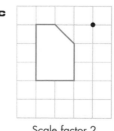

Scale factor 2

d

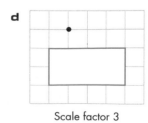

Scale factor 3

D

2 Copy each of these diagrams onto squared paper and enlarge it by scale factor 2, using the origin as the centre of enlargement.

a

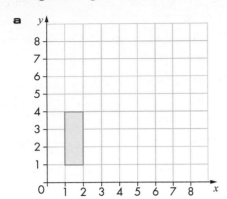

b

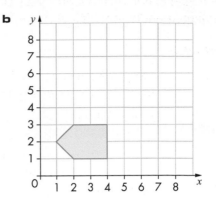

c

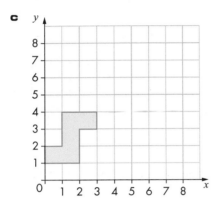

> **HINTS AND TIPS**
>
> Even if you are using a counting square method, you can always check by using the ray method.

3 Copy each of these diagrams onto squared paper and enlarge it by scale factor 2, using the given centre of enlargement.

a

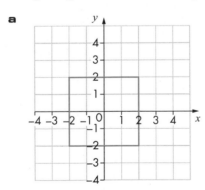

Centre of enlargement (−1, 1)

b

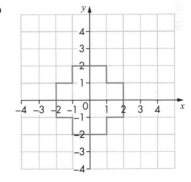

Centre of enlargement (−2, −3)

4 A designer is told to use the following routine.

- Start with a rectangle ABCD.
- Reflect ABCD in the line AC.
- Rotate the whole new shape about C through 180°.
- Enlarge the whole shape scale factor 2, centre of enlargement point A.

Start with any rectangle of your choice and create the design above.

C

5 Enlarge each of these shapes by a scale factor of $\frac{1}{2}$ about the given centre of enlargement.

6 Copy this diagram onto squared paper.

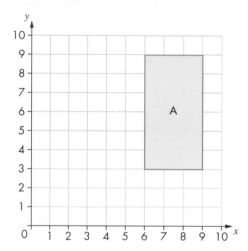

a Enlarge the rectangle A by scale factor $\frac{1}{3}$ about the origin. Label the image B.

b Write down the ratio of the lengths of the sides of rectangle A to the lengths of the sides of rectangle B.

c Work out the ratio of the perimeter of rectangle A to the perimeter of rectangle B.

d Work out the ratio of the area of rectangle A to the area of rectangle B.

B

AU 7 Copy this diagram onto squared paper.

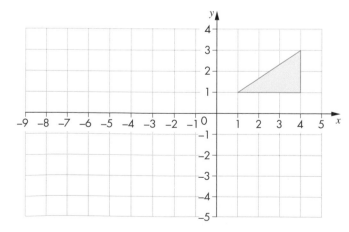

Enlarge the triangle by scale factor −2 about the origin.

8 Copy the diagram onto squared paper.

a Enlarge A by a scale factor of 3 about a centre (4, 5).

b Enlarge B by a scale factor $\frac{1}{2}$ about a centre (−1, −3).

c Enlarge B by scale factor $-\frac{1}{2}$ about a centre (−3, −1).

d What is the centre of enlargement and scale factor which maps B onto A?

e What is the centre of enlargement and scale factor which maps A onto B?

f What is the centre of enlargement and scale factor which maps the answer to part **b** to the answer to part **c**?

g What is the centre of enlargement and scale factor which maps the answer to part **c** to the answer to part **b**?

h What is the connection between the scale factors and the centres of enlargement in parts **d** and **e**, and in parts **f** and **g**?

PS 9 Triangle A has vertices with coordinates (2, 1), (4, 1) and (4, 4).

Triangle B has vertices with coordinates (−5, 1), (−5, 7) and (−1, 7).

Describe fully the single transformation that maps triangle A onto triangle B.

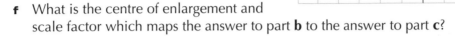

7.6 Combined transformations

This section will show you how to:	Key words
• combine transformations	enlargement reflection rotation transformation translation

Examination questions often require you to use more than one **transformation**. In this exercise, you will revise the transformations you have met so far.

Remember, to describe:

● a **translation** fully, you need to use a vector

● a **reflection** fully, you need to use a mirror line

● a **rotation** fully, you need a centre of rotation, an angle of rotation and the direction of turn

● an **enlargement** fully, you need a centre of enlargement and a scale factor

D

C

1 The point P(3, 4) is **reflected** in the x-axis, then rotated by 90° clockwise about the origin. What are the coordinates of the image of P?

2 A point Q(5, 2) is rotated by 180°, then reflected in the x-axis.

   a What are the coordinates of the image point of Q?

   b What single transformation would have taken point Q directly to the image point?

3 Describe fully the transformations that will map the shaded triangle onto each of the triangles A–F.

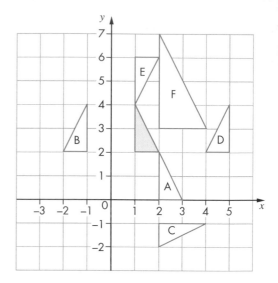

4 Describe fully the transformations that will result in the following movements.

   a T_1 to T_2

   b T_1 to T_6

   c T_2 to T_3

   d T_6 to T_2

   e T_6 to T_5

   f T_5 to T_4

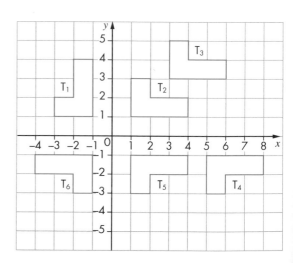

5 **a** Plot a triangle T with vertices (1, 1), (2, 1), (1, 3).

   b Reflect triangle T in the y-axis and label the image T_b.

   c Rotate triangle T_b 90° anticlockwise about the origin and label the image T_c.

   d Reflect triangle T_c in the y-axis and label the image T_d.

   e Describe fully the transformation that will move triangle T_d back to triangle T.

PS **6** Describe fully at least three different transformations that could move the square labelled S to the square labelled T.

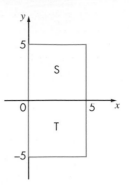

PS **7** The point A(4, 4) has been transformed to the point A′(4, −4). Describe as many different transformations as you can that could transform point A to point A′.

AU **8** Copy the diagram onto squared paper.

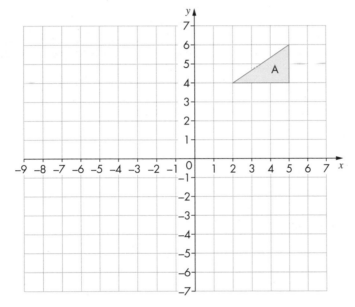

a Triangle A is translated by the vector $\begin{pmatrix} -1.5 \\ -3 \end{pmatrix}$ to give triangle B.

Triangle B is then enlarged by a scale factor −2 about the origin to give triangle C.

Draw triangles B and C on the diagram.

b Describe fully the single transformation that maps triangle C onto triangle A.

GRADE BOOSTER

D You can reflect a 2D shape in a line $x = a$ or $y = b$

D You can rotate a 2D shape about the origin

D You can enlarge a 2D shape by a whole number scale factor

C You can translate a 2D shape by a vector

C You can reflect a 2D shape in the line $y = x$ or $y = -x$

C You can rotate a 2D shape about any point

C You can enlarge a 2D shape by a fractional scale factor

C You can enlarge a 2D shape about any point

B You know the conditions to show two triangles are congruent

B You can enlarge a 2D shape by a negative scale factor

A You can prove two triangles are congruent

What you should know now

● How to translate a 2D shape by a vector

● How to reflect a 2D shape in any line

● How to rotate a 2D shape about any point and through any angle

● How to enlarge a 2D shape about any point using a positive, fractional or negative scale factor

● How to show that two triangles are congruent

1 Enlarge the shape by scale factor 2, using the origin as the centre of enlargement. *(3 marks)*

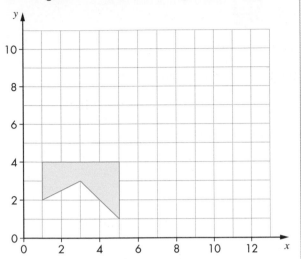

AQA, June 2009, Module 5, Paper 2 Higher, Question 1

2 Triangles A, B and C are shown on the grid.

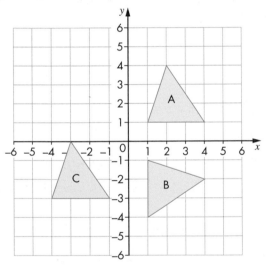

a Describe fully the **single** transformation that maps triangle A onto triangle B. *(3 marks)*

b Write down the vector which describes the translation of triangle A onto triangle C.
(1 mark)

AQA, May 2009, Paper 1, Question 10(a)(b)

3 The diagram shows two rectangles A and B.

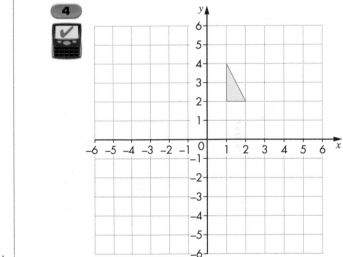

Complete the sentences.

a Rectangle B is a reflection of rectangle A in the line … *(1 mark)*

b Rectangle B is a translation of rectangle A by the vector… *(1 mark)*

c Rectangle B is a rotation of rectangle A through … degrees about the point … *(2 marks)*

AQA, June 2007, Module 5, Paper 1 Higher, Question 1(a)(b)(c)

4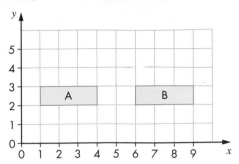

a Reflect the shaded triangle in the line $y = -x$.

Label this new triangle with the letter A
. *(2 marks)*

b Rotate the original shaded triangle by a quarter-turn anticlockwise about (0, 1).

Label this new triangle with the letter B. *(2 marks)*

AQA, June 2005, Paper 2 Higher, Question 3(a)(b)

5 The diagram shows two triangles, A and B.

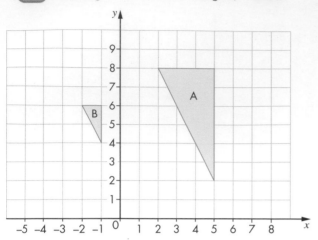

a Describe fully the single transformation that maps triangle A onto triangle B. *(3 marks)*

b On the diagram, draw the image of triangle A after it has been reflected in the line $y = x$. Label your image C. *(2 marks)*

AQA, June 2007, Paper 1 Higher, Question 6(a)(b)

6 The diagram shows four shapes, A, B, C and D.

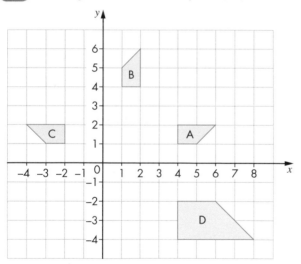

a Describe fully the single transformation that takes shape A onto shape B. *(2 marks)*

b Describe fully the single transformation that takes shape B onto shape C. *(3 marks)*

c Describe fully the single transformation that takes shape C onto shape D. *(3 marks)*

AQA, June 2006, Paper 1 Higher, Question 4(a)(b)(c)

7 ABC is an isosceles triangle.

 M is the midpoint of AC.

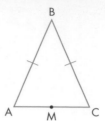

Prove that triangles ABM and CBM are congruent. *(4 marks)*

AQA, November 2007, Paper 2 Higher, Question 15

8 XYZ is an isosceles triangle in which XZ = XY.

M and N are points on XZ and XY such that angle MYZ = angle NZY.

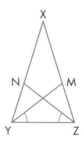

Prove that triangles YMZ and ZNY are congruent. *(4 marks)*

AQA, June 2006, Paper 1, Question 12

Worked Examination Questions

AU **1** The grid shows several transformations of the shaded triangle.

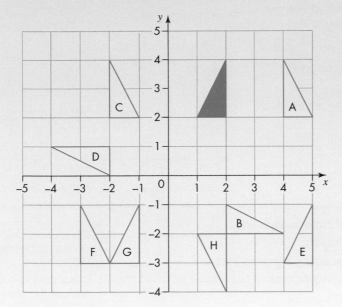

a Write down the letter of the shape:

   i after the shaded triangle is reflected in the line $x = 3$

   ii after the shaded triangle is translated by the vector $\begin{pmatrix} 3 \\ -5 \end{pmatrix}$

   iii after the shaded triangle is rotated 90° clockwise about 0.

b Describe fully the single transformation that takes triangle F onto triangle G.

1 a i A ——————————— | $x = 3$ is the vertical line passing through $x = 3$ on the x-axis. This scores 1 mark.

  ii E ——————————— | Move the triangle 3 squares to the right and 5 squares down. This scores 1 mark.

  iii B ——————————— | Use tracing paper to help you. Trace the shaded triangle, pivot the paper on 0 with your pencil point and rotate the paper through 90° clockwise. This scores 1 mark.

b A reflection in the line $x = -2$. ——— | The vertical mirror line passes through $x = -2$ on the x-axis. This scores 1 mark for method of identifying reflection and 1 mark for accuracy of mirror line.

Total: 5 marks

Worked Examination Questions

2 Triangle ABC has vertices A(6, 0), B(6, 9), C(9, 3).

a Rotate triangle ABC through 180° about the point (2, 4). Label the image triangle R.

b Enlarge triangle ABC by scale factor $\frac{1}{3}$ from the centre of enlargement (3, 0). Label the image triangle E.

c Describe fully the single transformation which maps triangle E to triangle R.

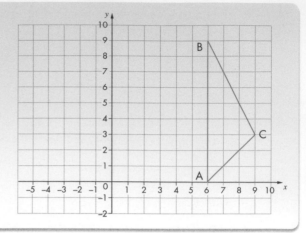

2 a Join each vertex to (2, 4) and rotate each line through 180° or use tracing paper.

b Use the ray method or the counting squares method. Remember, a fractional scale factor makes the image smaller.

This scores 1 method mark for rotating the triangle 180° about any point.

This scores 1 accuracy mark for the correct rotation.

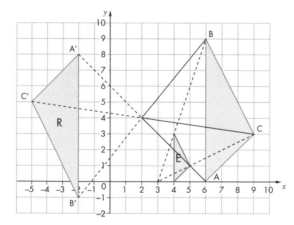

This scores 1 method mark for enlarging the triangle by scale factor $\frac{1}{3}$ about any point.

This scores 1 accuracy mark for the correct enlargement.

c

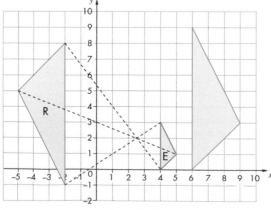

An enlargement of scale factor –3 about the point $(2\frac{1}{2}, 2)$.
Draw in the ray lines to find the centre of enlargement.

This scores 1 mark for enlargement of scale factor –3.

This scores 1 mark for $(2\frac{1}{2}, 2)$.

(Total: 6 marks)

Worked Examination Questions

3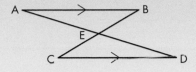

In the diagram AB and CD are parallel.

E is the midpoint of AD.

Prove triangle ABE is congruent to triangle CDE.

3 You will be expected to give reasons for each statement you make.

AE = DE (E is midpoint of AD) —————— This scores 1 mark for method.

∠BAE = ∠CDE (alternate angles) —————— This scores 1 mark for method.

∠AEB = ∠CED (opposite angles) —————— Or you could use ∠ABE = ∠DCE (alternate angles).

So △ABE ≡ △CDE (ASA) ——————

(Total: 3 marks)

This scores 1 accuracy mark for third statement with correct conclusion.

You would lose a mark if you missed out any of the reasons.

Enlargement is used in many aspects of life. How many can you think of?

Discuss these with the person sitting next to you or as a whole class.

Getting started

- What two things do you need to describe an enlargement?
- When an object is enlarged, what stays the same?
- When an object is enlarged, what changes?
- If an object is enlarged by a scale factor of 3, what is the ratio of the lengths in the image to the corresponding lengths in the object?
- If an object is enlarged by a scale factor of 2, what is the ratio of the area of the image to the area of the object?

Getting started (continued)

Which set of photographs is the odd one out? Explain why.

Look at these images. How can you tell that they are all based on the same original photograph?

Which do you think is the original? Which are enlargements? Why?

Your task

Use a digital camera to take at least two photographs. Use them to make a display or poster to explain enlargement. To complete the task successfully, you should answer at least two of the following questions about enlargement.

1 What happens to the image when you move the centre of enlargement?

2 Compare what happens to the image when you have a scale factor that is:
   - a whole number
   - a number between 0 and 1
   - a negative number.

3 What is the relationship between the scale factor and the properties of the object and image? For example, consider how the scale factor affects the relationships between lengths or areas in the object and image.

Note

If you do not have a digital camera available, use a suitable computer program to produce and enlarge a simple image, logo or other shape for your display or poster.

For anything, from a house to a landscape gardening project, designers need to construct plans accurately, to be sure that everything will fit together properly. This will also give the people putting it together a blueprint to work from.

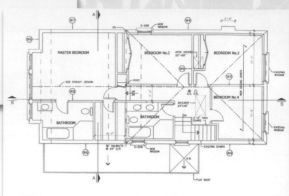

The need for accurate drawings is clear in bridge construction. Bridge engineers are responsible for producing practical bridge designs to meet the requirements of their employers. For example, a bridge intended to carry traffic over a newly constructed railway needs to be strong enough to bear the weight of the traffic and stable enough to counteract the effects of the moving traffic and strong winds. The designers produce a blueprint that has all the measurements, including heights, weights and angles, clearly marked on it. Construction workers then use this blueprint to build the bridge to the exact specifications set by the designers and engineers.

Generally, the construction workers work on both ends of the bridge at the same time, meeting in the middle. The blueprints are therefore essential for making sure that the bridge is safe and that the bridge meets in the middle.

Accurately-drawn blueprints were essential in the construction of the Golden Gate Bridge, which crosses the San Francisco Bay. When it was constructed in the 1930s, it was the longest suspension bridge in the world. The bridge engineers (who included Joseph Strauss and Charles Alton Ellis) had to draw precise blueprints to make sure that they had all the information necessary to build this innovative bridge and that it would be built correctly.

By contrast, a bridge built at a stadium for the Maccabiah Games in Israel was built without proper planning and without accurate blueprints. This led to the bridge collapsing soon after its construction in 1997, killing four athletes and injuring 64 people.

Just like a bridge engineer, you must be accurate in your construction, working with a freshly-sharpened pencil and a good pair of compasses, measuring and drawing angles carefully and drawing construction lines as faintly as possible.

In this chapter you will start with simple constructions of triangles, moving on to more complex bisectors and then to plotting loci, which are paths of whole sets of points obeying certain rules or criteria.

Geometry: Constructions

1 Constructing triangles

2 Bisectors

3 Defining a locus

4 Loci problems

This chapter will show you ...

D how to construct triangles

C how to bisect a line and an angle

C how to construct perpendiculars

C how to define a locus

C how to solve locus problems

Visual overview

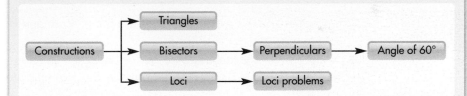

What you should already know

- How to measure lines and angles **(KS3 level 5, GCSE grade F)**
- How to use scale drawings **(KS3 level 5, GCSE grade E)**

Quick check

1 Measure the following lines.

a _____

b _____

c _____

2 Measure the following angles.

a   **b**

Constructing triangles

This section will show you how to:
- construct triangles, using compasses, a protractor and a straight edge

Key words
angle
compasses
construct
side

There are three ways of **constructing** a triangle. Which one you use depends on what information you are given about the triangle.

When carrying out geometric constructions, always use a sharp pencil (preferably grade 2H rather than HB) to give you thin, clear lines. These may be called faint or feint lines. The examiner will be marking your construction and will be looking for accuracy, which requires fine, clean lines and points as small as you can make them, while ensuring they are clearly visible.

All three sides known

EXAMPLE 1

Construct a triangle with **sides** that are 5 cm, 4 cm and 6 cm long.

- **Step 1:** Draw the longest side as the base. In this case, the base will be 6 cm, which you draw using a ruler. (The diagrams in this example are drawn at half-size.)

- **Step 2:** Deal with the second longest side, in this case the 5 cm side. Open the **compasses** to a radius of 5 cm (the length of the side), place the point on one end of the 6 cm line and draw a short faint arc, as shown here.

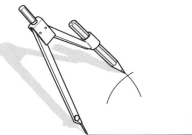

- **Step 3:** Deal with the shortest side, in this case the 4 cm side. Open the compasses to a radius of 4 cm, place the point on the other end of the 6 cm line and draw a second short faint arc to intersect the first arc, as shown here.

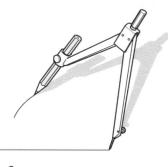

- **Step 4:** Complete the triangle by joining each end of the base line to the point where the two arcs intersect.

Note: The arcs are construction lines and so must be left in to show the examiner how you constructed the triangle.

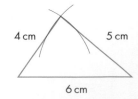

4 cm   5 cm
6 cm

FM Functional Maths   **AU** (AO2) Assessing Understanding   **PS** (AO3) Problem Solving

Two sides and the included angle known

EXAMPLE 2

Draw a triangle ABC, in which AB is 6 cm, BC is 5 cm and the included **angle** ABC is 55°. (The diagrams in this example are drawn at half-size.)

- **Step 1:** Draw the longest side, AB, as the base. Label the ends of the base A and B.

    A ——————————— B

- **Step 2:** Place the protractor along AB with its centre on B and make a point on the diagram at the 55° mark.

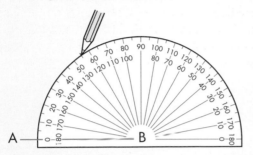

- **Step 3:** Draw a *faint* line from B through the 55° point. From B, using a pair of compasses, measure 5 cm along this line.

- Label the point where the arc cuts the line as C.

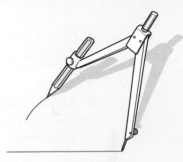

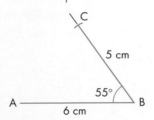

- **Step 4:** Join A and C to complete the triangle.

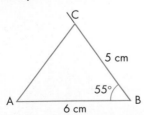

Note: Remember to use clean, sharp lines so that the examiner can see how the triangle has been constructed.

Two angles and a side known

When you know two angles of a triangle, you also know the third.

EXAMPLE 3

Draw a triangle ABC, in which AB is 7 cm, angle BAC is 40° and angle ABC is 65°.

- **Step 1:** As before, start by drawing the base, which here has to be 7 cm. Label the ends A and B.

A ———————————————————— B

- **Step 2:** Centre the protractor on A and mark the angle of 40°. Draw a clear, clean line from A through this point.

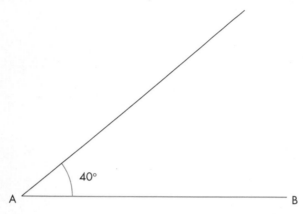

- **Step 3:** Centre the protractor on B and mark the angle of 65°. Draw a clear, clean line from B through this point, to intersect the 40° line drawn from A. Label the point of intersection as C.

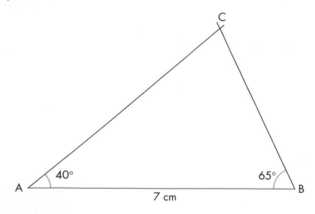

EXERCISE 8A

1 Draw the following triangles accurately and measure the sides and angles not given in the diagram.

a

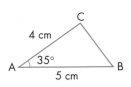

b

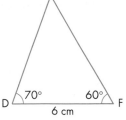

c

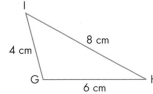

d

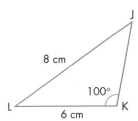

e

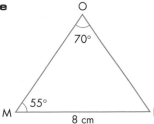

f

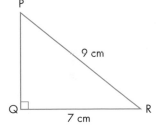

2 a Draw a triangle ABC, where AB = 7 cm, BC = 6 cm and AC = 5 cm.

b Measure the sizes of ∠ABC, ∠BCA and ∠CAB.

3 Draw an isosceles triangle that has two sides of length 7 cm and the included angle of 50°.

a Measure the length of the base of the triangle.

b What is the area of the triangle?

4 A triangle ABC has ∠ABC = 30°, AB = 6 cm and AC = 4 cm. There are two different triangles that can be drawn from this information.

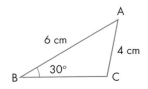

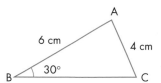

What are the two different lengths that BC can be?

5 Construct an equilateral triangle of side length 5 cm.

a Measure the height of the triangle.

b What is the area of this triangle?

6 Construct a parallelogram with sides of length 5 cm and 8 cm and with an angle of 120° between them.

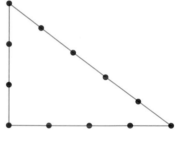

a Measure the height of the parallelogram.

b What is the area of the parallelogram?

7 Groundsmen painting white lines on a sports field may use a knotted rope, like the one shown below.

It has 12 equally-spaced knots.
It can be laid out to give a triangle, like this.

It will always be a right-angled triangle. This helps the groundsmen to draw lines perpendicular to each other.

Here are two more examples of such ropes.

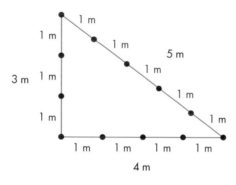

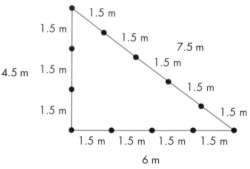

a Show, by constructing each of the above triangles (use a scale of 1 cm : 1 m), that each is a right-angled triangle.

b Choose a different triangle that you think might also be right-angled. Use the same knotted-rope idea to check.

PS 8 Construct the triangle with the largest area which has a total perimeter of 12 cm.

AU 9 Anil says that, as long as he knows all three angles of a triangle, he can draw it. Explain why Anil is wrong.

This section will show you how to:
- construct the bisectors of lines and angles
- construct angles of 60° and 90°

Key words
angle bisector
bisect
line bisector
perpendicular bisector

To **bisect** means to divide in half. So a bisector divides something into two equal parts.

- A **line bisector** divides a straight line into two equal lengths.
- An **angle bisector** is the straight line that divides an angle into two equal angles.

To construct a line bisector

It is usually more accurate to construct a line bisector than to measure its position (the midpoint of the line).

- **Step 1:** Here is a line to bisect.

- **Step 2:** Open your compasses to a radius of about three-quarters of the length of the line. Using each end of the line as a centre, and without changing the radius of your compasses, draw two intersecting arcs.

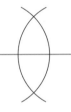

- **Step 3:** Join the two points at which the arcs intersect. This line is the **perpendicular bisector** of the original line.

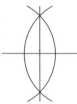

To construct an angle bisector

It is much more accurate to construct an angle bisector than to measure its position.

- **Step 1:** Here is an angle to bisect.

- **Step 2:** Open your compasses to any reasonable radius that is less than the length of the lines forming the angle. If in doubt, go for about 3 cm. With the vertex of the angle as centre, draw an arc through both lines.

- **Step 3:** With centres at the two points at which this arc intersects the lines, draw two more arcs so that they intersect.

- **Step 4:** Join the point at which these two arcs intersect to the vertex of the angle.

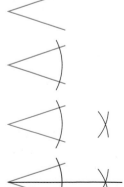

This line is the angle bisector.

To construct an angle of 60°

It is more accurate to construct an angle of 60° than to measure and draw it with a protractor.

- **Step 1:** Draw a line and mark a point on it.

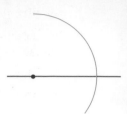

- **Step 2:** Open the compasses to a radius of about 4 cm.
  Using the point as the centre, draw an arc that crosses the line and extends almost above the point.

- **Step 3:** Keep the compasses set to the same radius.
  Using the point where the first arc crosses the line as a centre, draw another arc that intersects the first one.

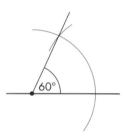

- **Step 4:** Join the original point to the point where the two arcs intersect.

- **Step 5:** Use a protractor to check that the angle is 60°.

To construct a perpendicular from a point on a line (an angle of 90°)

This construction will produce a perpendicular from a point A on a line.

- Open your compasses to about 2 or 3 cm.
  With point A as centre, draw two short arcs to intersect the line at each side of the point.

- Now extend the radius of your compasses to about 4 cm. With centres at the two points at which the arcs intersect the line, draw two arcs to intersect at X above the line.

- Join AX.

  AX is perpendicular to the line.

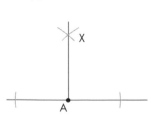

Note: If you needed to construct a 90° angle at the end of a line, you would first have to extend the line.

You could be even more accurate by also drawing two arcs underneath the line, which would give three points in line.

To construct a perpendicular from a point to a line

This construction will produce a perpendicular from a point A to a line.

● With point A as centre, draw an arc which intersects the line at two points.

● With centres at these two points of intersection, draw two arcs to intersect each other both above and below the line.

● Join the two points at which the arcs intersect. The resulting line passes through point A and is perpendicular to the line.

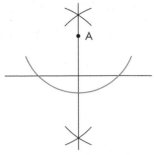

Examination note: When a question says *construct*, you must *only* use compasses, not a protractor. When it says *draw*, you may use whatever you can to produce an accurate diagram. But also note, when constructing you may use your protractor to check your accuracy.

EXERCISE 8B

1 Draw a line 7 cm long and bisect it. Check your accuracy by seeing if each half is 3.5 cm.

> **HINTS AND TIPS**
>
> Remember that examiners want to see your construction lines.

2 Draw a circle of about 4 cm radius.

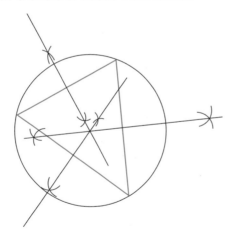

Draw a triangle inside the circle so that the corners of the triangle touch the circle.

Bisect each side of the triangle.

The bisectors should all meet at the same point, which should be the centre of the circle.

3 **a** Draw any triangle with sides that are between 5 cm and 10 cm.

b On each side construct the line bisector.

All your line bisectors should intersect at the same point.

c Using this point as the centre, draw a circle that goes through every vertex of the triangle.

4 Repeat question **2** with a different triangle and check that you get a similar result.

5 **a** Draw the following quadrilateral.

b Construct the line bisector of each side. These all should intersect at the same point.

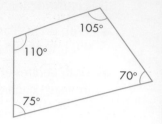

c Use this point as the centre of a circle that goes through the quadrilateral at each vertex. Draw this circle.

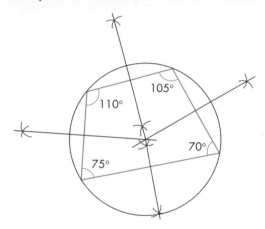

6 **a** Draw an angle of 50°.

b Construct the angle bisector.

c Check how accurate you have been by measuring each half. Both should be 25°.

7 Draw a circle with a radius of about 3 cm.

Draw a triangle so that the sides of the triangle are tangents to the circle.

Bisect each angle of the triangle.

The bisectors should all meet at the same point, which should be the centre of the circle.

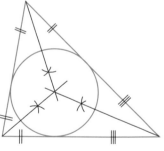

8 **a** Draw any triangle with sides that are between 5 cm and 10 cm.

b At each angle construct the angle bisector. All three bisectors should intersect at the same point.

c Use this point as the centre of a circle that just touches the sides of the triangle.

9 Repeat question **8** with a different triangle.

FM 10 Gianni and Anna have children living in Bristol and Norwich. Gianni is about to start a new job in Birmingham. They are looking on a map of Britain for places they might move to.

Anna says, "I want to be the same distance from both children."

Gianni says, "I want to be as close to Birmingham as possible."

Find the largest city that would suit both Gianni and Anna. Use a map of the UK to help you.

PS **11** Draw a circle with radius about 4 cm.

Draw a quadrilateral, **not** a rectangle, inside the circle so that each vertex is on the circumference.

Construct the bisector of each side of the quadrilateral.

Where is the point where these bisectors all meet?

AU **12** Briefly outline how you would construct a triangle with angles 90°, 60° and 30°.

13 **a** Draw a line AB, 6 cm long, and construct an angle of 90° at A.

b Bisect this angle to construct an angle of 45°.

14 **a** Draw a line AB, 6 cm long, and construct an angle of 60° at A.

b Bisect this angle to construct an angle of 30°.

15 Draw a line AB, 6 cm long, and mark a point C, 4 cm above the middle of the line.

Construct the perpendicular from the point C to the line AB.

8.3 Defining a locus

This section will show you how to:
● draw a locus for a given rule

Key words
equidistant
loci
locus

A **locus** (plural **loci**) is the movement of a point according to a given rule.

EXAMPLE 4

A point P that moves so that it is always at a distance of 5 cm from a fixed point A will have a locus that is a circle of radius 5 cm.

You can express this mathematically by saying the locus of the point P is such that AP = 5 cm.

EXAMPLE 5

A point P that moves so that it is always the same distance from two fixed points A and B will have a locus that is the perpendicular bisector of the line joining A and B.

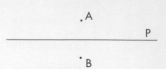

You can express this mathematically by saying:

the locus of the point P is such that AP = BP.

A point that is always the same distance from two points is **equidistant** from the two points.

EXAMPLE 6

A point that is always 5 m from a long, straight wall will have a locus that is a line parallel to the wall and 5 m from it.

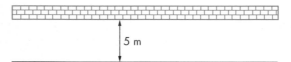

5 m

EXAMPLE 7

A point that moves so that it is always 5 cm from a line AB will have a locus that is a racetrack shape around the line.

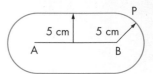

In your GCSE examination, you will usually get practical situations rather than abstract mathematical ones.

EXAMPLE 8

Imagine a grassy, flat field in which a horse is tethered to a stake by a rope that is 10 m long. What is the shape of the area that the horse can graze?

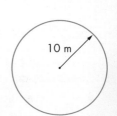

In reality, the horse may not be able to reach the full 10 m if the rope is tied round its neck but ignore fine details like that. You 'model' the situation by saying that the horse can move around in a 10 m circle and graze all the grass within that circle.

In this example, the locus is the whole of the area inside the circle.

You can express this mathematically as:

the locus of the point P is such that AP $\leqslant$ 10 m.

EXERCISE 8C

1 A is a fixed point. Sketch the locus of the point P in each of these situations.

a AP = 2 cm   **b** AP = 4 cm   **c** AP = 5 cm

2 A and B are two fixed points 5 cm apart. Sketch the locus of the point P for each of these situations.

a AP = BP   **b** AP = 4 cm and BP = 4 cm

c P is always within 2 cm of the line AB

FM 3 a A horse is tethered in a field on a rope 4 m long. Describe or sketch the area that the horse can graze.

b The horse is still tethered by the same rope but there is now a long, straight fence running 2 m from the stake. Sketch the area that the horse can now graze.

4 ABCD is a square of side 4 cm. In each of the following loci, the point P moves only inside the square. Sketch the locus in each case.

a AP = BP   **b** AP < BP   **c** AP = CP

d CP < 4 cm   **e** CP > 2 cm   **f** CP > 5 cm

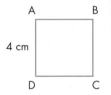

5 One of the following diagrams is the locus of a point on the rim of a bicycle wheel as it moves along a flat road. Which is it?

6 Draw the locus of the centre of the wheel for the bicycle in question **5**.

PS 7 ABC is a triangle.

The region R is defined as the set of points inside the triangle such that:

● they are closer to the line AB than the line AC
● they are closer to the point A than the point C.

Using a ruler and compasses, construct the region R.

AU 8 ABCD is a rectangle.

Copy the diagram and draw the locus of all points that are 2 cm from the edges of the rectangle.

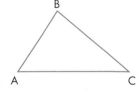

Loci problems

Most of the **loci** problems in your GCSE examination will be of a practical nature, as in the next example.

EXAMPLE 9

Imagine that a radio company wants to find a site for a transmitter. The transmitter must be the same distance from Doncaster and Leeds and within 20 miles of Sheffield.

In mathematical terms, this means they are concerned with the perpendicular bisector between Leeds and Doncaster and the area within a circle of radius 20 miles from Sheffield.

The diagram, drawn to a **scale** of 1 cm = 10 miles, illustrates the situation and shows that the transmitter can be built anywhere along the thick part of the blue line.

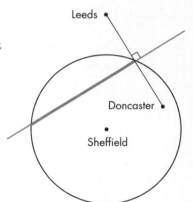

EXAMPLE 10

A radar station in Birmingham has a range of 150 km (that is, it can pick up any aircraft within a radius of 150 km). Another radar station in Norwich has a range of 100 km.

Can an aircraft be picked up by both radar stations at the same time?

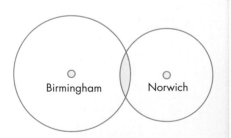

The situation is represented by a circle of radius 150 km around Birmingham and another circle of radius 100 km around Norwich. The two circles overlap, so an aircraft could be picked up by both radar stations when it is in the overlap.

EXAMPLE 11

A dog is tethered by a rope, 3 m long, to the corner of a shed, 4 m by 2 m. What is the area that the dog can guard effectively?

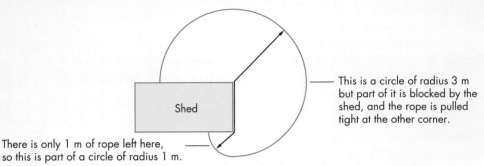

This is a circle of radius 3 m but part of it is blocked by the shed, and the rope is pulled tight at the other corner.

There is only 1 m of rope left here, so this is part of a circle of radius 1 m.

EXERCISE 8D

For questions **1** to **7**, you should start by sketching the picture given in each question on a 6 × 6 grid, each square of which is 1 cm by 1 cm. The scale for each question is given.

FM 1 A goat is tethered by a rope, 7 m long, in a corner of a field with a fence at each side. What is the locus of the area that the goat can graze? Use a scale of 1 cm ≡ 2 m.

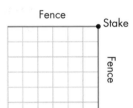

FM 2 In a field, a horse is tethered to a stake by a rope 6 m long. What is the locus of the area that the horse can graze? Use a scale of 1 cm ≡ 2 m.

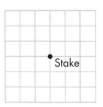

FM 3 A cow is tethered to a rail at the top of a fence 6 m long. The rope is 3 m long. Sketch the area that the cow can graze. Use a scale of 1 cm ≡ 2 m.

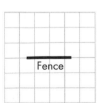

FM 4 A horse is tethered to a stake near a corner of a fenced field, at a point 4 m from each fence. The rope is 6 m long. Sketch the area that the horse can graze. Use a scale of 1 cm ≡ 2 m.

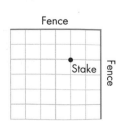

FM **5** A horse is tethered to a corner of a shed, 2 m by 1 m. The rope is 2 m long. Sketch the area that the horse can graze. Use a scale of 1 cm ≡ 1 m.

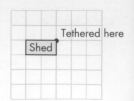

FM **6** A goat is tethered by a 4 m rope to a stake at one corner of a pen, 4 m by 3 m. Sketch the area of the pen on which the goat cannot graze. Use a scale of 1 cm ≡ 1 m.

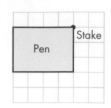

FM **7** A puppy is tethered to a stake by a rope, 1.5 m long, on a flat lawn on which are two raised brick flower beds. The stake is situated at one corner of a bed, as shown. Sketch the area that the puppy is free to roam in. Use a scale of 1 cm ≡ 1 m.

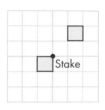

For questions **8** to **15**, you should use a copy of the map opposite. For each question, trace the map and mark on those points that are relevant to that question.

FM **8** A radio station broadcasts from London on a frequency of 1000 kHz with a range of 300 km. Another radio station broadcasts from Glasgow on the same frequency with a range of 200 km.

   a Sketch the area to which each station can broadcast.

   b Will they interfere with each other?

   c If the Glasgow station increases its range to 400 km, will they then interfere with each other?

FM **9** The radar at Leeds airport has a range of 200 km. The radar at Exeter airport has a range of 200 km.

   a Will a plane flying over Birmingham be detected by the Leeds radar?

   b Sketch the area where a plane can be picked up by both radars at the same time.

FM **10** A radio transmitter is to be built according to these rules.

   i It has to be the same distance from York and Birmingham.

   ii It must be within 350 km of Glasgow.

   iii It must be within 250 km of London.

   a Sketch the line that is the same distance from York and Birmingham.

   b Sketch the area that is within 350 km of Glasgow and 250 km of London.

   c Show clearly the possible places at which the transmitter could be built.

Glasgow

Newcastle
upon Tyne

North Sea

York
Leeds

Irish Sea

Manchester
Sheffield

Norwich

Birmingham

London

Bristol

Exeter

0   50   100   150   200   250   300   350 km

FM 11 A radio transmitter centred at Birmingham is designed to give good reception in an area greater than 150 km and less than 250 km from the transmitter. Sketch the area of good reception.

FM 12 Three radio stations pick up a distress call from a boat in the Irish Sea. The station at Glasgow can tell from the strength of the signal that the boat is within 300 km of the station. The station at York can tell that the boat is between 200 km and 300 km from York. The station at London can tell that it is less than 400 km from London. Sketch the area where the boat could be.

FM 13 Sketch the area that is between 200 km and 300 km from Newcastle upon Tyne, and between 150 km and 250 km from Bristol.

FM 14 An oil rig is situated in the North Sea in such a position that it is the same distance from Newcastle upon Tyne and Manchester. It is also the same distance from Sheffield and Norwich. Draw the line that shows all the points that are the same distance from Newcastle upon Tyne and Manchester. Repeat for the points that are the same distance from Sheffield and Norwich and find out where the oil rig is located.

FM 15 Whilst looking at a map, Fred notices that his house is the same distance from Glasgow, Norwich and Exeter. Where is it?

16 Wathsea Harbour is as shown in the diagram. A boat sets off from point A and steers so that it stays the same distance from the sea wall and the West Pier. Another boat sets off from B and steers so that it stays the same distance from the East Pier and the sea wall. Copy the diagram. On your diagram show accurately the path of each boat.

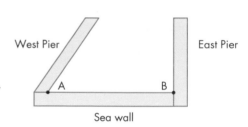

PS 17 Tariq wanted to fly himself from the Isle of Wight north, towards Scotland. He wanted to remain at the same distance from London as Bristol as far as he could.

Once he is past London and Bristol, which city should he aim toward to keep him, as accurately as possible, the same distance from London and Bristol? Use the map to help you.

AU 18 A distress call is heard by coastguards in both Newcastle and Bristol. The signal strength suggests that the call comes from a ship that is the same distance from both places. Explain how the coastguards could find the area of sea to search.

GRADE BOOSTER

c You can construct line and angle bisectors

c You can describe and draw the locus of a point from a given rule

c You can use loci to solve problems

B You can construct a perpendicular from a point on a line

B You can construct a perpendicular from a point to a line

B You can construct angles of 60° and 90°

What you should know now

- How to construct line and angle bisectors
- How to construct perpendiculars
- How to construct angles without using a protractor
- Understand what is meant by a locus
- How to solve problems, using loci

1 The diagram shows a sketch of a parallelogram.

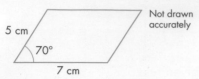

Not drawn accurately

Make an accurate drawing of the parallelogram. *(3 marks)*

AQA, November 2008, Module 5, Paper 1 Higher, Question 3

2 In trapezium PQRS, the sides PQ and SR are parallel.

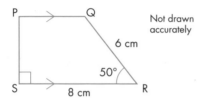

Not drawn accurately

Make an accurate drawing of the trapezium.
(4 marks)

AQA, June 2009, Module 5, Paper 2 Higher, Question 5

3 **a** Draw a line PQ 10 cm long. Now, using ruler and compasses only, construct the perpendicular bisector of the line PQ.
(2 marks)

b Complete the sentence.

The perpendicular bisector of the line PQ is the locus of points that are... *(1 mark)*

AQA, June 2008, Module 5, Paper 2 Higher, Question 9

4 ABCD is a quadrilateral.

The region R is defined as the set of points inside ABCD that are:

closer to the side AB than the side AD

and closer to the point D than the point C.

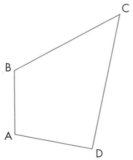

Using a ruler and compasses, copy the diagram and construct **accurately** the region R.

Label the region clearly with the letter R.
(4 marks)

AQA, June 2009, Paper 2 Higher, Question 20

5 The diagram shows an L shape.

Copy the diagram and draw the locus of all points 2 cm from the L shape.

(3 marks)

AQA, June 2005, Paper 1 Higher, Question 5

6 **a** Using a ruler and compasses only, construct an angle of 60°. *(2 marks)*

b Two lifeboat stations A and B receive a distress call from a boat.

The boat is within 6 kilometres of station A.

The boat is within 8 kilometres of station B.

Trace the diagram and shade the possible area where the boat could be. *(2 marks)*

Scale: 1 cm represents 1 km

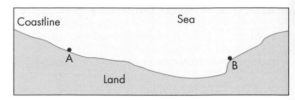

AQA, Specimen Paper 2008, Module 5, Paper 2 Higher, Question 8

7 The diagram shows a scale drawing of a straight road.

A walker is at point P.

P
×

Scale
1 cm represents 0.5 km

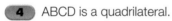

Road

a Copy the diagram and use a ruler and compasses to construct the perpendicular from the point P to the road. You **must** show all your construction lines and arcs.
(3 marks)

b Find the shortest real distance from the walker to the road. *(2 marks)*

AQA, November 2007, Paper 2 Higher, Question 3

C   D

8 There are two TV transmitters on an island.

The transmitter at A has a range of 40 km.

The transmitter at B has a range of 60 km.

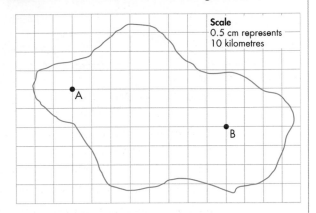

Scale
0.5 cm represents 10 kilometres

Copy the diagram and show clearly the area in which the signal from both transmitters can be received. *(3 marks)*

AQA, June 2007, Paper 2 Higher, Question 2

9 The diagram shows two triangles A and B.

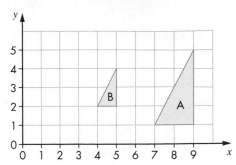

a Describe fully the transformation that maps triangle A onto triangle B. *(3 marks)*

b On a copy of the diagram draw the image of triangle B after it is reflected in the line $y = x$. *(2 marks)*

AQA, November 2005, Paper 1 Higher, Question 6

Worked Examination Questions

1 Here is a sketch of a triangle. PR = 6.4 cm, QR = 7.7 cm and angle R = 35°.

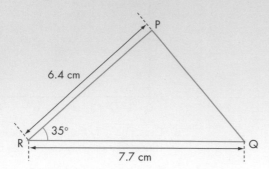

6.4 cm

35°

R

7.7 cm

Q

P

a Make an accurate drawing of the triangle.

b Measure the size of angle Q on your drawing.

1 a **Make an accurate drawing, using these steps.**

Step 1: Draw the base as a line 7.7 cm long.
You can draw this and measure it with a ruler,
although using a pair of compasses is more accurate.

> This scores 1 mark for the angle and line.

Step 2: Measure the angle at R as 35°.
Draw a faint line at this angle.

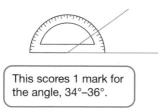

> This scores 1 mark for the angle, 34°–36°.

Step 4: Join P to Q.

P

R

Q

Step 3: Using a pair of compasses, draw
an arc 6.4 cm long from R. Where this
crosses the line from Step 2, make this P.

> This scores 1 mark for the second side.

> This scores 1 mark for completing the triangle.

b Measure the angle Q. It is 56°.

> This scores 1 mark for this angle 56° ± 2°. If your actual angle was not 56° but you measured it accurately, then you would still get the mark.

(**Total:** 4 marks)

Worked Examination Questions

FM **2** Some wind turbines follow a design based on **arcs** within an **equilateral triangle**.

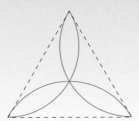

Construct this design, based on an equilateral triangle with sides of length 5 cm.

2 Start with the equilateral triangle.

> This scores 1 mark for method for correctly constructing this figure.

Construct the line bisectors of each side.

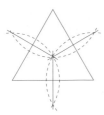

> This scores 1 mark for method for showing correct construction for at least two arcs.
>
> This scores 1 mark for accuracy for correctly constructing at least two of them.

Where these bisectors all meet gives the centre of the triangle.

> This scores 1 mark for method for all bisectors meeting at same point.

Join each vertex to this centre point and bisect each of these lines, extending the new bisectors to intersect with the bisectors of the sides of the triangle.

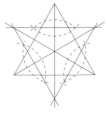

> This scores 1 mark for method for attempting to construct bisectors on at least two of the correct lines.
>
> This scores 1 mark for accuracy for correctly identifying at least two correct centres.

These points where the lines intersect are the centres of the arcs. Set the compasses to the distance between one of these points and the nearest vertex and draw the arcs from each point.

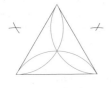

> This scores 1 mark for accuracy for correctly constructing this final figure.

Total: 7 marks

Worked Examination Questions

3 The map shows three boats, A, B and C, on a lake. Along one edge of the lake there is a straight path.

Treasure lies at the bottom of the lake.

The treasure is:

    between 150 m and 250 m from B,

    nearer to A than C,

    more than 100 m from the path.

Using a ruler and compasses only, shade the region in which the treasure lies.

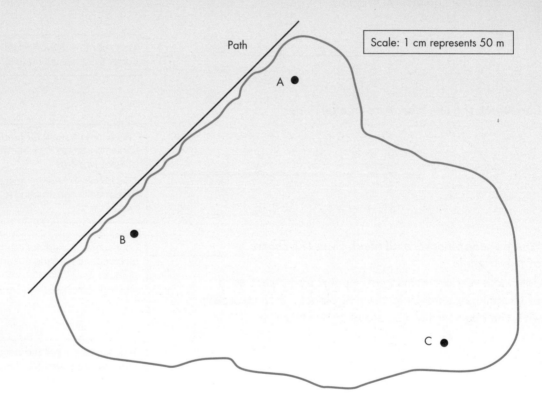

You must show clearly all your construction arcs.

Worked Examination Questions

3 Draw two circles with centre at B with radii 3 cm and 5 cm. ——————— This scores 1 mark.

Draw the perpendicular bisector of AC. ——————— This scores 1 mark.

Draw a parallel line 2 cm from the path. ——————— This scores 1 mark.

The region required is shaded on the diagram. ——————— This scores 1 mark.

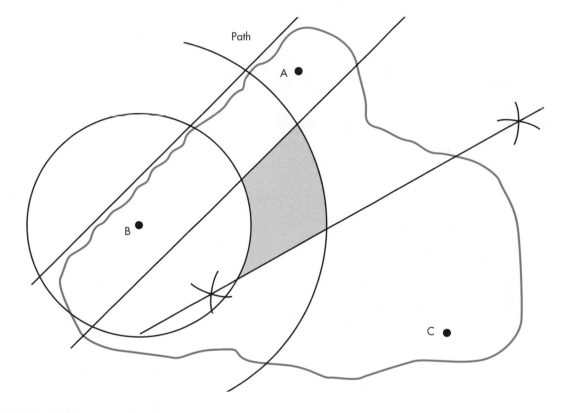

Total: 4 marks

You already know that architects and engineers must construct accurate diagrams, to be certain that the buildings and constructions they have designed will be built correctly. However, did you know that the same principles used by architects and engineers to construct diagrams are also used when planning sports pitches, whether it is your local playing field or a Premier League football club?

In this task you will take on the role of the grounds staff of a football pitch. You will need to negotiate many variables to ensure that the pitch is drawn up correctly and can be maintained thoroughly.

Your task

As a member of the grounds staff you have been asked to prepare the pitch ready for the new football season.

The club needs the pitch designed according to FIFA's specifications.

1 Construct a scale drawing of the football pitch, to be used in laying out the pitch on the football field. Be sure to label all the dimensions of the pitch.

2 The pitch will need to be regularly watered in order to keep it in good condition. For this, you will need to design a comprehensive sprinkler system. On a copy of your drawing of the pitch, mark up where the sprinklers should go, ensuring that the maximum possible area of the pitch is watered at any one time.

Getting started
Discuss these questions with a partner.

● What shapes do you see on sports fields? Do these shapes vary, depending on the sports that take place on these pitches?

● What angles do you see on sports fields?

● How are shapes drawn on to sports fields?

FIFA specifications

The field

The field of play must be rectangular, divided into two halves by a halfway line. The centre mark is indicated at the midpoint of the halfway line and a circle with a radius of 9.15 m (10 yards) is marked around it.

The field dimensions should be as follows.

	Minimum	Maximum
Length	90 m (approx. 100 yards)	120 m (approx. 130 yards)
Width	45 m (approx. 50 yards)	90 m (approx. 100 yards)

The goal area

The goal mouth is 7.3 metres (8 yards) wide. The goal area is 5.5 m (6 yards) wide by 18.3 m (12 yards) long.

The penalty area

The penalty area is 16.5 m (18 yards) wide by 40.3 m (44 yards) long.

Within each penalty area there is a penalty mark 11 m (12 yards) from the midpoint between the goalposts and equidistant from them. An arc with a radius of 9.15 m (10 yards) from each penalty mark is drawn outside the penalty area.

The corner arc

A flagpost is placed in each corner. A quarter-circle with a radius of 1 m (approximately 1 yard) is drawn at each corner flag post, inside the field of play.

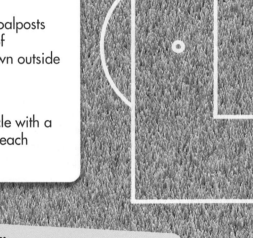

Hint: Use the internet to research football pitches and FIFA's specifications further.

Why this chapter matters

Thales of Miletus (624–547 BC) was a Greek philosopher and one of the Seven Sages of Greece. He is believed to have been the first person to use similar triangles to find the height of tall objects.

Thales discovered that, at a particular time of day, the height of an object and the length of its shadow were the same. He used this observation to calculate the height of the Egyptian pyramids. Later, he took this knowledge back to Greece. His observations are considered to be the forerunner of the technique of using similar triangles to solve such problems.

A clinometer is an instrument used to measure the height of objects from a distance. Using a clinometer, you can apply the geometry of triangles to determine the height visually, rather than by physically measuring it. Clinometers are commonly used to measure the heights of trees, buildings and towers, mountains and other objects for which taking physical measurements might be impractical.

Astronomers use the geometry of triangles to measure the distance to nearby stars. They take advantage of the Earth's journey in its orbit around the Sun to obtain the maximum distance between two measurements. They observe the star twice, from the same point on Earth and at the same time of day, but six months apart.

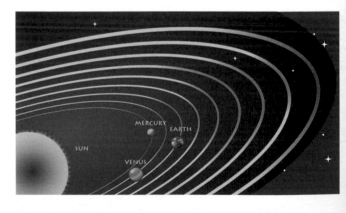

Telescopes and binoculars also use the geometry of triangles. The Hubble Space Telescope took this image of the Eagle Nebula. This star-forming region is located 6500 light years from Earth. It is only about 6 million years old and the dense clouds of interstellar gas are still collapsing to form new stars.

A light year is the distance that a ray of light travels in one year.

It is about 5 878 630 000 000 miles, or just under 10^{13} km.

Measures: Similarity

1 Similar triangles

2 Areas and volumes of similar shapes

This chapter will show you ...

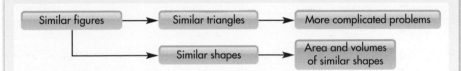

C how to work out the scale factor for two similar shapes

B how to work out lengths of sides in similar figures

to **A** **A*** how to work out areas and volumes of similar shapes

Visual overview

Similar figures → Similar triangles → More complicated problems

Similar figures → Similar shapes → Area and volumes of similar shapes

What you should already know

- How to use and simplify ratios **(KS3 level 6, GCSE grade D)**
- How to enlarge a shape by a given scale factor **(KS3 level 6, GCSE grade D–C)**
- How to solve equations **(KS3 level 6, GCSE grade D–C)**

Quick check

1 Simplify the following ratios.

   a $15 : 20$ **b** $24 : 30$

   c $6 : 1\frac{1}{2}$ **d** $7.5 : 5$

2 Solve the following equations.

   a $\dfrac{x}{4} = \dfrac{7}{2}$ **b** $\dfrac{x}{2} = \dfrac{5}{4}$

   c $\dfrac{x}{4} = \dfrac{x-2}{3}$ **d** $\dfrac{x+4}{x} = \dfrac{5}{3}$

This section will show you how to:
- show two triangles are similar
- work out the scale factor between similar triangles

Key words

ratio
scale factor
similar
similar triangles

Triangles are **similar** if their corresponding angles are equal. Their corresponding sides are then in the same **ratio**.

These two right-angled triangles are **similar triangles**.

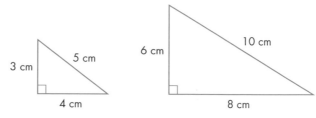

The scale factor of the enlargement = 2

The ratios of the lengths of corresponding sides all cancel to the same ratio.

    3 : 6 = 4 : 8 = 5 : 10 = 1 : 2

All corresponding angles are equal.

EXAMPLE 1

The triangles ABC and PQR are similar. Find the length of the side PR.

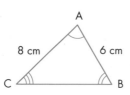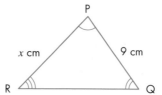

Take two pairs of corresponding sides, one pair of which must contain the unknown side. Form each pair into a fraction, so that x is on top. Since these fractions must be equal,

$$\frac{PR}{AC} = \frac{PQ}{AB}$$

$$\frac{x}{8} = \frac{9}{6}$$

To find x:

$$x = \frac{9 \times 8}{6} \text{ cm} \quad \Rightarrow \quad x = \frac{72}{6} = 12 \text{ cm}$$

FM Functional Maths   **AU** (AO2) Assessing Understanding   **PS** (AO3) Problem Solving

EXERCISE 9A

1 These diagrams are drawn to scale. What is the **scale factor** of the enlargement in each case?

a

b

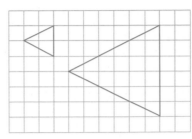

HINTS AND TIPS

If you need to revise enlargements, look back at Section 7.5.

AU **2** Are these pairs of shapes similar? If so, give the scale factor. If not, give a reason.

a
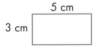

5 cm

3 cm

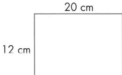

20 cm

12 cm

b

12 cm

5 cm

22 cm

15 cm

3 **a** Explain why these triangles are similar.

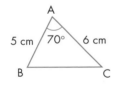

A

5 cm 70° 6 cm

B   C

P

15 cm 70° 18 cm

Q   R

b Give the ratio of the sides.

c Which angle corresponds to angle C?

d Which side corresponds to side QP?

4 **a** Explain why these triangles are similar.

b Which angle corresponds to angle A?

c Which side corresponds to side AC?

B

6 cm

A   5 cm   C

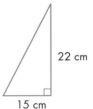

Q

9 cm

P   7.5 cm   R

5 **a** Explain why triangle ABC is similar to triangle AQR.

b Which angle corresponds to the angle at B?

c Which side of triangle AQR corresponds to side AC of triangle ABC? Your answers to question **4** may help you.

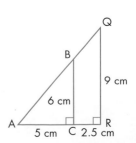

Q

B

9 cm

6 cm

A   5 cm   C 2.5 cm   R

B

6 In the diagrams **a** to **f**, each pair of shapes are similar but not drawn to scale.

a Find x.

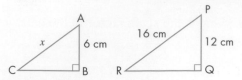

b Find PQ.

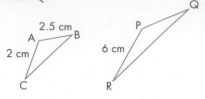

c Find x and y.

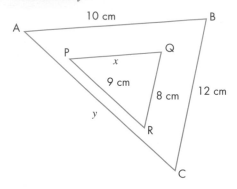

d Find x and y.

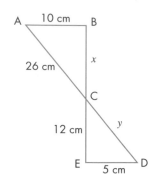

e Find the lengths of AB and PQ.

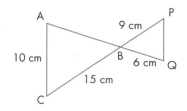

f Find the length of QR.

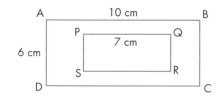

7 a Explain why these two triangles are similar.

b What is the ratio of their sides?

c Use Pythagoras' theorem to calculate the length of side AC of triangle ABC.

d Write down the length of the side PR of triangle PQR.

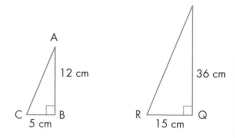

FM 8 Sean is standing next to a tree.

His height is 1.6 m and he casts a shadow that has a length of 2.4 m.

The tree casts a shadow that has a length of 7.8 m.

Use what you know about similar triangles to work out the height of the tree, h.

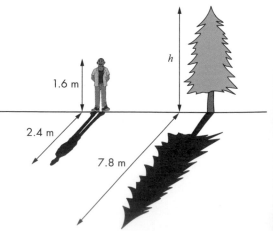

PS **9** Here are two rectangles.

Explain why the two rectangles are not similar.

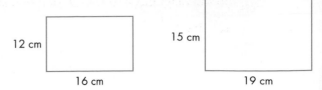

12 cm

16 cm

15 cm

19 cm

AU **10** Triangle ABC is similar to triangle CDE.

Jay says that the length of DE is 14 cm.

Explain why Jay is wrong.

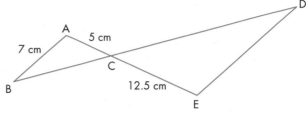

A

5 cm

7 cm

C

B

12.5 cm

D

E

Further examples of similar triangles

EXAMPLE 2

Find the lengths marked x and y in the diagram (not drawn to scale).

Triangles AED and ABC are similar. So using the corresponding sides CB, DE with AC, AD gives,

$$\frac{x}{5} = \frac{10}{4}$$

$$\Rightarrow x = \frac{10 \times 5}{4} = 12.5$$

Using the corresponding sides AE, AB with AD, AC gives,

$$\frac{y + 6}{6} = \frac{10}{4} \Rightarrow y + 6 = \frac{10 \times 6}{4} = 15$$

$$\Rightarrow \quad y = 15 - 6 = 9$$

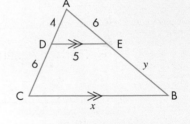

A

4

6

D

5

E

6

C

x

B

y

EXAMPLE 3

Ahmed wants to work out the height of a tall building. He walks 100 paces from the building and sticks a pole, 2 m long, vertically into the ground. He then walks another 10 paces on the same line and notices that when he looks from ground level, the top of the pole and the top of the building are in line. How tall is the building?

First, draw a diagram of the situation and label it.

Using corresponding sides ED, CB with AD, AB gives,

$$\frac{x}{2} = \frac{110}{10}$$

$$\Rightarrow \quad x = \frac{110 \times 2}{10} = 22 \text{ m}$$

Hence the building is 22 m high.

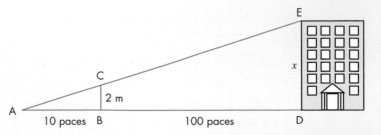

E

C

2 m

A

10 paces   B

100 paces

D

x

EXERCISE 9B

1 In each of the cases below, state a pair of similar triangles and find the length marked *x*. Separate the similar triangles if it makes it easier for you.

a

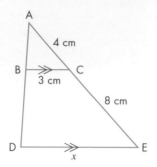

b

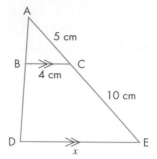

2 a Find the value of *x*.

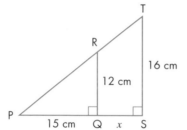

b Find the length of CE.

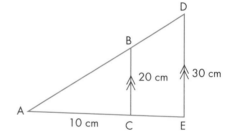

c Find the values of *x* and *y*.

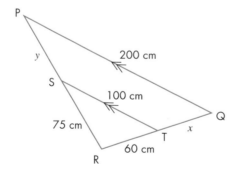

d Find the values of *x* and *y*.

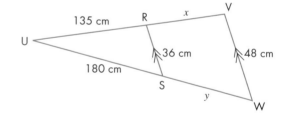

e Find the lengths of DC and EB.

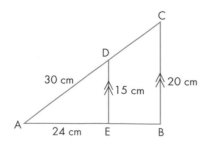

FM 3 This diagram shows a method of working out the height of a tower.

A stick, 2 m long, is placed vertically 120 m from the base of a tower so that the top of the tower and the top of the stick are in line with a point on the ground 3 m from the base of the stick. How high is the tower?

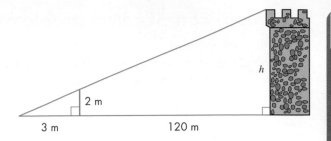

FM 4 It is known that a factory chimney is 330 feet high. Patrick paces out distances as shown in the diagram, so that the top of the chimney and the top of the flag pole are in line with each other. How high is the flag pole?

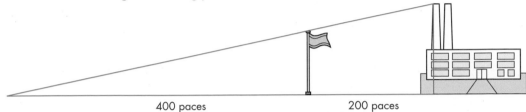

400 paces   200 paces

FM 5 The height of a golf flag is 1.5 m. Use the diagram to find the height of the tree.

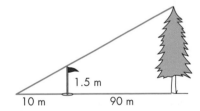

10 m   90 m

FM 6 Find the height of a pole that casts a shadow of 1.5 m when, at the same time, a man 165 cm tall, casts a shadow of 75 cm.

7 Bob, a builder, is making this wooden frame for a roof.

In the diagram, triangle ABC is similar to triangle AXY.

AB = 1.5 m, BX = 3.5 m and XY = 6 m

Work out the length of wood that Bob needs to make BC.

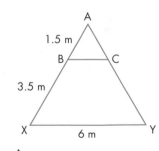

PS 8 Triangle ABC is similar to triangle ACD.

AC = 9 cm and CD = 6 cm

Work out the length of BC.

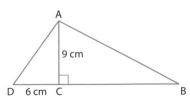

AU 9 In the diagram triangle ABC is similar to triangle AXY.

Which of the following is the correct length of BX?

Explain how you decide.

a 2 cm   **b** 3 cm

c 4 cm   **d** 5 cm

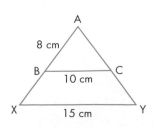

More complicated problems

The information given in a similar triangle situation can be more complicated than anything you have met so far, and you will need to have good algebraic skills to deal with it. Example 4 is typical of the more complicated problem you may be asked to solve, so follow it through carefully.

EXAMPLE 4

Find the value of x in this triangle.

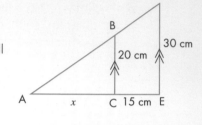

You know that triangle ABC is similar to triangle ADE.

Splitting up the triangles may help you to see what will be needed.

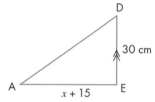

So your equation will be:

$$\frac{x + 15}{x} = \frac{30}{20}$$

Cross multiplying (moving each of the two bottom terms to the opposite side and multiplying) gives:

$$20x + 300 = 30x$$
$$\Rightarrow \quad 300 = 10x \Rightarrow x = 30 \text{ cm}$$

EXERCISE 9C

Find the lengths x or x and y in the diagrams **1** to **6**.

B

1
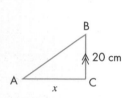

2
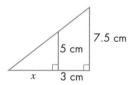

3
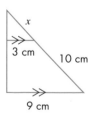
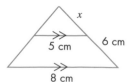

4
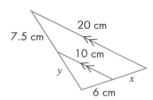

5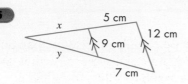

6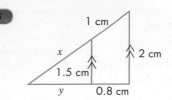

B

9.2 Areas and volumes of similar shapes

This section will show you how to:
- solve problems involving the area and volume of similar shapes

Key words
area ratio
area scale factor
length ratio
linear scale factor
volume ratio
volume scale factor

There are relationships between the lengths, areas and volumes of similar shapes.

You saw on pages 196–198 that when a 2D shape is enlarged by a given scale factor to form a new, similar shape, the corresponding lengths of the original shape and the new shape are all in the same ratio, which is equal to the scale factor. This scale factor of the lengths is called the **length ratio** or **linear scale factor**.

Two similar shapes also have an **area ratio**, which is equal to the ratio of the squares of their corresponding lengths. The area ratio, or **area scale factor**, is the square of the length ratio.

Likewise, two 3D shapes are similar if their corresponding lengths are in the same ratio. Their **volume ratio** is equal to the ratio of the cubes of their corresponding lengths. The volume ratio, or **volume scale factor**, is the cube of the length ratio.

Generally, the relationship between similar shapes can be expressed as:

Length ratio $x : y$ Area ratio $x^2 : y^2$ Volume ratio $x^3 : y^3$

EXAMPLE 5

A model yacht is made to a scale of $\frac{1}{20}$ of the size of the real yacht. The area of the sail of the model is 150 cm^2. What is the area of the sail of the real yacht?

At first sight, it may appear that you do not have enough information to solve this problem, but it can be done as follows.

Linear scale factor $= 1 : 20$
Area scale factor $= 1 : 400$ (square of the linear scale factor)
Area of real sail $= 400 \times$ area of model sail
            $= 400 \times 150$ cm^2
            $= 60\,000$ cm$^2 = 6$ m^2

EXAMPLE 6

A bottle has a base radius of 4 cm, a height of 15 cm and a capacity of 650 cm^3. A similar bottle has a base radius of 3 cm.

a What is the length ratio?

b What is the volume ratio?

c What is the volume of the smaller bottle?

a The length ratio is given by the ratio of the two radii, that is 4 : 3.

b The volume ratio is therefore $4^3 : 3^3 = 64 : 27$.

c Let v be the volume of the smaller bottle. Then the volume ratio is:

$$\frac{\text{volume of smaller bottle}}{\text{volume of larger bottle}} = \frac{v}{650} = \frac{27}{64}$$

$$\Rightarrow v = \frac{27 \times 650}{64} = 274 \text{ cm}^3 \text{ (3 significant figures)}$$

EXAMPLE 7

The cost of a tin of paint , height 12 cm, is £3.20 and its label has an area of 24 cm^2.

a If the cost is based on the amount of paint in the tin, what is the cost of a similar tin, 18 cm high?

b Assuming the labels are similar, what will be the area of the label on the larger tin?

a The cost of the paint is proportional to the volume of the tin.

Length ratio = 12 : 18 = 2 : 3

Volume ratio = $2^3 : 3^3$ = 8 : 27

Let P be the cost of the larger tin. Then the cost ratio is:

$$\frac{\text{cost of larger tin}}{\text{cost of smaller tin}} = \frac{P}{3.2}$$

Therefore,

$$\frac{P}{3.2} = \frac{27}{8}$$

$$\Rightarrow P = \frac{27 \times 3.2}{8} = £10.80$$

b Area ratio = $2^2 : 3^2$ = 4 : 9

Let A be the area of the larger label. Then the area ratio is:

$$\frac{\text{larger label area}}{\text{smaller label area}} = \frac{A}{24}$$

Therefore,

$$\frac{A}{24} = \frac{9}{4}$$

$$\Rightarrow A = \frac{9 \times 24}{4} = 54 \text{ cm}^2$$

EXERCISE 9D

1 The length ratio between two similar solids is 2 : 5.

   a What is the area ratio between the solids?

   b What is the volume ratio between the solids?

2 The length ratio between two similar solids is 4 : 7.

   a What is the area ratio between the solids?

   b What is the volume ratio between the solids?

3 Copy and complete this table.

Linear scale factor	Linear ratio	Linear fraction	Area scale factor	Volume scale factor
2	1 : 2	$\frac{2}{1}$		
3				
$\frac{1}{4}$	4 : 1	$\frac{1}{4}$		$\frac{1}{64}$
			25	
				$\frac{1}{1000}$

4 A shape has an area of 15 cm². What is the area of a similar shape with lengths that are three times the corresponding lengths of the first shape?

FM 5 A toy brick has a surface area of 14 cm². What would be the surface area of a similar toy brick with lengths that are:

   a twice the corresponding lengths of the first brick

   b three times the corresponding lengths of the first brick?

6 A rug has an area of 12 m². What area would be covered by rugs with lengths that are:

   a twice the corresponding lengths of the first rug

   b half the corresponding lengths of the first rug?

7 A brick has a volume of 300 cm³. What would be the volume of a similar brick whose lengths are:

   a twice the corresponding lengths of the first brick

   b three times the corresponding lengths of the first brick?

FM 8 A tin of paint, 6 cm high, holds a half a litre of paint. How much paint would go into a similar tin which is 12 cm high?

FM 9 A model statue is 10 cm high and has a volume of 100 cm³. The real statue is 2.4 m high. What is the volume of the real statue? Give your answer in m³.

10 A small tin of paint costs 75p. What is the cost of a larger similar tin with height twice that of the smaller tin? Assume that the cost is based only on the volume of paint in the tin.

11 A small trinket box of width 2 cm has a volume of 10 cm³. What is the width of a similar trinket box with a volume of 80 cm³?

FM 12 A cinema sells popcorn in two different-sized tubs that are similar in shape.

Show that it is true that the big tub is better value.

Popcorn

10 cm   20 cm

Small tub
60p

Large tub
£4.00p

Better value if you buy the Big tub

PS 13 The diameters of two ball bearings are given below.
Work out:

   a the ratio of their radii

   b the ratio of their surface areas

   c the ratio of their volumes.

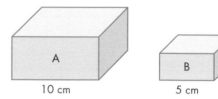

6 mm   8 mm

AU 14 Cuboid A is similar to cuboid B.

The length of cuboid A is 10 cm and the length of cuboid B is 5 cm.

The volume of cuboid A is 720 cm³.

A

10 cm

B

5 cm

Shona says that the volume of cuboid B must be 360 cm³.

Explain why she is wrong.

More complex problems using area and volume ratios

In some problems involving similar shapes, the length ratio is not given, so we have to start with the area ratio or the volume ratio. We usually then need to first find the length ratio in order to proceed with the solution.

EXAMPLE 8

A manufacturer makes a range of clown hats that are all similar in shape. The smallest hat is 8 cm tall and uses 180 cm² of card. What will be the height of a hat made from 300 cm² of card?

The area ratio is 180 : 300

Therefore, the length ratio is $\sqrt{180} : \sqrt{300}$ (do not calculate these yet)

Let the height of the larger hat be H, then

$$\frac{H}{8} = \frac{\sqrt{300}}{\sqrt{180}} = \sqrt{\frac{300}{180}}$$

$$\Rightarrow H = 8 \times \sqrt{\frac{300}{180}} = 10.3 \text{ cm (1 decimal place)}$$

EXAMPLE 9

A supermarket stocks similar small and large tins of soup. The areas of their labels are 110 cm² and 190 cm² respectively. The weight of a small tin is 450 g. What is the weight of a large tin?

The area ratio is 110 : 190

Therefore, the length ratio is $\sqrt{110} : \sqrt{190}$ (do not calculate these yet)

So the volume (weight) ratio is $(\sqrt{110})^3 : (\sqrt{190})^3$.

Let the weight of a large tin be W, then

$$\frac{W}{450} = \frac{(\sqrt{190})^3}{(\sqrt{110})^3} = \left(\sqrt{\frac{190}{110}}\right)^3$$

$$\Rightarrow \quad W = 450 \times \left(\sqrt{\frac{190}{110}}\right)^3 = 1020 \text{ g} \quad \text{(3 significant figures)}$$

EXAMPLE 10

Two similar tins hold 1.5 litres and 2.5 litres of paint respectively. The area of the label on the smaller tin is 85 cm². What is the area of the label on the larger tin?

The volume ratio is 1.5 : 2.5

Therefore, the length ratio is $\sqrt[3]{1.5} : \sqrt[3]{2.5}$ (do not calculate these yet)

So the area ratio is $(\sqrt[3]{1.5})^2 : (\sqrt[3]{2.5})^2$

Let the area of the label on the larger tin be A, then

$$\frac{A}{85} = \frac{(\sqrt[3]{2.5})^2}{(\sqrt[3]{1.5})^2} = \left(\sqrt[3]{\frac{2.5}{1.5}}\right)^2$$

$$\Rightarrow \quad A = 85 \times \left(\sqrt[3]{\frac{2.5}{1.5}}\right)^2 = 119 \text{ cm}^2 \quad \text{(3 significant figures)}$$

EXERCISE 9E

FM 1 A firm produces three sizes of similar-shaped labels for its products. Their areas are 150 cm², 250 cm² and 400 cm². The 250 cm² label just fits around a can of height 8 cm. Find the heights of similar cans around which the other two labels would just fit.

2 A firm makes similar gift boxes in three different sizes: small, medium and large. The areas of their lids are as follows.

    Small: 30 cm²   Medium: 50 cm²   Large: 75 cm²

The medium box is 5.5 cm high. Find the heights of the other two sizes.

A*

A*

3 A cone of height 8 cm can be made from a piece of card with an area of 140 cm^2. What is the height of a similar cone made from a similar piece of card with an area of 200 cm^2?

4 It takes 5.6 litres of paint to paint a chimney which is 3 m high. What is the tallest similar chimney that can be painted with 8 litres of paint?

5 A piece of card, 1200 cm^2 in area, will make a tube 13 cm long. What is the length of a similar tube made from a similar piece of card with an area of 500 cm^2?

6 All television screens (of the same style) are similar. If a screen of area 220 cm^2 has a diagonal length of 21 cm, what will be the diagonal length of a screen of area 350 cm^2?

7 Two similar statues, made from the same bronze, are placed in a school. One weighs 300 g, the other weighs 2 kg. The height of the smaller statue is 9 cm. What is the height of the larger statue?

FM 8 A supermarket sells similar cans of pasta rings in three different sizes: small, medium and large. The sizes of the labels around the cans are as follows.

  Small can: 24 cm^2 Medium can: 46 cm^2 Large can: 78 cm^2

The medium size can is 6 cm tall with a weight of 380 g. Calculate these quantities.

  a The heights of the other two sizes

  b The weights of the other two sizes

9 A statue weighs 840 kg. A similar statue was made out of the same material but two-fifths the height of the first one. What was the weight of the smaller statue?

10 A model stands on a base of area 12 cm^2. A smaller but similar model, made of the same material, stands on a base of area 7.5 cm^2. Calculate the weight of the smaller model if the larger one is 3.5 kg.

FM 11 Steve fills two similar jugs with orange juice.

The first jug holds 1.5 litres of juice and has a base diameter of 8 cm.

The second jug holds 2 litres of juice. Work out the base diameter of the second jug.

PS 12 The total surface areas of two similar cuboids are 500 cm^2 and 800 cm^2.

If the width of one of the cuboids is 10 cm, calculate the two possible widths for the other cuboid.

AU 13 The volumes of two similar cylinders are 256 cm^3 and 864 cm^3.

Which of the following gives the ratio of their surface areas?

  a 2 : 3   **b** 4 : 9   **c** 8 : 27

GRADE BOOSTER

C You can work out unknown lengths in 2D shapes, using scale factors

B You can use ratios and equations to find unknown lengths in similar triangles

A You can solve problems, using area and volume scale factors

A* You can solve more complex problems, using area and volume scale factors

What you should know now

- How to find the ratios between two similar shapes
- How to work out unknown lengths, areas and volumes of similar 3D shapes
- How to solve practical problems, using similar shapes
- How to solve problems, using area and volume ratios

1 Triangles ABC and DEF are similar.

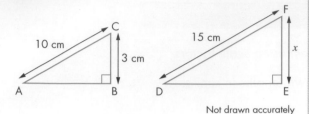

Not drawn accurately

Work out the length of EF, marked x on the diagram.

(3 marks)

AQA, May 2008, Module 5, Paper 1 Higher, Question 9(b)

2 Triangles ABC and PQR are similar.

AB = 5 cm, BC = 6 cm, and QR = 21 cm

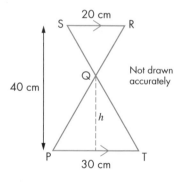

Not drawn accurately

Calculate the length of PQ. *(3 marks)*

AQA, May 2008, Paper 1, Question17

3 In the diagram SR is parallel to PT.

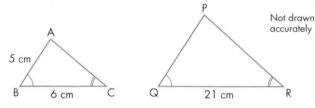

Not drawn accurately

SQT and RQP are straight lines.

SR = 20 cm and
PT = 30 cm

The total height of the two triangles is 40 cm.

Use similar triangles to calculate the height, h cm, of triangle PQT.

(3 marks)

AQA, June 2006, Paper 1, Question 10

4 ABC and XYZ are similar triangles with right angles at B and Y.

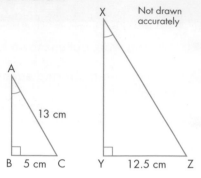

Not drawn accurately

AC = 13 cm, BC = 5 cm and YZ = 12.5 cm

Work out the length of XY. *(5 marks)*

AQA, November 2006, Paper 1, Question 11

5 The diagram shows three mathematically similar containers.

Not drawn accurately

small   medium   large

This table shows some information about the containers.

	Height (cm)	Area of top of container (cm²)	Volume (cm³)
small	12	X	400
medium	24	500	
large	36		Y

Calculate the missing entries, X and Y.

(4 marks)

AQA, November 2007, Paper 1, Question 19

6 **a** Explain why the volume of a cube increases by a factor of 8 when the side length is doubled. *(2 marks)*

ALIEN

Place in water and it becomes 6 times bigger!

b June recently bought a small toy in a local shop.

It was originally 8 cm tall.

After she placed it in water it grew to a similarly shaped alien.

The height was then 14.5 cm.

Is the claim on the pack justified? *(3 marks)*

AQA, June 2005, Paper 2, Question 21(a)(b)

A   B

Worked Examination Questions

PS **1** Triangles ABC and CDE are similar.

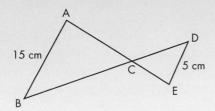

AB = 15 cm and DE = 5 cm

The length of BD is 24 cm.

Work out the lengths of BC and CD.

1 AB : DE = 15 : 5 = 3 : 1 ——————
> AB and DE are corresponding sides in similar triangles. This gets 1 method mark.

So the ratio BC : CD is also 3 : 1 ——————
> BC and CD are another pair of corresponding sides.

BD = 24 cm, divide this in the ratio 3 : 1 ——————
> The ratio has 4 parts, so 24 ÷ 4 = 6.

So BC = 18 cm ——————
> This gets 1 mark for accuracy.

and CD = 6 cm ——————
> This gets 1 mark for accuracy.

Total: 3 marks

Worked Examination Questions

AU **2** A manufacturer makes cylindrical boxes in two different sizes.

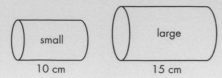

	small	large
	10 cm	15 cm

The two boxes are similar.

The length of the small box is 10 cm.

The length of the large box is 15 cm.

Some information about the boxes is given in the table.

	length	surface area	volume
small	10 cm	224 cm^2	270 cm^3
large	15 cm		

Complete the table.

2 Ratio of lengths = 10 : 15 = 2 : 3 ——— *Or scale factor = 1.5*

So ratio of areas = 4 : 9 ——— *Square the length ratios or area scale factor = 1.5^2 = 2.25*
This gets 1 mark for method.

Surface area of large box = $\dfrac{224 \times 9}{4}$ = 504 cm^2 ——— *Or 224 × 2.25*
This gets 1 mark for accuracy.

Ratio of volumes = 8 : 27 ——— *Cube the length ratios or volume scale factor = 1.5^3 = 3.375*
This gets 1 mark for method.

Volume of large box = $\dfrac{270 \times 27}{8}$ = 911 cm^3 (3 sf) ——— *Or 270 × 3.375*
This gets 1 mark for accuracy.

	length	surface area	volume
small	10 cm	224 cm^2	270 cm^3
large	15 cm	504 cm^2	911 cm^3 (3 sf)

Total: 4 marks

Worked Examination Questions

FM **3** A camping gas container is in the shape of a cylinder with a hemispherical top. The dimensions of the container are shown in the diagram.

It is decided to increase the volume of the container by **20%**.
The new container is mathematically **similar** to the old one.

Calculate the base **diameter** of the new container.

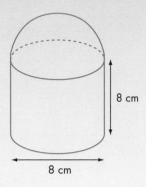

8 cm

8 cm

3 Old volume : New volume = 100% : 120% = 1 : 1.2

> First find the volume scale factor.
> This gets 1 mark for method.

$\sqrt[3]{1} : \sqrt[3]{1.2} = 1 : 1.06265$

> Take the cube root to get the linear scale factor.
> This gets 1 mark for method.

New diameter = Old diameter × 1.06265
= 8 × 1.06265 = 8.5 cm

> Multiply the old diameter by the linear scale factor to get the new diameter.
> This gets 1 mark for accuracy.

Total: 3 marks

Professional model-makers make scale models for all kinds of purposes. These models help people to visualise what things will look like in reality. An architect may need a scale model of a shopping centre, to show local people what it would be like. A film-maker may want a scale model of a dinosaur, to use for special effects.

Getting started

A transport museum displays scale models. Sometimes it takes these models into schools to show children.

Museum department	Model	Scale
Aeroplanes	*Concorde*	1 : 50
Trains	*Orient Express* single cabin	1 : 5
Automobiles	Rolls Royce *Phantom*	1 : 8

● Why didn't the model-maker use the same scale for *Concorde* as for the Rolls Royce *Phantom*?

● The dimensions of the bed in the model of the *Orient Express* cabin are 38 cm × 17 cm. Work out the dimensions of a bed on the real *Orient Express*.

● The wing area of the model *Concorde* is 1432 cm^2. Work out the wing area for the real *Concorde*. Give your answer in square metres (m^2).

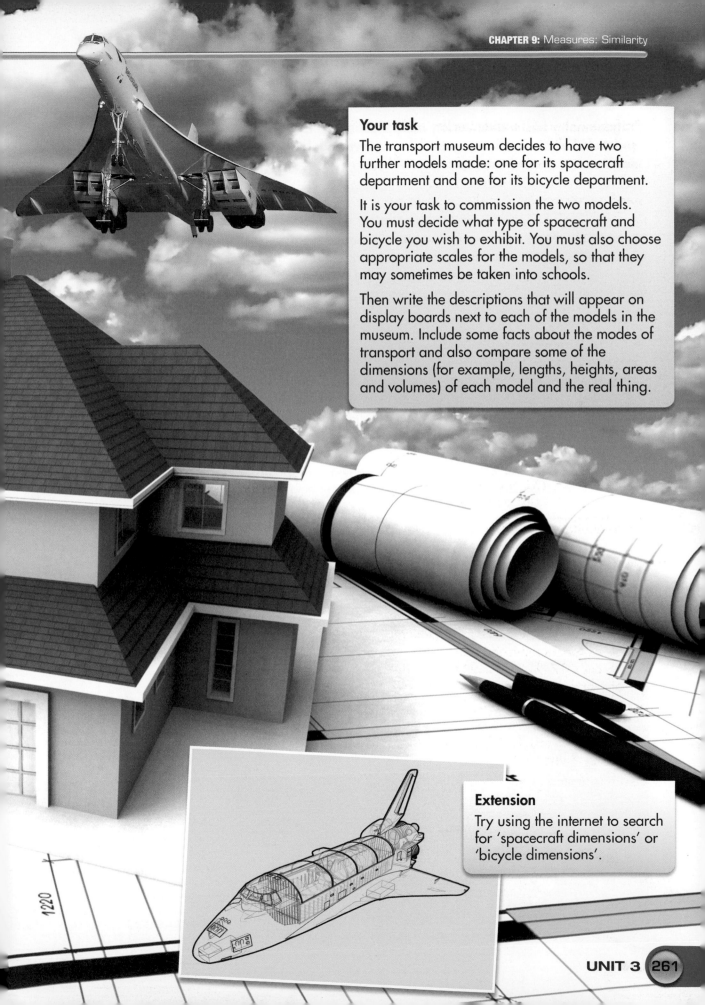

Your task

The transport museum decides to have two further models made: one for its spacecraft department and one for its bicycle department.

It is your task to commission the two models. You must decide what type of spacecraft and bicycle you wish to exhibit. You must also choose appropriate scales for the models, so that they may sometimes be taken into schools.

Then write the descriptions that will appear on display boards next to each of the models in the museum. Include some facts about the modes of transport and also compare some of the dimensions (for example, lengths, heights, areas and volumes) of each model and the real thing.

Extension

Try using the internet to search for 'spacecraft dimensions' or 'bicycle dimensions'.

Why this chapter matters

Trigonometry has a wide variety of applications. It is used in practical fields such as navigation, land surveying, building, engineering and astronomy.

In surveying, trigonometry is used extensively in triangulation. This is a process for establishing the location of a point by measuring angles or bearings to this point, from two other known points at either end of a fixed baseline.

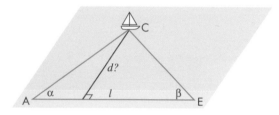

Triangulation can be used to calculate the position and distance from the shore to a ship. The observer at A measures the angle α between the shore and the ship, and the observer at B does likewise for angle β. With the length, *l*, or the position of A and B known, then the sine rule can be applied to find the position of the ship at C and the distance, *d*.

Marine sextants like this are used to measure the angle of the Sun or stars with respect to the horizon. Using trigonometry and a marine chronometer, the ship's navigator can determine the position of the ship on the sea.

The Canadarm2 robotic manipulator in the International Space Station is operated by controlling the angles of its joints. Calculating the final position of the astronaut at the end of the arm requires repeated use of trigonometry in three dimensions.

Geometry: Trigonometry

This chapter will show you ...

to **A** **A*** how to use trigonometric ratios to solve more complex 2D problems and 3D problems

to **A** **A*** how to use the sine and cosine rules to solve problems involving non right-angled triangles

to **A** **A*** how to find the area of a triangle using formula $A = \frac{1}{2}ab \sin C$

Visual overview

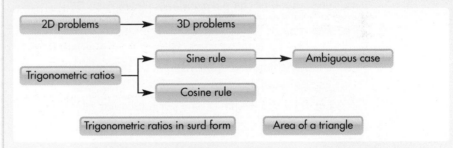

What you should already know

- How to find the sides of right-angled triangles using Pythagoras' theorem (**KS3 level 7, GCSE grade C**)
- How to find angles and sides of right-angled triangles using sine, cosine and tangent (**KS3 level 8, GCSE grade B**)

Quick check

Calculate the value of x in each of these right-angled triangles.

Give your answers to 3 significant figures.

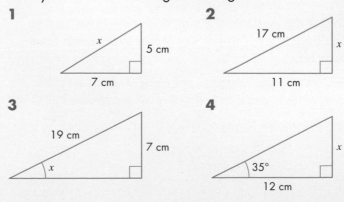

1

x, 5 cm, 7 cm

2

17 cm, x, 11 cm

3

19 cm, 7 cm, x

4

$35°$, x, 12 cm

This section will show you how to:
- use trigonometric ratios and Pythagoras' theorem to solve more complex two-dimensional problems

Key words
cosine
Pythagoras' theorem
sine
tangent

This lesson brings together previous work on **Pythagoras' theorem**, circle theorems and trigonometric ratios – **sine** (sin), **cosine** (cos) and **tangent** (tan).

EXAMPLE 1

In triangle ABC , AB = 6 cm, BC = 9 cm and angle ABC = 52°. Calculate:

a the length of the perpendicular from A to BC

b the area of the triangle.

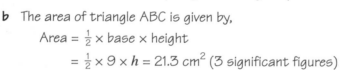

a Drop the perpendicular from A to BC to form the right-angled triangle ADB.

Let h be the length of the perpendicular AD. Then,

$h = 6 \sin 52° = 4.73$ (3 significant figures)

b The area of triangle ABC is given by,

Area = $\frac{1}{2}$ × base × height

= $\frac{1}{2}$ × 9 × h = 21.3 cm^2 (3 significant figures)

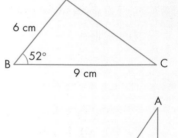

EXAMPLE 2

SR is a diameter of a circle of radius 25 cm. PQ is a chord at right angles to SR. X is the midpoint of PQ. The length of XR is 1 cm. Calculate the length of the arc PQ.

To find the length of the arc PQ, you need first to find the angle it subtends at the centre of the circle. (See page 163.)

So join P to the centre of the circle O to obtain the angle POX, which is equal to half the angle subtended by PQ at O.

In right-angled triangle POX,

OX = OR − XR

OX = 25 − 1 = 24 cm

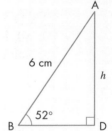

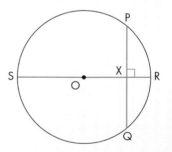

FM Functional Maths **AU** (AO2) Assessing Understanding **PS** (AO3) Problem Solving

Therefore,

$$\cos x = \frac{24}{25}$$

$$\Rightarrow x = \cos^{-1} 0.96 = 16.26°$$

So, the angle subtended at the centre by the arc PQ is $2 \times 16.26° = 32.52°$, giving the length of the arc PQ as:

$$\frac{32.52}{360} \times 2 \times \pi \times 25 = 14.2 \text{ cm} \qquad \text{(3 significant figures)}$$

EXERCISE 10A

1 AC and BC are tangents to a circle of radius 7 cm. Calculate the length of AB.

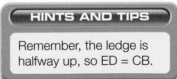

2 CD, length 20 cm, is a diameter of a circle. AB, length 12 cm, is a chord at right angles to DC. Calculate the angle AOB.

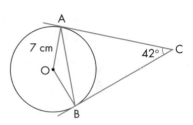

3 Calculate the length of AB in the diagram.

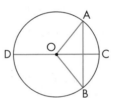

FM 4 A building has a ledge halfway up, as shown in the diagram. Alf measures the length AB as 100 m, the angle CAB as 31° and the angle EAB as 42°. Use this information to calculate the width of the ledge CD.

HINTS AND TIPS

Remember, the ledge is halfway up, so ED = CB.

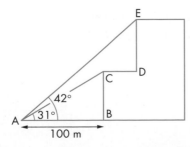

5 AB and CD are two equal, perpendicular chords of a circle that intersect at X. The circle is of radius 6 cm and the angle COA is 113°. Calculate:

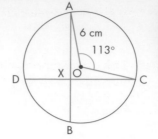

a the length AC

b the angle XAO

c the length XB.

6 A vertical flagpole PQ is held by a wooden framework, as shown in the diagram. The framework is in the same vertical plane. Angle SRP = 25°, SQ = 6 m and PR = 4 m. Calculate the size of the angle QRP.

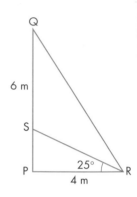

FM **7** A mine descends from ground level for 500 m at an angle of 13° to the horizontal and then continues for another 300 m at an angle of 17° to the horizontal, as shown in the diagram. A mining company decides to drill a vertical shaft to join up with the bottom of the mine as shown. How far along the surface from the opening, marked x on the diagram, do they need to drill down?

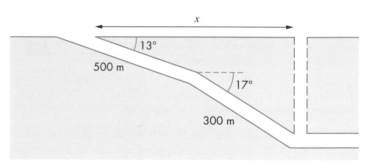

PS **8** **a** Use Pythagoras' theorem to work out the length of AC.

Leave your answer in surd form.

b Write down the values of:

   i cos 45°   **ii** sin 45°   **iii** tan 45°

leaving your answers in surd form.

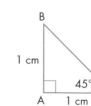

AU **9** In the diagram, AD = 5 cm, AC = 8 cm and AB = 12 cm.

Calculate angle CAB.

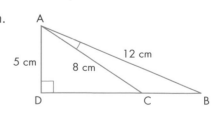

10.2 Some 3D problems

This section will show you how to:

- use trigonometric ratios and Pythagoras' theorem to solve more complex three-dimensional problems

Key words

cosine
Pythagoras' theorem
sine
tangent

Solving a problem set in three dimensions nearly always involves identifying a right-angled triangle that contains the length or angle required. This triangle will have to contain (apart from the right angle) two known measures from which the required calculation can be made.

It is essential to extract the triangle you are going to use from its 3D situation and redraw it as a separate, plain, right-angled triangle. (It is rarely the case that the required triangle appears as a true right-angled triangle in its 3D representation. Even if it does, you should still redraw it as a separate figure.)

Annotate the redrawn triangle with the known quantities and the unknown quantity that is to be found. Then use the trigonometric ratios **sine** (sin), **cosine** (cos) and **tangent** (tan), **Pythagoras' theorem** and the circle theorems to solve the triangle.

EXAMPLE 3

A, B and C are three points at ground level. They are in the same horizontal plane. C is 50 km east of B. B is north of A. C is on a bearing of 050° from A.

An aircraft, flying in an easterly direction, passes over B and over C at the same height. When it passes over B, the angle of elevation from A is 12°. Find the angle of elevation of the aircraft from A when it is over C.

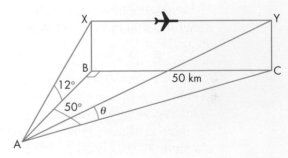

First, draw a diagram containing all the known information.

Next, use the right-angled triangle ABC to calculate AB and AC.

$$AB = \frac{50}{\tan 50°} = 41.95 \text{ km} \quad \text{(4 significant figures)}$$

$$AC = \frac{50}{\sin 50°} = 65.27 \text{ km} \quad \text{(4 significant figures)}$$

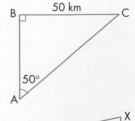

Then use the right-angled triangle ABX to calculate BX, and hence CY.

$$BX = 41.95 \tan 12° = 8.917 \text{ km} \quad \text{(4 significant figures)}$$

Finally, use the right-angled triangle ACY to calculate the required angle of elevation, θ.

$$\tan \theta = \frac{8.917}{65.27} = 0.1366$$

$$\Rightarrow \theta = \tan^{-1} 0.1366 = 7.8° \quad \text{(1 decimal place)}$$

Always write down intermediate working values to at least 4 significant figures, or use the answer on your calculator display to avoid inaccuracy in the final answer.

EXAMPLE 4

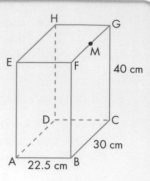

The diagram shows a cuboid 22.5 cm by 40 cm by 30 cm. M is the midpoint of FG.

Calculate these angles.

a ABE

b ECA

c EMH

a The right-angled triangle containing the angle required is ABE.

Solving for α gives,

$$\tan \alpha = \frac{40}{22.5} = 1.7777$$

$$\Rightarrow \alpha = \tan^{-1} 1.7777 = 60.6° \qquad \text{(3 significant figures)}$$

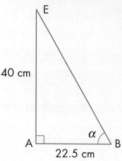

b The right-angled triangle containing the angle required is ACE, but for which only AE is known. Therefore, you need to find AC by applying Pythagoras' theorem to the right-angled triangle ABC.

$$x^2 = (22.5)^2 + (30)^2 \text{ cm}^2$$

$$\Rightarrow x = 37.5 \text{ cm}$$

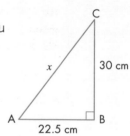

Returning to triangle ACE,

$$\tan \beta = \frac{40}{37.5} = 1.0666$$

$$\Rightarrow \beta = 46.8° \qquad \text{(3 significant figures)}$$

c EMH is an isosceles triangle.

Drop the perpendicular from M to N, the midpoint of HE, to form two right-angled triangles. Angle HMN equals angle EMN, and HN = NE = 15 cm.

Taking triangle MEN,

$$\tan \theta = \frac{15}{22.5} = 0.66666$$

$$\Rightarrow \theta = \tan^{-1} 0.66666 = 33.7°$$

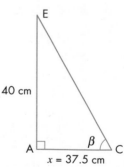

Therefore, angle HME is $2 \times 33.7° = 67.4°$ (3 significant figures)

EXERCISE 10B

1 A vertical flagpole AP stands at the corner of a rectangular courtyard ABCD.

Calculate the angle of elevation of P from C.

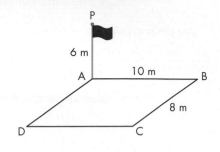

2 The diagram shows a pyramid. The base is a horizontal rectangle ABCD, 20 cm by 15 cm. The length of each sloping edge is 24 cm. The apex, V, is over the centre of the rectangular base. Calculate:

a the size of the angle VAC

b the height of the pyramid

c the volume of the pyramid

d the size of the angle between the face VAD and the base ABCD.

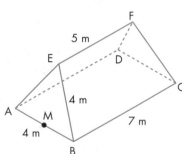

FM 3 The diagram shows the roof of a building. The base ABCD is a horizontal rectangle 7 m by 4 m. The triangular ends are equilateral triangles. Each side of the roof is an isosceles trapezium. The length of the top of the roof, EF, is 5 m. Calculate:

a the length EM, where M is the midpoint of AB

b the size of angle EBC

c the size of the angle between the face EAB and the base ABCD

d the surface area of the roof (excluding the base).

e Tiles cost £25 per square metre. How much would it cost to tile the roof?

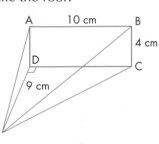

4 ABCD is a vertical rectangular plane. EDC is a horizontal triangular plane. Angle CDE = 90°, AB = 10 cm, BC = 4 cm and ED = 9 cm. Calculate:

a angle AED   **b** angle DEC

c EC   **d** angle BEC.

5 The diagram shows a tetrahedron, each face of which is an equilateral triangle of side 6 m. The lines AN and BM meet the sides CB and AC at a right angle. The lines AN and BM intersect at X, which is directly below the vertex, D. Calculate:

a the distance AX

b the angle between the side DBC and the base ABC.

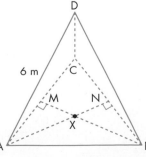

A*

PS **6** The lengths of the sides of a cuboid are a, b and c.

Show that the length of the diagonal XY is:

$$\sqrt{a^2 + b^2 + c^2}$$

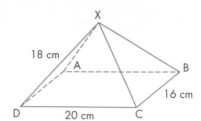

AU **7** In the diagram, XABCD is a right pyramid with a rectangular base.

Ellie says that the angle between the edge XD and the base ABCD is 56.3°.

Work out the correct answer to show that Ellie is wrong.

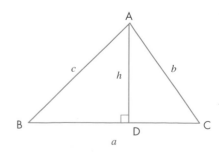

10.3 Solving any triangle

This section will show you how to:	Key words
• use the sine rule and the cosine rule to find sides and angles in any triangle	cosine rule included angle sine rule

We have already established that any triangle has six measurements: three sides and three angles. To solve a triangle (that is, to find any unknown angles or sides), we need to know at least three of the measurements. Any combination of three measurements – except that of all three angles – is enough to work out the rest. In a right-angled triangle, one of the known measurements is, of course, the right angle.

When we need to solve a triangle which contains no right angle, we can use one or the other of two rules, depending on what is known about the triangle. These are the **sine rule** and the **cosine rule**.

The sine rule

Take a triangle ABC and draw the perpendicular from A to the opposite side BC.

From right-angled triangle ADB,

$$h = c \sin B$$

From right-angled triangle ADC,

$$h = b \sin C$$

Therefore,

$$c \sin B = b \sin C$$

which can be rearranged to give:

$$\frac{c}{\sin C} = \frac{b}{\sin B}$$

By drawing a perpendicular from each of the other two vertices to the opposite side (or by algebraic symmetry), we see that

$$\frac{a}{\sin A} = \frac{c}{\sin C} \quad \text{and that} \quad \frac{a}{\sin A} = \frac{b}{\sin B}$$

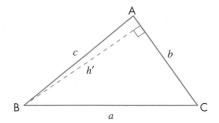

These are usually combined in the form

$$\frac{a}{\sin A} = \frac{b}{\sin B} = \frac{c}{\sin C}$$

— Find side

which can be inverted to give:

$$\text{or} \quad \frac{\sin A}{a} = \frac{\sin B}{b} = \frac{\sin C}{c}$$

— Find angle

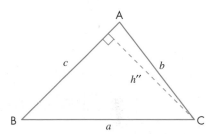

Usually, a triangle is not conveniently labelled, as in these diagrams. So, when using the sine rule, it is easier to remember to proceed as follows: take each side in turn, divide it by the sine of the angle opposite and then equate the resulting quotients.

Note:

- When you are calculating a *side*, use the rule with the *sides on top*.
- When you are calculating an *angle*, use the rule with the *sines on top*.

EXAMPLE 5

In triangle ABC, find the value of x.

Use the sine rule with sides on top, which gives:

$$\frac{x}{\sin 84°} = \frac{25}{\sin 47°}$$

$$\Rightarrow x = \frac{25 \sin 84°}{\sin 47°} = 34.0 \text{ cm} \quad \text{(3 significant figures)}$$

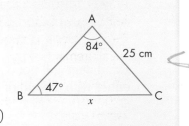

EXAMPLE 6

In the triangle ABC, find the value of the acute angle x.

Use the sine rule with sines on top, which gives:

$$\frac{\sin x}{7} = \frac{7 \sin 40°}{6}$$

$$\Rightarrow \sin x = \frac{7 \sin 40°}{6} = 0.7499$$

$$\Rightarrow x = \sin^{-1} 0.7499 = 48.6° \quad \text{(3 significant figures)}$$

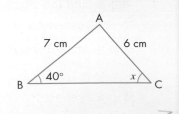

The ambiguous case

It is possible to find the sine of an angle that is greater than 90° (see Chapter 11).

For example, sin 30° = sin 150° = 0.5. (Notice that the two angles add up to 180°.)

So sin 25° = sin 155° and sin 100° = sin 80°

EXAMPLE 7

In triangle ABC, AB = 9 cm, AC = 7 cm and angle ABC = 40°. Find the angle ACB.

As you sketch triangle ABC, note that C can have two positions, giving two different configurations.

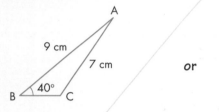 **or**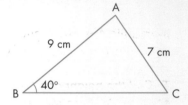

But you still proceed as in the normal sine rule situation, obtaining:

$$\frac{\sin C}{9} = \frac{\sin 40°}{7}$$

$$\Rightarrow \sin C = \frac{9 \sin 40°}{7}$$

$$= 0.8264$$

Keying inverse sine on the calculator gives C = 55.7°. But there is another angle with a sine of 0.8264, given by (180° − 55.7°) = 124.3°.

These two values for C give the two different situations shown above.

When an illustration of the triangle is given, it will be clear whether the required angle is acute or obtuse. When an illustration is not given, the more likely answer is an acute angle.

Examiners will not try to catch you out with the ambiguous case. They will indicate clearly, either with the aid of a diagram or by stating it, what is required.

EXERCISE 10C

1 Find the length x in each of these triangles.

a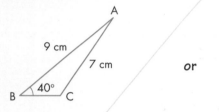

b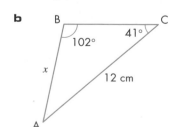

c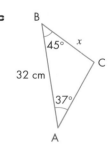

2 Find the angle x in each of these triangles.

a

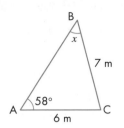

b

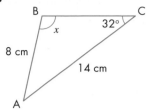

c

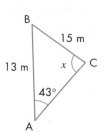

3 In triangle ABC, the angle at A is 38°, the side AB is 10 cm and the side BC is 8 cm. Find the two possible values of the angle at C.

4 In triangle ABC, the angle at A is 42°, the side AB is 16 cm and the side BC is 14 cm. Find the two possible values of the side AC.

FM 5 To find the height of a tower standing on a small hill, Mary made some measurements (see diagram).

From a point B, the angle of elevation of C is 20°, the angle of elevation of A is 50°, and the distance BC is 25 m.

a Calculate these angles.

  i ABC

  ii BAC

b Using the sine rule and triangle ABC, calculate the height h of the tower.

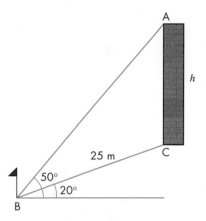

PS 6 Use the information on this sketch to calculate the width, w, of the river.

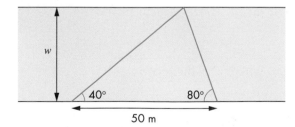

FM 7 An old building is unsafe and is protected by a fence. A demolition company is employed to demolish the building and has to work out the height BD, marked h on the diagram.

Calculate the value of h, using the given information.

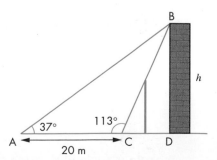

A*

8 A weight is hung from a horizontal beam using two strings. The shorter string is 2.5 m long and makes an angle of 71° with the horizontal. The longer string makes an angle of 43° with the horizontal. What is the length of the longer string?

FM 9 An aircraft is flying over an army base. Suddenly, two searchlights, 3 km apart, are switched on. The two beams of light meet on the aircraft at an angle of 125° vertically above the line joining the searchlights. One of the beams of light makes an angle of 31° with the horizontal. Calculate the height of the aircraft.

FM 10 Two ships leave a port in directions that are 41° from each other. After half an hour, the ships are 11 km apart. If the speed of the slower ship is 7 km/h, what is the speed of the faster ship?

FM 11 A rescue helicopter is based at an airfield at A.

The helicopter is sent out to rescue a man who has had an accident on a mountain at M, due north of A.

The helicopter then flies on a bearing of 145° to a hospital at H as shown on the diagram.

Calculate the direct distance from the mountain to the hospital.

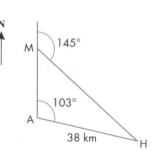

AU 12 Choose four values of θ, $0° < \theta < 90°$, to show that $\sin \theta = \sin (180° - \theta)$.

13 Triangle ABC has an obtuse at angle B.

Calculate the size of angle ABC.

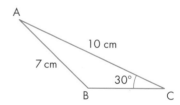

PS 14 For any triangle ABC, prove the sine rule:

$$\frac{a}{\sin A} = \frac{b}{\sin B} = \frac{c}{\sin C}$$

The cosine rule

Take the triangle, shown on the right, where D is the foot of the perpendicular to BC from A.

Using Pythagoras' theorem on triangle BDA:
$$h^2 = c^2 - x^2$$

Using Pythagoras' theorem on triangle ADC:
$$h^2 = b^2 - (a - x)^2$$

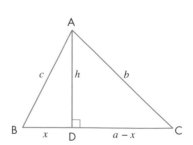

Therefore,
$$c^2 - x^2 = b^2 - (a - x)^2$$
$$c^2 - x^2 = b^2 - a^2 + 2ax - x^2$$
$$\Rightarrow c^2 = b^2 - a^2 + 2ax$$

From triangle BDA, $x = c \cos B$.

Hence,

$$c^2 = b^2 - a^2 + 2ac \cos B$$

Rearranging gives:

$$b^2 = a^2 + c^2 - 2ac \cos B$$

By algebraic symmetry:

$$a^2 = b^2 + c^2 - 2bc \cos A \quad \text{and} \quad c^2 = a^2 + b^2 - 2ab \cos C$$

This is the cosine rule, which can be best remembered by the diagram on the right, where:

$$a^2 = b^2 + c^2 - 2bc \cos A$$

Note the symmetry of the rule and how the rule works using two adjacent sides and the angle between them (the **included angle**).

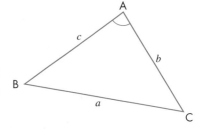

The formula can be rearranged to find any of the three angles.

$$\cos A = \frac{b^2 + c^2 - a^2}{2bc}$$

$$\cos B = \frac{a^2 + c^2 - b^2}{2ac}$$

$$\cos C = \frac{a^2 + b^2 - c^2}{2ab}$$

Note that the cosine rule $a^2 = b^2 + c^2 - 2bc \cos A$ is given in the formula sheets in the GCSE examination but the rearranged formula for the angle is not given. You are advised to learn this as trying to rearrange usually ends up with an incorrect formula.

EXAMPLE 8

Find x in this triangle.

By the cosine rule:

$$x^2 = 6^2 + 10^2 - 2 \times 6 \times 10 \times \cos 80°$$
$$x^2 = 115.16$$
$$\Rightarrow x = 10.7 \qquad \text{(3 significant figures)}$$

EXAMPLE 9

Find x in this triangle.

By the cosine rule:

$$\cos x = \frac{5^2 + 7^2 - 8^2}{2 \times 5 \times 7} = 0.1428$$

$$\Rightarrow x = 81.8° \qquad \text{(3 significant figures)}$$

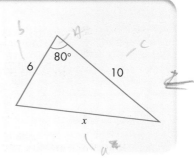

$8^2 = 5^2 + 7^2 - 2 \times 5 \times 7 \times \cos x$

$64 = 25 + 49 - 70 \cos x$

It is possible to find the cosine of an angle that is greater than 90° (see Chapter 11). For example, $\cos 120° = -\cos 60° = -0.5$. (Notice the minus sign; the two angles add up to 180°.)

So $\cos 150° = -\cos 30° = -0.866$

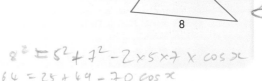

$64 - 25 - 49 = -70 \cos x$

$-10 = -70 \cos x$

$0.14 = \cos x$

$\cos^{-1} 0.14 = x = 81.7°$

EXAMPLE 10

A ship sails from a port on a bearing of 055° for 40 km. It then changes course to 123° for another 50 km. On what course should the ship be steered to get it straight back to the port?

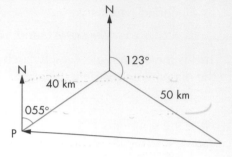

Previously, you have solved this type of problem using right-angled triangles. This method could be applied here but it would involve at least six separate calculations.

With the aid of the cosine and sine rules, however, you can reduce the solution to two separate calculations, as follows.

The course diagram gives the triangle PAB (on the right), where angle PAB is found by using alternate angles and angles on a line.
55° + (180° − 123°) = 112°

Let ϕ be the bearing to be steered, then

$$\phi = \theta + 55° + 180°$$

To find θ, you first have to obtain PB(= x), using the cosine rule.

$$x^2 = 40^2 + 50^2 - 2 \times 40 \times 50 \times \cos 112° \text{ km}^2$$

(Remember: the cosine of 112° is negative.)

$$\Rightarrow x^2 = 5598.43 \text{ km}^2$$
$$\Rightarrow x = 74.82 \text{ km}$$

You can now find θ from the sine rule.

$$\frac{\sin \theta}{50} = \frac{\sin 112°}{74.82}$$

$$\Rightarrow \sin \theta = \frac{50 \times \sin 112°}{74.82} = 0.6196$$

$$\Rightarrow \theta = 38.3°$$

So the ship should be steered on a bearing of:

$$38.3° + 55° + 180° = 273.3°$$

EXERCISE 10D

1 Find the length x in each of these triangles.

a
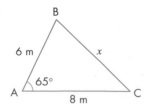

b
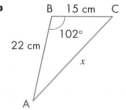

c
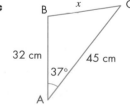

2 Find the angle x in each of these triangles.

a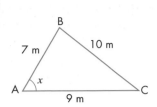

b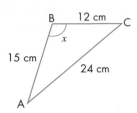

c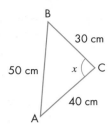

d Explain the significance of the answer to part **c**.

3 In triangle ABC, AB = 5 cm, BC = 6 cm and angle ABC = 55°. Find AC.

4 A triangle has two sides of length 40 cm and an angle of 110°. Work out the length of the third side of the triangle.

5 The diagram shows a trapezium ABCD.
AB = 6.7 cm, AD = 7.2 cm, CB = 9.3 cm and
angle DAB = 100°.

Calculate:

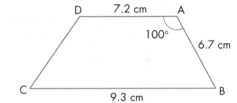

a the length DB   **b** angle DBA

c angle DBC   **d** the length DC

e the area of the trapezium.

6 A quadrilateral ABCD has AD = 6 cm, DC = 9 cm, AB = 10 cm and BC = 12 cm. Angle ADC = 120°. Calculate angle ABC.

7 A triangle has two sides of length 30 cm and an angle of 50°. Unfortunately, the position of the angle is not known. Sketch the two possible triangles and use them to work out the two possible lengths of the third side of the triangle.

FM 8 A ship sails from a port on a bearing of 050° for 50 km then turns on a bearing of 150° for 40 km. A crewman is taken ill, so the ship drops anchor. What course and distance should a rescue helicopter from the port fly to reach the ship in the shortest possible time?

> **HINTS AND TIPS**
>
> Bearings can be revised on page 141.

9 The three sides of a triangle are given as $3a$, $5a$ and $7a$. Calculate the smallest angle in the triangle.

10 ABCD is a trapezium where AB is parallel to CD. AB = 4 cm, BC = 5 cm, CD = 8 cm, DA = 6 cm. A line BX is parallel to AD and cuts DC at X. Calculate:

a angle BCD   **b** the length BD.

PS 11 Two ships, X and Y, leave a port at 9 am.

Ship X travels at an average speed of 20 km/h on a bearing of 075° from the port.

Ship Y travels at an average speed of 25 km/h on a bearing of 130° from the port.

Calculate the distance between the two ships at 11 am.

A*

AU **12** Choose four values of θ, $0° < \theta < 90°$, to show that $\cos \theta = -\cos(180° - \theta)$.

AU **13** Calculate the size of the largest angle in the triangle ABC.

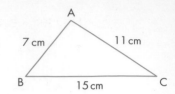

Choosing the correct rule

When solving triangles, there are only four situations that can occur, each of which can be solved completely in three stages.

Two sides and the included angle

1   Use the cosine rule to find the third side.

2   Use the sine rule to find either of the other angles.

3   Use the sum of the angles in a triangle to find the third angle.

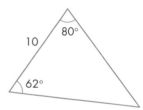

Two angles and a side

1   Use the sum of the angles in a triangle to find the third angle.

2, 3 Use the sine rule to find the other two sides.

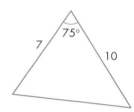

Three sides

1   Use the cosine rule to find one angle.

2   Use the sine rule to find another angle.

3   Use the sum of the angles in a triangle to find the third angle.

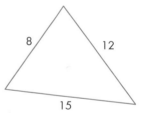

Two sides and a non-included angle

This is the ambiguous case already covered (page 272).

1   Use the sine rule to find the two possible values of the appropriate angle.

2   Use the sum of the angles in a triangle to find the two possible values of the third angle.

3   Use the sine rule to find the two possible values for the length of the third side.

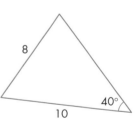

Note: Apply the sine rule wherever you can – it is always easier to use than the cosine rule. You should never need to use the cosine rule more than once.

EXERCISE 10E

1 Find the length or angle *x* in each of these triangles.

a
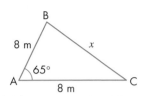

b
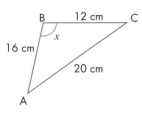

c
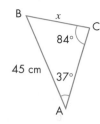

d
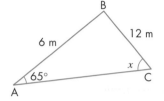

e
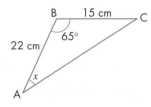

f
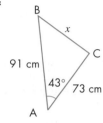

g
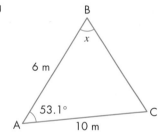

h
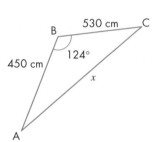

i
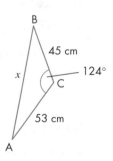

2 The hands of a clock have lengths 3 cm and 5 cm. Find the distance between the tips of the hands at 4 o'clock.

3 A spacecraft is seen hovering at a point which is in the same vertical plane as two towns, X and F, which are on the same level. Its distances from X and F are 8.5 km and 12 km respectively. The angle of elevation of the spacecraft when observed from F is 43°. Calculate the distance between the two towns.

FM 4 Two boats, Mary Jo and Suzie, leave port at the same time. Mary Jo sails at 10 knots on a bearing of 065°. Suzie sails on a bearing of 120° and after 1 hour Mary Jo is on a bearing of 330° from Suzie. What is Suzie's speed? (1 knot = 1 nautical mile per hour)

> **HINTS AND TIPS**
>
> Bearings can be revised on page 141.

5 Two ships leave port at the same time, Darling Dave sailing at 12 knots on a bearing of 055°, and Merry Mary at 18 knots on a bearing of 280°.

a How far apart are the two ships after 1 hour?

b What is the bearing of Merry Mary from Darling Dave?

PS 6 Triangle ABC has sides with lengths a, b and c, as shown in the diagram.

a What can you say about the angle BAC, if $b^2 + c^2 - a^2 = 0$?

b What can you say about the angle BAC, if $b^2 + c^2 - a^2 > 0$?

c What can you say about the angle BAC, if $b^2 + c^2 - a^2 < 0$?

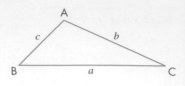

AU 7 The diagram shows a sketch of a field ABCD.
A farmer wants to put a new fence round the perimeter of the field.

Calculate the perimeter of the field.

Give your answer to an appropriate degree of accuracy.

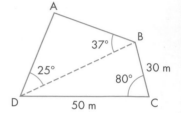

10.4 Trigonometric ratios in surd form

This section will show you how to:
● work out trigonometric ratios in surd form

Key words

cosine

Pythagoras' theorem

sine

surd

surd form

tangent

Solving triangles often involves finding square roots. Unless a number has an exact square root, the value on a calculator can only be an approximation. The exact value of the square root of 2, for example, is often written as $\sqrt{2}$. This expression, using the square root symbol, is a **surd**, and answers given in this way are in **surd form**.

EXAMPLE 11

Using an equilateral triangle with sides of 2 units, write down expressions for the sine, cosine and tangent of 60° and 30°. Give answers in surd form.

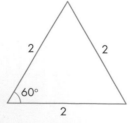 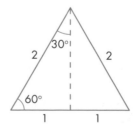 

Divide the equilateral triangle into two equal right-angled triangles. Taking one of them, use **Pythagoras' theorem** and the definition of **sine**, **cosine** and **tangent** to obtain:

$$\sin 60° = \frac{\sqrt{3}}{2} \qquad \cos 60° = \frac{1}{2} \qquad \tan 60° = \sqrt{3}$$

$$\text{and} \quad \sin 30° = \frac{1}{2} \qquad \cos 30° = \frac{\sqrt{3}}{2} \qquad \tan 30° = \frac{1}{\sqrt{3}} = \frac{\sqrt{3}}{3}$$

EXAMPLE 12

Using a right-angled isosceles triangle in which the equal sides are 1 unit, find the sine, cosine and tangent of 45°. Give answers in surd form.

By Pythagoras' theorem, the hypotenuse of the triangle is $\sqrt{2}$ units.

From the definition of sine, cosine and tangent,

$$\sin 45° = \frac{1}{\sqrt{2}} = \frac{\sqrt{2}}{2} \qquad \cos 45° = \frac{1}{\sqrt{2}} = \frac{\sqrt{2}}{2} \qquad \tan 45° = 1$$

These results can be summarised in a table.

You do not need to learn these results, but it is useful to know how to work them out.

θ	$\cos \theta$	$\sin \theta$	$\tan \theta$
30°	$\frac{\sqrt{3}}{2}$	$\frac{1}{2}$	$\frac{\sqrt{3}}{3}$
45°	$\frac{\sqrt{2}}{2}$	$\frac{\sqrt{2}}{2}$	1
60°	$\frac{1}{2}$	$\frac{\sqrt{3}}{2}$	$\sqrt{3}$

When solving problems, you can write trigonometric ratios as numerical values or in surd form, in which case you do not need a calculator.

EXAMPLE 13

ABC is a right-angled triangle.

a Write down the value of $\tan x$.

b Work out the values of $\cos x$ and $\sin x$, giving your answers in simplified surd form.

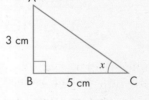

a $\tan x = \frac{3}{5}$

b Using Pythagoras' theorem, $AC = \sqrt{34}$.

$$\text{So } \cos x = \frac{5}{\sqrt{34}} = \frac{5\sqrt{34}}{34}$$

$$\text{and } \sin x = \frac{3}{\sqrt{34}} = \frac{3\sqrt{34}}{34}$$

EXERCISE 10F

AU **1** The sine of angle x is $\frac{4}{5}$. Work out the cosine of angle x.

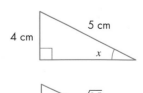

AU **2** The cosine of angle x is $\frac{3}{\sqrt{15}}$. Work out the sine of angle x.

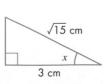

A*

PS **3** The lengths of the two short sides of a right-angled triangle are $\sqrt{6}$ and $\sqrt{13}$. Write down the exact value of the hypotenuse of this triangle, and the exact value of the sine, cosine and tangent of the smallest angle in the triangle.

PS **4** The tangent of angle A is $\frac{6}{11}$. Use this to write down possible lengths of two sides of the triangle.

a Calculate the length of the third side of the triangle.

b Write down the exact values of sin A and cos A.

PS **5** Calculate the exact value of the area of an equilateral triangle of side 6 cm.

6 Work out the exact value of the area of a right-angled isosceles triangle with hypotenuse 40 cm.

7 Work out the length of AB in the triangle ABC.

Give your answer in simplified surd form.

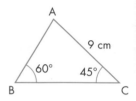

10.5 Using sine to find the area of a triangle

This section will show you how to:	Key words
• work out the area of a triangle if you know two sides and the included angle	area area sine rule cosine rule included angle sine rule

In triangle ABC, the vertical height is BD and the base is AC.

Let BD = h and AC = b, then the **area** of the triangle is given by:

$\frac{1}{2} \times$ AC $\times$ BD $= \frac{1}{2}bh$

However, in triangle BCD,

$h =$ BC sin $C = a$ sin C

where BC = a.

Substituting into $\frac{1}{2}bh$ gives:

$\frac{1}{2}b \times (a \sin C) = \frac{1}{2}ab \sin C$

as the area of the triangle.

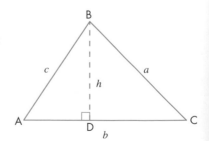

By taking the perpendicular from A to its opposite side BC, and the perpendicular from C to its opposite side AB, we can show that the area of the triangle is also given by:

$\frac{1}{2}ac \sin B$ and $\frac{1}{2}bc \sin A$

Note the pattern: the area is given by the product of two sides multiplied by the sine of the **included angle**. This is the **area sine rule**. Starting from any of the three forms, it is also possible to use the **sine rule** to establish the other two.

EXAMPLE 14

Find the area of triangle ABC.

Area $= \frac{1}{2}ab \sin C$

Area $= \frac{1}{2} \times 5 \times 7 \times \sin 38° = 10.8$ cm^2

(3 significant figures)

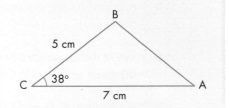

EXAMPLE 15

Find the area of triangle ABC.

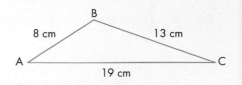

You have all three sides but no angle. So first you must find an angle in order to apply the area sine rule.

Find angle C, using the **cosine rule**.

$\cos C = \dfrac{a^2 + b^2 - c^2}{2ab}$

$ = \dfrac{13^2 + 19^2 - 8^2}{2 \times 13 \times 19} = 0.9433$

$\Rightarrow C = \cos^{-1} 0.9433 = 19.4°$

(Keep the exact value in your calculator memory.)

Now apply the area sine rule.

$\frac{1}{2}ab \sin C = \frac{1}{2} \times 13 \times 19 \times \sin 19.4°$

$\phantom{\frac{1}{2}ab \sin C} = 41.0$ cm^2 (3 significant figures)

EXERCISE 10G

1 Find the area of each of the following triangles.

a Triangle ABC where BC = 7 cm, AC = 8 cm and angle ACB = 59°

b Triangle ABC where angle BAC = 86°, AC = 6.7 cm and AB = 8 cm

c Triangle PQR where QR = 27 cm, PR = 19 cm and angle QRP = 109°

d Triangle XYZ where XY = 231 cm, XZ = 191 cm and angle YXZ = 73°

e Triangle LMN where LN = 63 cm, LM = 39 cm and angle NLM = 85°

A

2 The area of triangle ABC is 27 cm². If BC = 14 cm and angle BCA = 115°, find AC.

3 The area of triangle LMN is 113 cm², LM = 16 cm and MN = 21 cm. Angle LMN is acute. Calculate these angles.

    a LMN   **b** MNL

4 In a quadrilateral ABCD, DC = 4 cm, BD = 11 cm, angle BAD = 32°, angle ABD = 48° and angle BDC = 61°. Calculate the area of the quadrilateral.

5 A board is in the shape of a triangle with sides 60 cm, 70 cm and 80 cm. Find the area of the board.

6 Two circles, centres P and Q, have radii of 6 cm and 7 cm respectively. The circles intersect at X and Y. Given that PQ = 9 cm, find the area of triangle PXQ.

7 The points A, B and C are on the circumference of a circle, centre O and radius 7 cm. AB = 4 cm and BC = 3.5 cm. Calculate:

    a angle AOB   **b** the area of quadrilateral OABC.

PS **8** Prove that for any triangle ABC,

$$\text{area} = \tfrac{1}{2}ab \sin C$$

9 **a** ABC is a right-angled isosceles triangle with short sides of 1 cm. Write down the value of sin 45°.

    b Calculate the area of triangle PQR. Give your answer in surd form.

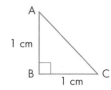

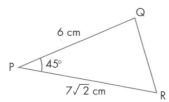

10 Sanjay is making a kite. The diagram shows a sketch of his kite.

Calculate the area of the material required to make the kite.

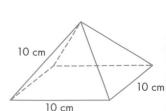

PS **11** An equilateral triangle has sides of length a.

Work out the area of the triangle, giving your answer in surd form.

AU **12** The lengths of all the sides of a square-based pyramid are 10 cm.

Which of these possible answers correctly gives the total surface area of the pyramid?

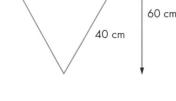

    a $100(1 + 2\sqrt{3})$ cm²   **b** $100(2 + \sqrt{3})$ cm²

    c $100(1 + \sqrt{3})$ cm²   **d** $100(1 + 2\sqrt{2})$ cm²

GRADE BOOSTER

A You can solve more complex 2D problems, using Pythagoras' theorem and trigonometry

A You can use the sine and cosine rules to calculate missing angles or sides in non-right-angled triangles

A You can find the area of a triangle using the formula area $= \frac{1}{2}ab \sin C$

A* You can use the sine and cosine rules to solve more complex problems involving non-right-angled triangles

A* You can solve 3D problems, using Pythagoras' theorem and trigonometric ratios

What you should know now

- How to use the sine and cosine rules
- How to find the area of a triangle, using area $= \frac{1}{2}ab \sin C$

1 ABCD is a quadrilateral.

AB = 12 cm, BC = 11 cm, CD = 10 cm and DA = 9 cm.

∠ABC = 74° and ∠DAC = 46°.

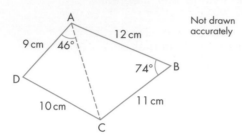

Not drawn accurately

a Use the cosine rule to find AC. *(3 marks)*

b Use the sine rule to find the size of angle ACD. *(3 marks)*

AQA, November 2008, Paper 2, Question 20(a)(b)

2 ABC is a triangle.

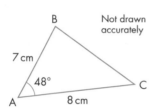

Not drawn accurately

a Calculate the length of side BC. *(3 marks)*

b Find the size of angle BCA. *(3 marks)*

AQA, November 2006, Paper 2, Question 16(a)(b)

3 In the triangle ABC, angle B = 95°, angle C = 24° and AC = 17 cm.

Not drawn accurately

a Calculate the length of AB.

(3 marks)

b Calculate the area of triangle ABC.

(3 marks)

AQA, June 2007, Module 5, Paper 2, Question 12(a)(b)

4 A prism ABCDEF with a right-angled triangular cross-section has dimensions as shown.

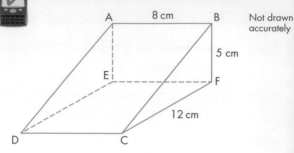

Not drawn accurately

a Calculate the length BD. *(3 marks)*

b Hence, or otherwise, calculate the angle BDF. *(2 marks)*

AQA, June 2008, Paper 2, Question 24

5 VABCD is a right pyramid on a square base.

V is vertically above the centre of the square.

VA = VB = VC = VD = 20 cm

AB = 15 cm

Calculate the angle between the edge VA and the base ABCD.

Not drawn accurately

6 Zoe wants to find the height of a tower on top of a cliff.

From point A she measures the angle of elevation of the top of the tower, T, as 48°.

She then walks 50 metres horizontally towards the tower to a point B, where the angle of elevation of T is 70°.

The height of the cliff is 60 metres.

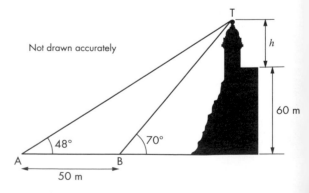

Not drawn accurately

Calculate the height, h, of the tower. *(6 marks)*

AQA, June 2006, Paper 2, Question 14

A* A

Worked Examination Questions

AU 1 The diagram shows a cuboid ABCDEFGH.
Calculate the size of angle AGE.

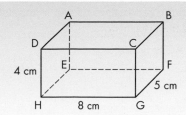

1 First draw the right-angled triangle EFG to find the length of EG.
Mark it x on the diagram.

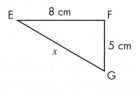

Find the length of EG by Pythagoras' theorem.

$x^2 = 8^2 + 5^2 = 89$

> Store $\sqrt{89}$ in your calculator or write down the answer to 4 significant figures.
> This line gets 1 mark for method.

So $x = \sqrt{89} = 9.434$ cm

> Answer gets 1 mark for accuracy ($\sqrt{89}$ is acceptable).

Now draw the right-angled triangle AGE and mark the required angle y.

$\tan y = \frac{O}{A}$

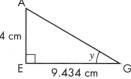

Use tangent to find angle y.

$\tan y = \dfrac{4}{9.434} = 0.4240$

> This gets 1 mark for method for this line.

So $y = \tan^{-1} 0.420$

$y = 23.0°$ (3 significant figures)

> This gets 1 mark for accuracy for the answer.

(**Total:** 4 marks)

Worked Examination Questions

FM **2** The diagram represents a level triangular piece of land. AB = 61 m, AC = 76 m and the area of the land is 2300 m².

Angle BAC is acute.

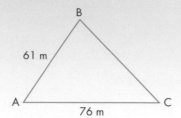

Calculate the length of BC. Give your answer to an appropriate degree of accuracy.

$\frac{1}{2} \times 61 \times 76 \times \sin A = 2300$

> Since the third side is unknown, we need to find an angle. Find angle BAC (= A) so that we can use the cosine rule. Use area = $\frac{1}{2}bc \sin A$.

$\therefore \sin BAC = \dfrac{4600}{4636} = 0.9922 \ldots$

> Use area = $\frac{1}{2}bc \sin A$ to set up an equation and solve it to get angle A. You are given that A is acute so there is no problem with any ambiguity.
>
> This gets 1 mark for method for this line.

$\therefore A = 82.86°$

> This gets 1 mark for accuracy for the answer. Now use the cosine rule to find BC.

$BC^2 = 61^2 + 76^2 - 2 \times 61 \times 76 \times \cos 82.9$
$ = 8343.75$

> Use the cosine rule to work out the side BC. If possible keep values in your calculator display but if you have to write down values then use at least 4 significant figures for trigonometric ratios and at least 1 decimal place for angles. This will avoid any inaccuracy in the final answer.
>
> This gets 1 mark for method for this line.

$BC = 91.3$ m (3 significant figures)

> The answer gets 1 mark for accuracy.

Total: 4 marks

Worked Examination Questions

PS 3   A **tetrahedron** has one face which is an equilateral triangle of side 6 cm and
three faces which are isosceles triangles with sides 6 cm, 9 cm and 9 cm.

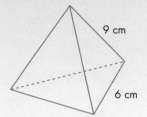

9 cm

6 cm

HINTS AND TIPS

A tetrahedron is a
triangle-based pyramid.

Calculate the surface area of the tetrahedron.

3   First work out the area of the base, which has angles of 60°.
Use area = $\frac{1}{2}ac$ sin B.

Area base = $\frac{1}{2}$ × 6 × 6 × sin 60° = 15.59 cm² (4 significant figures) ──────

This gets 1 mark for
accuracy of the
answer.

Next, work out the top angle in one of the
isosceles triangles, using the cosine rule.

$$\cos x = \frac{9^2 + 9^2 - 6^2}{2 \times 9 \times 9} = 0.7778$$ ──────

This gets 1 mark for
method.

So x = 38.9° ──────

Keep the exact value
in your calculator.

This gets 1 mark for
accuracy.

Work out the area of one side face
and then add all faces together.

Area side face = $\frac{1}{2}$ × 9 × 9 × sin 38.9°
                = 25.46 cm² (4 significant figures) ──────

This gets 1 mark for
method.

Total area   = 3 × 25.46 + 15.59 = 92.0 cm² (3 significant figures) ──────

This answer gets
1 mark for accuracy.

Remember to include
the units (cm²) in your
final answer.

Total: 4 marks

Forest researchers collect data about trees. Sometimes they measure heights. To do this, they use a piece of equipment that extends as far as the tree top. However, the equipment can be bulky and may require more than one person to operate it. Instead, many forest researchers simply use a clinometer, which is a small instrument used for measuring angles of elevation and depression, and trigonometry.

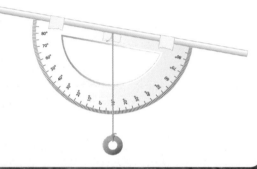

Getting started

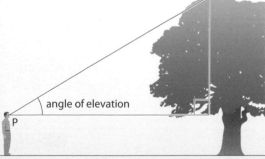

angle of elevation

P

A forest researcher measures the angle of elevation of the top of the tree.

- What other measurement should the researcher find, to help him calculate the height of the tree?
- Which trigonometric ratio would the researcher use?

English oaks

Tree number	Distance from base of trunk (m)	Angle of elevation of top of tree	Angle of elevation of lowest branch
001	16.3	45°	15°
002	10	58°	20°
003	24.5	49°	14°
004	15	55°	17°
005	12.4	52°	21°

Your task

The table shows information a researcher collected for the English oaks in one particular forest.

The forest owner would like to install camping tree-houses in three of the English oak trees. She would like each tree-house to be at a different height, with a different incline for each ladder, to appeal to a range of holiday-makers. For safety reasons:

- a tree-house must be no higher than 5.5 m from the ground
- the angle between the tree-house ladder and the ground must be 75° or less.

Look at the table and choose three trees for the tree-houses. Decide on the height above the ground and the length of the ladder required for each tree-house.

Then, write a leaflet advertising your three tree-houses to holiday-makers.

Remember to include information about heights and ladders. What other mathematical information might you include?

Why this chapter matters

There are many curves that can be seen in everyday life. Did you know that all these curves can be represented mathematically?

Below are a few examples of simple curves that you may have come across. Can you think of others?

Many road signs are circular.

The examples above all show circular-based curves. However, in mathematics, curves can take many shapes. These can be demonstrated using a cone, as shown on the right and below. If you can make a cone out of plasticine or modelling clay, then you can prove this principle yourself. As you look at these curves, try to think of where you have seen them in your own life.

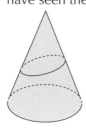

If you slice the cone at an angle to the base, the shape you are left with is an ellipse

The curve that will be particularly important in this chapter is the parabola. Car headlights are shaped like parabolas.

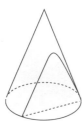

If you slice the cone parallel to its side, the shape you are left with is a parabola.

All parabolas are quadratic graphs. During the course of this chapter you will be looking at how to use quadratic equations to draw graphs that have this kind of curve.

A chain hanging freely between two supports forms a curve called a catenary.

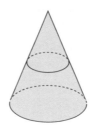

If you slice the cone parallel to the base, the shape you are left with is a circle.

If you slice the cone vertically, the shape you are left with is a hyperbola.

The suspension cables on the Humber Bridge are also parabolas.

Algebra: More graphs and equations

This chapter will show you ...

- **C** how to draw quadratic graphs
- **A** how to recognise and find the significant points of a quadratic graph
- **A** how to recognise and draw cubic, reciprocal and exponential graphs
- **A** how to use graphs to find the solutions to one linear and one non-linear pair of simultaneous equations
- **A*** how to use the sine and cosine graphs to find angles with the same sine and cosine between 0° and 360°
- **A*** how to use the method of intersection to solve one quadratic equation, using the graph of another quadratic equation and an appropriate straight line

Visual overview

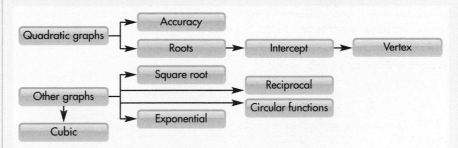

What you should already know

- How to draw linear graphs (KS3 level 6, GCSE grade D)
- How to find the equation of a graph, using the gradient-intercept method (KS3 level 8, GCSE grade B)

Quick check

1 Draw the graph of $y = 3x - 1$ for values of x from -2 to $+3$.

2 Give the equation of the graph shown.

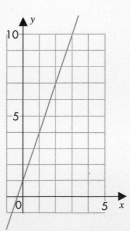

Quadratic graphs

This section will show you how to:
- draw and read values from quadratic graphs

Key words
parabola
quadratic

A **quadratic** graph has a term in x^2 in its equation. All of the following are quadratic equations and each would produce a quadratic graph.

$y = x^2$ $\qquad\qquad$ $y = x^2 + 5$ $\qquad\qquad$ $y = x^2 - 3x$

$y = x^2 + 5x + 6$ $\qquad$ $y = 3x^2 - 5x + 4$

EXAMPLE 1

Draw the graph of $y = x^2 + 5x + 6$ for $-5 \leqslant x \leqslant 3$.

Make a table, as shown below. Work out the values in each row (x^2, $5x$, 6) separately, adding them together to obtain the values of y. Then plot the points from the table.

x	−5	−4	−3	−2	−1	0	1	2	3
y^2	25	16	9	4	1	0	1	4	9
$+5x$	−25	−20	−15	−10	−5	0	5	10	15
$+6$	6	6	6	6	6	6	6	6	6
y	6	2	0	0	2	6	12	20	30

Note that in an examination paper you may be given only the first and last rows, with some values filled in. For example,

x	−5	−4	−3	−2	−1	0	1	2	3
y	6		0		2				30

In this case, you would either construct your own table, or work out the remaining y-values with a calculator.

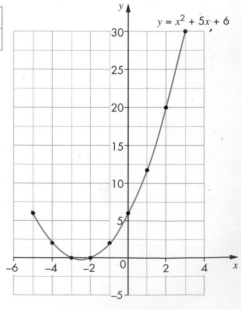

FM Functional Maths $\quad$ **AU** (AO2) Assessing Understanding $\quad$ **PS** (AO3) Problem Solving

EXAMPLE 2

a Complete the table for $y = 3x^2 - 5x + 4$ for $-1 \leqslant x \leqslant 3$, then draw the graph.

x	−5	−0.5	0	0.5	1	1.5	2	2.5	3
y	12		0	2.25	2			10.25	16

b Use your graph to find the value of y when $x = 2.2$.

c Use your graph to find the values of x that give a y-value of 9.

a The table gives only some values. So you either set up your own table with $3x^2$, $-5x$ and $+4$, or calculate each y-value. For example, on the majority of scientific calculators, the value for -0.5 will be worked out as:

Check that you get an answer of 7.25

If you want to make sure that you are doing the correct arithmetic with your calculator, try some values for x for which you know the answer. For example, try $x = 0.5$, and see whether your answer is 2.25

The complete table should be:

x	−1	−0.5	0	0.5	1	1.5	2	2.5	3
y	12	7.25	4	2.25	2	3.25	6	10.25	16

The graph is shown on the right.

b To find the corresponding y-value for any value of x, you start on the x-axis at that x-value, go up to the curve, across to the y-axis and read off the y-value. This procedure is marked on the graph with arrows.

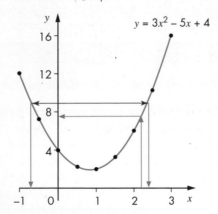

Always show these arrows because even if you make a mistake and misread the scales, you may still get a mark.

When $x = 2.2$, $y = 7.5$.

c This time start at 9 on the y-axis and read off the two x-values that correspond to a y-value of 9. Again, this procedure is marked on the graph with arrows.

When $y = 9$, $x = -0.7$ or $x = 2.4$.

A quadratic curve drawn correctly will always give a smooth curve, called a **parabola**.

Drawing accurate graphs

Although it is difficult to draw accurate curves, examiners work to a tolerance of only 1 mm. Here are some of the more common ways in which marks are lost in an examination.

- When the points are too far apart, a curve tends to 'wobble'.
- Drawing curves in small sections leads to 'feathering'.
- The place where a curve should turn smoothly is drawn 'flat'.
- A line is drawn through a point that, clearly, has been incorrectly plotted.

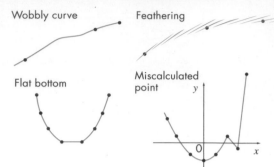

Here are some tips which will make it easier for you to draw smooth, curved lines.

- If you are *right-handed*, turn your paper or exercise book round so that you draw from left to right. Your hand is steadier this way than when you are trying to draw from right to left or away from your body. If you are *left-handed*, you should find drawing from right to left the more accurate way.
- Move your pencil over the points as a practice run without drawing the curve.
- Do one continuous curve and only stop at a plotted point.
- Use a *sharp* pencil and do not press too heavily, so that you may easily rub out mistakes.

Normally, in an examination, grids are provided with the axes clearly marked, so the examiner can place a transparent master over a graph and see immediately whether any lines are badly drawn or points are misplotted. Remember: a tolerance of 1 mm is all that you are allowed.

You do not need to work out all values in a table. You need only to work out the *y*-value. The other rows in the table are just working lines to break down the calculation. Learn how to calculate *y*-values with a calculator as there is no credit given for setting up tables in examinations.

EXERCISE 11A

In this exercise, suitable ranges are suggested for the axes. You can use any type of graph paper.

1 **a** Copy and complete the table or use a calculator to work out values for the graph of $y = 3x^2$ for values of x from -3 to 3.

x	-3	-2	-1	0	1	2	3
y	27		3			12	

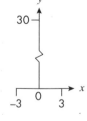

b Use your graph to find the value of y when $x = -1.5$.

c Use your graph to find the values of x that give a y-value of 10.

2 **a** Copy and complete the table or use a calculator to work out values for the graph of $y = x^2 + 2$ for values of x from -5 to 5.

x	-5	-4	-3	-2	-1	0	1	2	3	4	5
$y = x^2 + 2$	27		11					6			

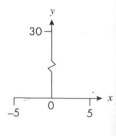

b Use your graph to find the value of y when $x = -2.5$.

c Use your graph to find the values of x that give a y-value of 14.

3 **a** Copy and complete the table or use a calculator to work out values for the graph of $y = x^2 - 2x - 8$ for values of x from -5 to 5.

x	-5	-4	-3	-2	-1	0	1	2	3	4	5
x^2	25		9					4			
$-2x$	10							-4			
-8	-8							-8			
y	27							-8			

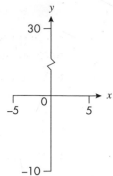

b Use your graph to find the value of y when $x = 0.5$.

c Use your graph to find the values of x that give a y-value of -3.

4 **a** Copy and complete the table or use a calculator to work out the values for the graph of $y = x^2 + 2x - 1$ for values of x from -3 to 3.

x	-3	-2	-1	0	1	2	3
x^2	9				1	4	
$+2x$	-6		-2			4	
-1	-1	-1				-1	
y	2					7	

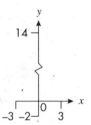

b Use your graph to find the y-value when $x = -2.5$.

c Use your graph to find the values of x that give a y-value of 1.

d On the same axes, draw the graph of $y = \frac{x}{2} + 2$.

e Where do the graphs $y = x^2 + 2x - 1$ and $y = \frac{x}{2} + 2$ cross?

5 **a** Copy and complete the table or use a calculator to work out values for the graph of $y = x^2 - x + 6$ for values of x from -3 to 3.

x	-3	-2	-1	0	1	2	3
x^2	9				1	4	
$-x$	3					-2	
$+6$	6					6	
y	18					8	

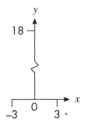

b Use your graph to find the y-value when $x = 2.5$.

c Use your graph to find the values of x that give a y-value of 8.

d Copy and complete the table or use a calculator to draw the graph of $y = x^2 + 5$ on the same axes.

x	-3	-2	-1	0	1	2	3
y	14		6				14

e Where do the graphs $y = x^2 - x + 6$ and $y = x^2 + 5$ cross?

6 a Copy and complete the table or use a calculator to work out values for the graph of $y = x^2 + 2x + 1$ for values of x from -3 to 3.

x	-3	-2	-1	0	1	2	3
x^2	9				1	4	
$+2x$	-6					4	
$+1$	1					1	
y	4						

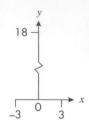

b Use your graph to find the y-value when $x = 1.7$.

c Use your graph to find the values of x that give a y-value of 2.

d On the same axes, draw the graph of $y = 2x + 2$.

e Where do the graphs $y = x^2 + 2x + 1$ and $y = 2x + 2$ cross?

7 a Copy and complete the table or use a calculator to work out values for the graph of $y = 2x^2 - 5x - 3$ for values of x from -2 to 4.

x	-2	-1.5	-1	-0.5	0	0.5	1	1.5	2	2.5	3	3.5	4
y	15	9			-3	-5				-3			9

b Where does the graph cross the x-axis?

PS 8 The diagram shows a side elevation of a cone with a cut parallel to one side.

The cone is divided into horizontal sections.

A plan view of the cone is shown.

Construction lines have been drawn to link the elevation and the plan.

Two of the intersecting points have been drawn on the plan.

Two points have also been drawn where the construction lines from the side elevation intersect with the construction lines from the plan.

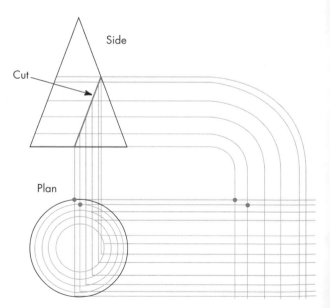

a Plot the rest of the points on the plan and join them with a smooth curve to see the plan view of the parabola.

b Plot the rest of the points on the intersecting lines and join them with a smooth curve to see the parabola.

PS **9** Copy the grid onto centimetre-squared paper.

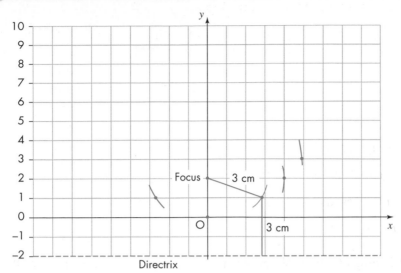

Mark a point at (0, 2). This is the focus.

Draw the line $y = -2$. This is the directrix.

A property of all parabolas is that all the points on a parabola are the same distance from the focus and the directrix.

The origin is 2 units away from both and this will be the lowest point of the parabola.

Set a pair of compasses to a radius of 3 cm. Using the focus as the centre, draw arcs on both sides to intersect with the line $y = 1$, which is 3 cm from the directrix.

Now set the compasses at 4 cm and draw arcs from the focus to intersect with $y = 2$.

Repeat with the compasses set to 5 cm, 6 cm, etc.

Once you have drawn all the points, join them with a smooth curve to show a parabola.

The parabola drawn has the equation $y = \frac{1}{8}x^2$.

AU **10** Here are the equations of three quadratic equations.

Parabola A: $y = 2x^2$

Parabola B: $y = -x^2$

Parabola C: $y = x^2 + 2$

Give a reason why each line may be the odd one out.

The significant points of a quadratic graph

This section will show you how to:

- recognise and calculate the significant points of a quadratic graph

Key words

intercept
maximum
minimum
roots
vertex

A quadratic graph has four points that are of interest to a mathematician. These are the points A, B, C and D on the diagram. The x-values at A and B are called the **roots**, and are where the graph crosses the x-axis. C is the point where the graph crosses the y-axis (the **intercept**) and D is the **vertex**, which is the lowest or highest point of the graph.

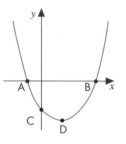

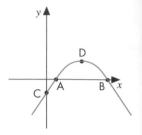

The roots

If you look at your answer to question **7** in Exercise 11A, you will see that the graph crosses the x-axis at $x = -0.5$ and $x = 3$. Since the x-axis is the line $y = 0$, the y-value at any point on the x-axis is zero. So, you have found the solution to the equation:

$0 = 2x^2 - 5x - 3$ that is $2x^2 - 5x - 3 = 0$

Equations of this type are known as *quadratic equations*.

You can solve quadratic equations by finding the values of x that make them true. Such values are called the roots of the equation. On the graph, these occur where the curve cuts the x-axis. So the roots of the quadratic equation $2x^2 - 5x - 3 = 0$ are -0.5 and 3.

Let's check these values.

For $x = 3.0$ $2(3)^2 - 5(3) - 3 = 18 - 15 - 3 = 0$

For $x = 0.5$ $2(-0.5)^2 - 5(-0.5) - 3 = 0.5 + 2.5 - 3 = 0$

You can find the roots of a quadratic equation by drawing its graph and finding where the graph crosses the x-axis.

EXAMPLE 3

a Draw the graph of $y = x^2 - 3x - 4$ for $-2 \leqslant x \leqslant 5$.

b Use your graph to find the roots of the equation $x^2 - 3x - 4 = 0$.

a Set up a table.

x	-2	-1	0	1	2	3	4	5
y^2	4	1	0	1	4	9	16	25
$-3x$	6	3	0	-3	-6	-9	-12	-15
-4	-4	-4	-4	-4	-4	-4	-4	-4
y	6	0	-4	-6	-6	-4	0	6

Draw the graph.

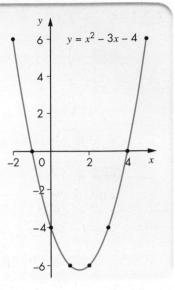

b The points where the graph crosses the x-axis are −1 and 4.

So, the roots of $x^2 - 3x - 4 = 0$ are $x = -1$ and $x = 4$.

Note that sometimes the quadratic graph may not cross the x-axis. In this case there are no roots. This was dealt with in Chapter 10 of Book 1.

The y-intercept

If you look at all the quadratic graphs you have drawn so far you will see a connection between the equation and the point where the graph crosses the y-axis. Very simply, the constant term of the equation $y = ax^2 + bx + c$ (that is, the value c) is where the graph crosses the y-axis. The intercept is at $(0, c)$.

The vertex

The lowest (or highest) point of a quadratic graph is called the *vertex*.

If it is the highest point, it is called the **maximum**.

If it is the lowest point, it is called the **minimum**.

It is difficult to find a general rule for this point, but the x-coordinate is always half-way between the roots. The easiest way to find the y-value is to substitute the x-value into the original equation.

Another way to find the vertex is to complete the square (you have met this in Chapter 10 of Book 1).

EXAMPLE 4

a Write the equation $x^2 - 3x - 4 = 0$ in the form $(x - p)^2 - q = 0$.

b What is the least value of the graph $y = x^2 - 3x - 4$?

a $(x - p)^2 - q = x^2 - 2px + p^2 - q = x^2 - 3x - 4$

So $p = 1\frac{1}{2}$ and $p^2 - q = -4$, $q = p^2 + 4 = (1\frac{1}{2})^2 + 4 = 6\frac{1}{4}$

b Looking at the graph drawn in Example 3 you can see that the minimum point is at $(1\frac{1}{2}, -6\frac{1}{4})$, so the least value is $-6\frac{1}{4}$.

You should be able to see the connection between the vertex point and the equation written in the 'completing the square' form.

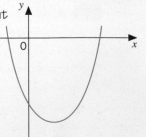

As a general rule when a quadratic is written in the form $(x - p)^2 + q$ then the minimum point is (p, q). Note the sign change of p.

Note: If the x^2 term is negative then the graph will be inverted and the vertex will be a maximum.

EXERCISE 11B

1 a Copy and complete the table to draw the graph of $y = x^2 - 4$ for $-4 \leqslant x \leqslant 4$.

x	-4	-3	-2	-1	0	1	2	3	4
y	12			-3				5	

b Use your graph to find the roots of $x^2 - 4 = 0$.

2 a Copy and complete the table and draw the graph of $y = x^2 - 9$ for $-4 \leqslant x \leqslant 4$.

x	-4	-3	-2	-1	0	1	2	3	4
y	7				-9			0	

b Use your graph to find the roots of $x^2 - 9 = 0$.

PS 3 a Look at the equations of the graphs you drew in questions **1** and **2**. Is there a connection between the numbers in each equation and its roots?

b Before you draw the graphs in parts **c** and **d**, try to predict what their roots will be.

c Copy and complete the table and draw the graph of $y = x^2 - 1$ for $-4 \leqslant x \leqslant 4$.

x	-4	-3	-2	-1	0	1	2	3	4
y	15				-1			8	

d Copy and complete the table and draw the graph of $y = x^2 - 5$ for $-4 \leqslant x \leqslant 4$.

x	-4	-3	-2	-1	0	1	2	3	4
y	11		-1					4	

e Were your predictions correct?

4 a Copy and complete the table and draw the graph of $y = x^2 + 4x$ for $-5 \leqslant x \leqslant 2$.

x	-5	-4	-3	-2	-1	0	1	2
x^2	25			4			1	
$+4x$	-20			-8			4	
y	5			-4			5	

b Use your graph to find the roots of the equation $x^2 + 4x = 0$.

5 a Copy and complete the table and draw the graph of $y = x^2 - 6x$ for $-2 \leqslant x \leqslant 8$.

x	-2	-1	0	1	2	3	4	5	6	7	8
x^2	4			1			16				
$-6x$	12			-6			-24				
y	16			-5			-8				

b Use your graph to find the roots of the equation $x^2 - 6x = 0$.

6 **a** Copy and complete the table and draw the graph of $y = x^2 + 3x$ for $-5 \leqslant x \leqslant 3$.

x	-5	-4	-3	-2	-1	0	1	2	3
y	10			-2				10	

b Use your graph to find the roots of the equation $x^2 + 3x = 0$.

PS 7 **a** Look at the equations of the graphs you drew in questions **4**, **5** and **6**. Is there a connection between the numbers in each equation and the roots?

b Before you draw the graphs in parts **c** and **d**, try to predict what their roots will be.

c Copy and complete the table and draw the graph of $y = x^2 - 3x$ for $-2 \leqslant x \leqslant 5$.

x	-2	-1	0	1	2	3	4	5
y	10			-2				10

d Copy and complete the table and draw the graph of $y = x^2 + 5x$ for $-6 \leqslant x \leqslant 2$.

x	-6	-5	-4	-3	-2	-1	0	1	2
y	6			-6				6	

e Were your predictions correct?

8 **a** Copy and complete the table and draw the graph of $y = x^2 - 4x + 4$ for $-1 \leqslant x \leqslant 5$.

x	-1	0	1	2	3	4	5
y	9				1		

b Use your graph to find the roots of the equation $x^2 - 4x + 4 = 0$.

c What happens with the roots?

9 **a** Copy and complete the table and draw the graph of $y = x^2 - 6x + 3$ for $-1 \leqslant x \leqslant 7$.

x	-1	0	1	2	3	4	5	6	7
y	10			-5			-2		

b Use your graph to find the roots of the equation $x^2 - 6x + 3 = 0$.

10 **a** Copy and complete the table and draw the graph of $y = 2x^2 + 5x - 6$ for $-5 \leqslant x \leqslant 2$.

x	-5	-4	-3	-2	-1	0	1	2
y								

b Use your graph to find the roots of the equation $2x^2 + 5x - 6 = 0$.

PS 11 Look back at questions **1** to **7**.

    a Write down the point of intersection of the graph with the y-axis for each one.

    b Write down the coordinates of the minimum point (vertex) of each graph for each one.

    c Explain the connection between these points and the original equation.

12 **a** Write the equation $y = x^2 - 4x + 4$ in the form $y = (x - p)^2 + q$.

    b Write down the minimum value of the equation $y = x^2 - 4x + 4$.

13 **a** Write the equation $y = x^2 - 6x + 3$ in the form $y = (x - p)^2 + q$.

    b Write down the minimum value of the equation $y = x^2 - 6x + 3$.

14 **a** Write the equation $y = x^2 - 8x + 2$ in the form $y = (x - p)^2 + q$.

    b Write down the minimum value of the equation $y = x^2 - 8x + 2$.

15 **a** Write the equation $y = -x^2 + 2x - 6$ in the form $y = -(x - p)^2 + q$.

    b Write down the maximum value of the equation $y = -x^2 + 2x - 6$.

PS 16 Look at your answers to questions **12** to **13**.

    a What is the connection between the maximum or minimum point and the values in the equation when written as $(x - a)^2 + b$?

    b Without drawing the curve, predict the minimum point of the graph:

        $y = x^2 + 10x - 3$.

AU 17 Masood draws a quadratic graph which has a minimum point at $(3, -7)$.

He forgets to label it and later cannot remember what the quadratic function was.

He knows it is of the form $y = x^2 + px + q$.

Can you help him?

AU 18 **a** The graph $y = x^2 + 4x + 2$ has a minimum point at $(-2, 2)$.

    Write down the minimum point of the graph $y = x^2 + 4x - 3$.

    b The graph $y = x^2 - 2ax + b$ has a minimum point at $(a, b - a^2)$.

    Write down the minimum points of:

        i $y = x^2 - 2ax + 2b$

        ii $y = x^2 - 4ax + b$

Other graphs

This section will show you how to:

- recognise and plot cubic, exponential and reciprocal graphs

Key words

asymptote
cubic
exponential function
reciprocal

Cubic graphs

A **cubic** function or graph is one that contains a term in x^3. The following are examples of cubic graphs.

$$y = x^3 \qquad y = x^3 + 3x \qquad y = x^3 + x^2 + x + 1$$

The techniques used to draw them are exactly the same as those for quadratic and reciprocal graphs.

Questions requiring an accurate drawing of a cubic graph are not very common in examinations, but questions asking if you can recognise a cubic graph occur quite often.

This is the basic graph $y = x^3$.

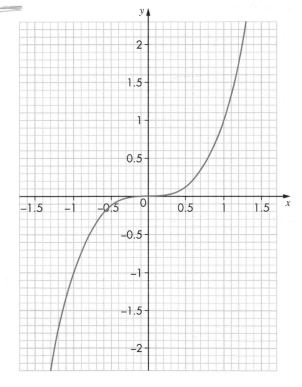

It has a characteristic shape which you should learn to recognise.

Example 5 shows you how to draw a cubic graph accurately.

You should use a calculator to work out the value of y and to round to 1 or 2 decimal places.

EXAMPLE 5

a Complete the table to draw the graph of $y = x^3 - x^2 - 4x + 4$ for $-3 \leqslant x \leqslant 3$.

x	-3	-2.5	-2	-1.5	-1	-0.5	0	0.5	1	1.5	2	2.5	3
y	-20.00		0.00		6.00		4.00	1.88				3.38	10.00

b Use your graph to give the roots of the equation $x^3 - x^2 - 4x + 4 = 0$.

c Write down the coordinates of:

    i the minimum vertex   **ii** the maximum vertex.

d Write down the coordinates of the point where the graph intersects the y-axis.

a The completed table (to 2 decimal places) is given below and the graph is shown below, right.

x	-3	-2.5	-2	-1.5	-1	-0.5	0	0.5	1	1.5	2	2.5	3
y	-20.00	-7.88	0.00	4.38	6.00	5.63	4.00	1.88	0.00	-0.88	0.00	3.38	10.00

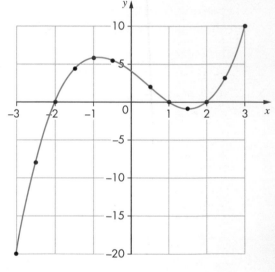

b Just as in quadratic graphs, the roots are the points where the graph crosses the x-axis.

So the roots are $x = -2$, 1 and 2.

Note that, in the table, these are the x-values where the y-value is 0.

c **i** The minimum vertex is at the point $(1.5, -0.88)$.

    ii The maximum vertex is at the point $(-1, 6)$.

    Note that the minimum and maximum values of the function are $\pm$ infinity, as the arms of the curve continue forever.

d Just as in the quadratic, this is the constant term in the equation, so the point is $(0, 4)$.

Reciprocal graphs

A **reciprocal** equation has the form $y = \dfrac{a}{x}$.

Examples of reciprocal equations are:

$$y = \frac{1}{x} \qquad y = \frac{4}{x} \qquad y = -\frac{3}{x}$$

All reciprocal graphs have a similar shape and some symmetry properties.

EXAMPLE 6

Complete the table to draw the graph of $y = \dfrac{1}{x}$ for $-4 \leqslant x \leqslant 4$.

x	−4	−3	−2	−1	1	2	3	4
y								

Values are rounded to two decimal places, as it is unlikely that you could plot a value more accurately than this. The completed table looks like this.

x	−4	−3	−2	−1	1	2	3	4
y	−0.25	−0.33	−0.5	−1	1	0.5	0.33	0.25

The graph plotted from these values is shown in **A**. This is not much of a graph and does not show the properties of the reciprocal function. If you take x-values from −0.8 to 0.8 in steps of 0.2, you get the next table.

Note that you cannot use $x = 0$ since $\dfrac{1}{0}$ is infinity.

x	−0.8	−0.6	−0.4	−0.2	0.2	0.4	0.6	0.8
y	−1.25	−1.67	−2.5	−5	5	2.5	1.67	1.25

Plotting these points as well gives the graph in **B**.

A

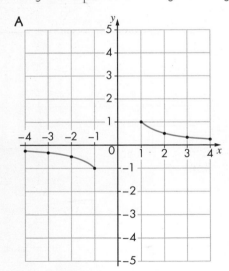

B

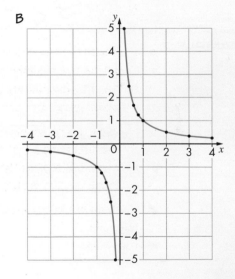

From the graph in **B**, the following properties can be seen.

- The lines $y = x$ and $y = -x$ are lines of symmetry.
- The closer x gets to zero, the nearer the graph gets to the y-axis.
- As x increases, the graph gets closer to the x-axis.

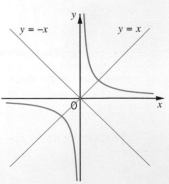

The graph never actually touches the axes, it just gets closer and closer to them. A line to which a graph gets closer but never touches or crosses is an **asymptote**.

These properties are true for *all* reciprocal graphs.

Exponential graphs

Equations that have the form $y = k^x$, where k is a positive number, are called **exponential functions**.

Exponential functions share the following properties.

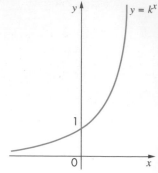

- When k is greater than 1, the value of y increases steeply as x increases, which you can see from the graph on the right.

- Also when k is greater than 1, as x takes on increasingly large negative values, the closer y gets to zero, and so the graph gets nearer and nearer to the negative x-axis. y never actually becomes zero and so the graph never touches the negative x-axis. That is, the negative x-axis is an asymptote to the graph. (See also previous page.)

- Whatever the value of k, the graph always intercepts the y-axis at 1, because here $y = k^0$.

- The reciprocal graph, $y = k^{-x}$, is the reflection in the y-axis of the graph of $y = k^x$, as you can see from the graph on the right.

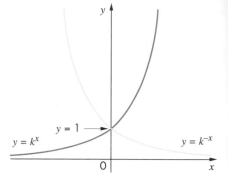

EXAMPLE 7

a Complete the table below for $y = 2^x$ for values of x from -5 to $+5$. (Values are rounded to 2 decimal places.)

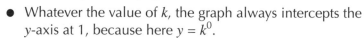

x	−5	−4	−3	−2	−1	0	1	2	3	4	5
$y = 2^x$	0.03	0.06	0.13			1	2	4			32

b Plot the graph of $y = 2^x$ for $-5 \leqslant x \leqslant 5$.

c Use your graph to estimate the value of y when $x = 2.5$.

d Use your graph to estimate the value of x when $y = 0.75$.

a The values missing from the table are:

   0.25, 0.5, 8 and 16

b Part of the graph (drawn to scale) is shown on the right.

c Draw a line vertically from $x = 2.5$ until it meets the graph and then read across. The y-value is 5.7.

d Draw a line horizontally from $y = 0.75$, the x-value is −0.4.

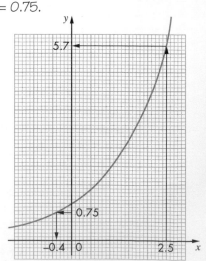

EXERCISE 11C

1 Sketch the graph of $y = -x^3$.

2 a Copy and complete the table to draw the graph of $y = 2x^3$ for $-3 \leqslant x \leqslant 3$.

x	–3	–2.5	–2	–1.5	–1	–0.5	0	0.5	1	1.5	2	2.5	3
y		–31.25		–6.75			0.00	0.25			16.00		

b Use your graph to find the y-value for an x-value of 2.7.

3 a Copy and complete the table to draw the graph of $y = x^3 + 3$ for $-3 \leqslant x \leqslant 3$.

x	–3	–2.5	–2	–1.5	–1	–0.5	0	0.5	1	1.5	2	2.5	3
y	–24.00	–12.63			2.00		3.00	3.13			11.00		30.00

b Use your graph to find the y-value for an x-value of 1.2.

c Find the root of the equation $x^3 + 3 = 0$.

4 a Copy and complete the table to draw the graph of $y = x^3 - 2x + 5$ for $-3 \leqslant x \leqslant 3$.

x	–3	–2.5	–2	–1.5	–1	–0.5	0	0.5	1	1.5	2	2.5	3
y	–16.00		1.00	4.63			5.00	4.13				15.63	

b Use the graph to find:

i the root of $x^3 - 2x + 5 = 0$

ii the approximate value of the coordinate of the maximum vertex

iii the approximate value of the coordinate of the minimum vertex

iv the coordinates of the point where the graph crosses the y-axis.

5 a Copy and complete the table to draw the graph of $y = \dfrac{2}{x}$ for $-4 \leqslant x \leqslant 4$.

x	0.2	0.4	0.5	0.8	1	1.5	2	3	4
y	10		4	2.5			1		0.5

b Use your graph to find:

i the y-value when $x = 2.5$ **ii** the x-value when $y = -1.25$.

6 a Copy and complete the table to draw the graph of $y^2 = 25x$ for $0 \leqslant x \leqslant 5$.

x	0	1	2	3	4	5
$\sqrt{x}$					2 and –2	
$y = 5\sqrt{x}$					10 and –10	

b Use your graph to find:

i the values of y when $x = 3.5$ **ii** the value of x when $y = 8$.

A

7 **a** Copy and complete the table to draw the graph of $y = \dfrac{5}{x}$ for $-20 \leqslant x \leqslant 20$.

x	0.2	0.4	0.5	1	2	5	10	15	20
y	25		10						0.25

b On the same axes, draw the line $y = x + 10$.

c Use your graph to find the x-values of the points where the graphs cross.

8 **a** Complete the table below for $y = 3^x$ for values of x from -4 to $+3$. (Values are rounded to 2 decimal places.)

x	-4	-3	-2	-1	0	1	2	3
$y = 3^x$	0.01	0.04			1	3		

b Plot the graph of $y = 3^x$ for $-4 \leqslant x \leqslant 3$. (Take the y-axis from 0 to 30.)

c Use your graph to estimate the value of y when $x = 2.5$.

d Use your graph to estimate the value of x when $y = 0.5$.

9 **a** Complete the table below for $y = (\tfrac{1}{2})^x$ for values of x from -5 to $+5$. (Values are rounded to 2 decimal places.)

x	-5	-4	-3	-2	-1	0	1	2	3	4	5
$y = (\tfrac{1}{2})^x$			8			1				0.06	0.03

b Plot the graph of $y = (\tfrac{1}{2})^x$ for $-5 \leqslant x \leqslant 5$. (Take the y-axis from 0 to 35.)

c Use your graph to estimate the value of y when $x = 2.5$.

d Use your graph to estimate the value of x when $y = 0.75$.

10 Write down whether each of these graphs is 'linear', 'quadratic', 'reciprocal', 'cubic', 'exponential' or 'none of these'.

a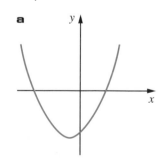

b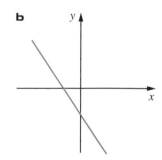

c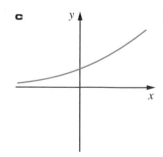

d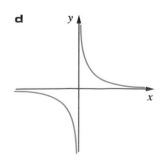

e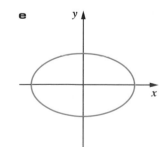

f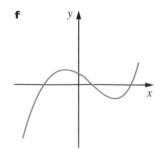

g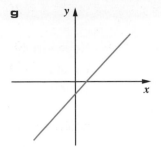

h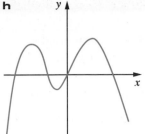

i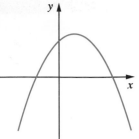

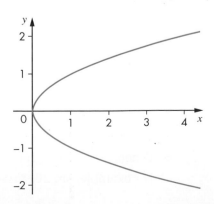

PS 11 One grain of rice is placed on the first square of a chess board. Two grains of rice are placed on the second square, four grains on the third square and so on.

a Explain why $y = 2^{(n-1)}$ gives the number of grains of rice on the nth square.

b Complete the table for the number of grains of rice on the first 10 squares.

Square	1	2	3	4	5	6	7	8	9	10
Grains	1	2	4							

c Use the rule to work out how many grains of rice there are on the 64th square.

d If 1000 grains of rice are worth 5p, how much is the rice on the 64th square worth?

PS 12 An extremely large sheet of paper is 0.01 cm thick. It is torn in half and one piece placed on top of the other. These two pieces are then torn in half and one half is placed on top of the other half to give a pile four sheets thick. This process is repeated 50 times.

a Complete the table to show how many pieces there are in the pile after each tear.

Tears	1	2	3	4	5	6	7	8
Pieces	2	4						

b Write down a rule for the number of pieces after n tears.

c How many pieces will there be piled up after 50 tears?

d How thick is this pile?

AU 13 A curve of the form $y = ab^x$ passes through the points (0, 5) and (2, 45).

Work out the values of a and b.

PS 14 The graph of $y^2 = x$ is shown below.

On a copy of this graph, sketch the following graphs.

a $y^2 + 2 = x$

b $2y^2 = x$

c $(y - 2)^2 = x$

11.4 Trigonometric ratios of angles between 90° and 360°

This section will show you how to:

- find the sine, cosine and tangent of any angle from 0° to 360°

Key words
circular function
cosine
sine
tangent

ACTIVITY

a Copy and complete this table, using your calculator and rounding to three decimal places.

x	sin x	x	sin x	x	sin x	x	sin x
0°		180°		180°		360°	
15°		165°		195°		335°	
30°		150°		210°		320°	
45°		135°		225°		315°	
60°		120°		240°		300°	
75°		105°		255°		285°	
90°		90°		270°		270°	

b Comment on what you notice about the **sine** of each acute angle, and the sines of its corresponding non-acute angles.

c Draw a graph of sin x against x. Take x from 0° to 360° and sin x from –1 to 1.

d Comment on any symmetries your graph has.

You should have discovered these three facts.

- When $90° < x < 180°$, $\sin x = \sin (180° - x)$
  For example, sin 153° = sin (180° – 153°) = sin 27° = 0.454
- When $180° < x < 270°$, $\sin x = -\sin (x - 180°)$
  For example, sin 214° = – sin (214° – 180°) = – sin 34° = – 0.559
- When $270° < x < 360°$, $\sin x = -\sin (360° - x)$
  For example, sin 287° = – sin (360° – 287°) = – sin 73° = – 0.956

Note:

- Each and every value of sine between –1 and 1 gives *two* angles between 0° and 360°.
- When the value of sine is positive, both angles are between 0° and 180°.
- When the value of sine is negative, both angles are between 180° and 360°.
- You can use the sine graph from 0° to 360° to check values approximately.

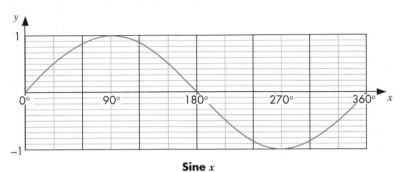

Sine x

EXAMPLE 8

Find the angles with a sine of 0.56.

You know that both angles are between 0° and 180°.

Using your calculator to find $\sin^{-1} 0.56$, you obtain 34.1°.

The other angle is, therefore,

180° – 34.1° = 145.9°

So, the angles are 34.1° and 145.9°.

EXAMPLE 9

Find the angles with a sine of –0.197.

You know that both angles are between 180° and 360°.

Using your calculator to find $\sin^{-1} 0.197$, you obtain 11.4°.

So the angles are

180° + 11.4° and 360° – 11.4°

which give 191.4° and 348.6°.

You can always use your calculator to check your answer to this type of problem by first keying in the angle and the appropriate trigonometric function (which would be sine in the above examples).

EXERCISE 11D

1 State the two angles between 0° and 360° for each of these sine values.

a 0.6   **b** 0.8   **c** 0.75   **d** −0.7

e −0.25   **f** −0.32   **g** −0.175   **h** −0.814

i 0.471   **j** −0.097   **k** 0.553   **l** −0.5

AU 2 Which of these values is the odd one out and why?

sin 36°   sin 144°   sin 234°   sin 324°

PS 3 The graph of sine x is cyclic, which means that it repeats forever in each direction.

a Write down one value of x greater than 360° for which the sine value is 0.978 147 600 73.

b Write down one value of x less than 0° for which the sine value is 0.978 147 600 73.

c Describe any symmetries of the graph of $y = \sin x$.

a Copy and complete this table, using your calculator and rounding to 3 decimal places.

x	cos x	x	cos x	x	cos x	x	cos x
0°		180°		180°		360°	
15°		165°		195°		335°	
30°		150°		210°		320°	
45°		135°		225°		315°	
60°		120°		240°		300°	
75°		105°		255°		285°	
90°		90°		270°		270°	

b Comment on what you notice about the cosines of the angles.

c Draw a graph of cos x against x. Take x from 0° to 360° and cos x from −1 to 1.

d Comment on the symmetry of the graph.

You should have discovered these three facts.

- When $90° < x < 180°$, $\cos x = -\cos (180 - x)°$
  For example, $\cos 161° = -\cos (180° - 161°) = -\cos 19° = -0.946$ (3 significant figures)
- When $180° < x < 270°$, $\cos x = -\cos (x - 180°)$
  For example, $\cos 245° = -\cos (245° - 180°) = -\cos 65° = -0.423$ (3 significant figures)
- When $270° < x < 360°$, $\cos x = \cos (360° - x)$
  For example, $\cos 310° = \cos (360° - 310°) = \cos 50° = 0.643$ (3 significant figures)

Note:

- Each and every value of cosine between –1 and 1 gives *two* angles between 0° and 360°.
- When the value of cosine is positive, one angle is between 0° and 90°, and the other is between 270° and 360°.
- When the value of cosine is negative, both angles are between 90° and 270°.
- You can use the cosine graph from 0° to 360° to check values approximately.

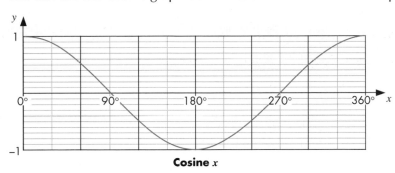

Cosine x

EXAMPLE 10

Find the angles with a cosine of 0.75.

One angle is between 0° and 90°, and the other is between 270° and 360°.

Using your calculator to find $\cos^{-1} 0.75$, you obtain 41.4°.

The other angle is, therefore,

  $360° - 41.4° = 318.6°$

So, the angles are 41.4° and 318.6°.

EXAMPLE 11

Find the angles with a cosine of –0.285.

You know that both angles are between 90° and 270°.

Using your calculator to find $\cos^{-1} 0.285$, you obtain 73.4°.

The two angles are, therefore,

  $180° - 73.4°$ and $180° + 73.4°$

which give 106.6° and 253.4°.

Here again, you can use your calculator to check your answer, by keying in cosine.

EXERCISE 11E

1 State the two angles between 0° and 360° for each of these cosine values.

   a 0.6   **b** 0.58   **c** 0.458   **d** 0.575

   e 0.185   **f** −0.8   **g** −0.25   **h** −0.175

   i −0.361   **j** −0.974   **k** 0.196   **l** 0.714

AU 2 Which of these values is the odd one out and why?

      cos 58°   cos 118°   cos 238°   cos 262°

PS 3 The graph of cosine x is cyclic, which means that it repeats forever in each direction.

   a Write down one value of x greater than 360° for which the cosine value is −0.669 130 606 36.

   b Write down one value of x less than 0° for which the cosine value is −0.669 130 606 36.

   c Describe any symmetries of the graph of $y = \cos x$.

EXERCISE 11F

1 Write down the sine of each of these angles.

   a 135°   **b** 269°   **c** 305°   **d** 133°

2 Write down the cosine of each of these angles.

   a 129°   **b** 209°   **c** 95°   **d** 357°

3 Write down the two possible values of x ($0° < x < 360°$) for each equation. Give your answers to 1 decimal place.

   a $\sin x = 0.361$ **b** $\sin x = -0.486$ **c** $\cos x = 0.641$

   d $\cos x = -0.866$ **e** $\sin x = 0.874$ **f** $\cos x = 0.874$

4 Find two angles such that the sine of each is 0.5.

5 $\cos 41° = 0.755$. What is $\cos 139°$?

6 Write down the value of each of the following, correct to 3 significant figures.

   a $\sin 50° + \cos 50°$ **b** $\cos 120° - \sin 120°$ **c** $\sin 136° + \cos 223°$

   d $\sin 175° + \cos 257°$ **e** $\sin 114° - \sin 210°$ **f** $\cos 123° + \sin 177°$

AU 7 It is suggested that $(\sin x)^2 + (\cos x)^2 = 1$ is true for all values of x. Test out this suggestion to see if you agree.

PS 8 Suppose the sine key on your calculator is broken, but not the cosine key. Show how you could calculate these.

     a   sin 25°   **b**   sin 130°

PS 9 Find a solution to each of these equations.

     a   sin $(x + 20°) = 0.5$ **b**   cos $(5x) = 0.45$

PS 10 Use any suitable method to find the solution to the equation $\sin x = (\cos x)^2$.

ACTIVITY

a Try to find tan 90°. What do you notice?

Which is the closest angle to 90° for which you can find the **tangent** on your calculator?

What is the largest value for tangent that you can get on your calculator?

b Find values of tan x where $0° < x < 360°$. Draw a graph of your results.

State some rules for finding both angles between 0° and 360° that have any given tangent.

EXAMPLE 12

Find the angles between 0° and 360° with a tangent of 0.875.

One angle is between 0° and 90°, and the other is between 180° and 270°.

Using your calculator to find $\tan^{-1} 0.875$, you obtain 41.2°.

The other angle is, therefore,

     180° + 41.2° = 221.2°

So, the angles are 41.2° and 221.2°.

EXAMPLE 13

Find the angles between 0° and 360° with a tangent of –1.5.

You know that one angle is between 90° and 180°, and that the other is between 270° and 360°.

Using your calculator to find $\tan^{-1} 1.5$, you obtain 56.3°.

The angles are, therefore,

     180° – 56.3° and 360° – 56.3°

which give 123.7° and 303.7°.

EXERCISE 11G

A*

1 State the angles between 0° and 360° which have each of these tangent values.

a 0.258	**b** 0.785	**c** 1.19	**d** 1.875	**e** 2.55
f −0.358	**g** −0.634	**h** −0.987	**i** −1.67	**j** −3.68
k 1.397	**l** 0.907	**m** −0.355	**n** −1.153	**o** 4.15
p −2.05	**q** −0.098	**r** 0.998	**s** 1.208	**t** −2.5

AU 2 Which of these values is the odd one out and why?

tan 45°   tan 135°   tan 235°   tan 315°

PS 3 The graph of tan x is cyclic, which means that it repeats forever in each direction.

a Write down one value of x greater than 360° for which the tangent value is 2.144 506 920 51.

b Write down one value of x less than 0° for which the tangent value is 2.144 506 920 51.

c Describe any symmetries of the graph of $y = \tan x$.

You may see the trigonometric functions sine, cosine and tangent referred to as **circular functions**. You could use the internet to find out more.

11.5 The circular function graphs

This section will show you how to:
- use the symmetry of the graphs $y = \sin x$, and $y = \cos x$ in answering questions
- understand that for every value of sine and cosine between 1 and −1 there are two angles between 0° and 360°

Key words
cosine
cyclic
inverse cosine
inverse sine
line symmetry
rotational symmetry
sine

You have just met **sine** and **cosine** graphs.

These graphs have some special properties.

- They are **cyclic**. This means that they repeat indefinitely in both directions.
- For every value of sine or cosine between −1 and 1 there are two angles between 0° and 360°, and an infinite number of angles altogether.

- The sine graph has **rotational symmetry** about (180°, 0) and has **line symmetry** between 0° and 180° about $x = 90°$, and between 180° and 360° about $x = 270°$.

- The cosine graph has line symmetry about $x = 180°$, and has rotational symmetry between 0° and 180° about (90°, 0) and between 180° and 360° about (270°, 0).

The graphs can be used to find angles with certain values of sine and cosine.

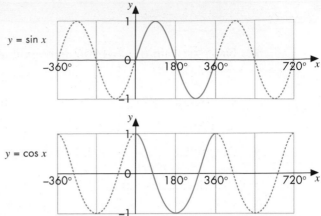

EXAMPLE 14

Given that sin 42° = 0.669, find another angle between 0° and 360° that also has a sine of 0.669.

Plot the approximate value 0.669 on the sine graph and use the symmetry to work out the other value.

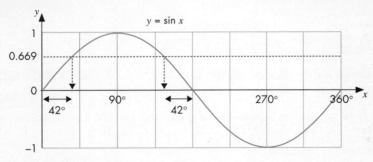

The other value is 180° − 42° = 138°

EXAMPLE 15

Given that cos 110° = −0.342, find two angles between 0° and 360° that have a cosine of +0.342.

Plot the approximate values −0.342 and 0.342 on the cosine graph and use the symmetry to work out the values.

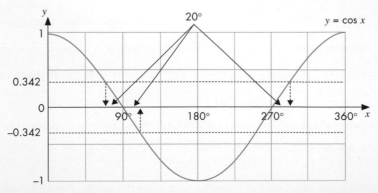

The required values are 90° − 20° = 70° and 270° + 20° = 290°

EXERCISE 11H

1 Given that sin 65° = 0.906, find another angle between 0° and 360° that also has a sine of 0.906.

2 Given that sin 213° = –0.545, find another angle between 0° and 360° that also has a sine of –0.545.

3 Given that cos 36° = 0.809, find another angle between 0° and 360° that also has a cosine of 0.809.

4 Given that cos 165° = –0.966, find another angle between 0° and 360° that also has a cosine of –0.966.

5 Given that sin 30° = 0.5, find two angles between 0° and 360° that have a sine of –0.5.

6 Given that cos 45° = 0.707, find two angles between 0° and 360° that have a cosine of –0.707.

PS 7 **a** Choose an acute angle a. Write down the values of:

    i   sin a **ii**   cos $(90° – a)$.

  b Repeat with another acute angle b.

  c Write down a rule connecting the sine of an acute angle x and the cosine of the complementary angle (i.e. the difference with 90°).

  d Find a similar rule for the cosine of x and the sine of its complementary angle.

8 Given that sin 26° = 0.438:

  a write down an angle between 0° and 90° that has a cosine of 0.438

  b find two angles between 0° and 360° that have a sine of –0.438

  c find two angles between 0° and 360° that have a cosine of –0.438.

AU 9 A formula used to work out the angle of a triangle is

$$\cos A = \frac{b^2 + c^2 - a^2}{2bc}$$

where a, b and c are the sides of the triangle and angle A is the angle opposite side a.

  a Work out the value of cos A for a triangle where $a = 20$, $b = 11$ and $c = 13$.

  b What is the size of angle A to the nearest degree? Use the **inverse cosine function** on your calculator.

PS 10 Another formula that can be used to work out the angle of a triangle is

$$\sin A = \frac{a\sin B}{b}$$

where a and b are sides of the triangle and A and B are angles opposite the sides a and b respectively.

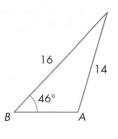

a Work out the value of sin *A* for this triangle, where *a* = 16, *b* = 14 and *B* = 46°.

b Use your calculator and the **inverse sine** function to find the value of *B*.

c Does your value from the calculator match the obtuse angle *A*?

d If not, explain why not.

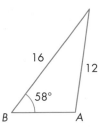

PS 11 Mike used the same rule as in question 10 to work out the size of angle *A* in this triangle.

a Work out the value of sin *A* for the triangle shown, where *a* = 16, *b* = 12 and *B* = 58°.

b Use your calculator and the inverse sine function to find the value of *B*.

c What happens? Can you explain why?

AU 12 State if the following rules are true or false.

a $\sin x = \sin(180° - x)$ **b** $\sin x = -\sin(360° - x)$ **c** $\cos x = \cos(360° - x)$

d $\sin x = -\sin(180° + x)$ **e** $\cos(180° - x) = \cos(180° + x)$

11.6 Solving equations, one linear and one non-linear, with graphs

This section will show you how to:
- solve a pair of simultaneous equations where one is linear and one is non-linear, using graphs

Key words
linear
non-linear
simultaneous equations

In Chapter 13 of Book 1, you learned how to use an algebraic method for solving a pair of **simultaneous equations** where one is **linear** (a straight line) and one is **non-linear** (a curve). In this section, you will learn how to do this graphically. You have seen in Chapter 12 of Book 1 how to find the solution to a pair of linear simultaneous equations. The same principle applies here. The point where the graphs cross gives the solution. However, in most cases, there are two solutions, because the straight line will cross the curve twice.

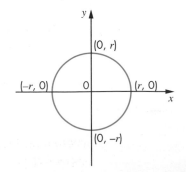

Most of the non-linear graphs will be quadratic graphs, but there is one other type you can meet. This is an equation of the form $x^2 + y^2 = r^2$, which is a circle, with the centre as the origin and a radius of *r*.

EXAMPLE 16

Find the approximate solutions of the pair of equations $y = x^2 + x - 2$ and $y = 2x + 3$ by graphical means.

Set up a table for the quadratic.

x	−4	−3	−2	−1	0	1	2	3	4
y	10	4	0	−2	−2	0	4	10	18

Draw both graphs on the same set of axes.

From the graph, the approximate solutions can be seen to be (−1.8, −0.6) and (2.8, 8.6).

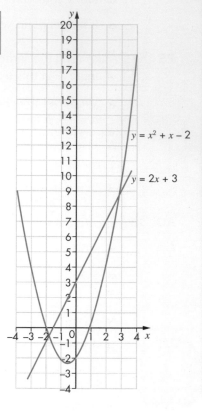

EXAMPLE 17

Find the approximate solutions of the pair of equations $x^2 + y^2 = 25$ and $y = x + 2$ by graphical means.

The curve is a circle of radius 5 centred on the origin.

From the graph, the approximate solutions can be seen to be (−4.4, −2.4), (2.4, 4.4).

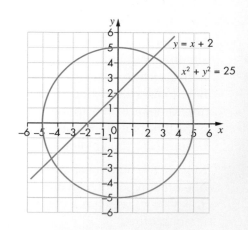

EXERCISE 11I

1 Use graphical methods to find the approximate or exact solutions to the following pairs of simultaneous equations. In this question, suitable ranges for the axes are given. In an examination a grid will be supplied.

    a $y = x^2 + 3x - 2$ and $y = x$ $(-5 \leqslant x \leqslant 5, -5 \leqslant y \leqslant 5)$

    b $y = x^2 - 3x - 6$ and $y = 2x$ $(-4 \leqslant x \leqslant 8, -10 \leqslant y \leqslant 20)$

    c $x^2 + y^2 = 25$ and $x + y = 1$ $(-6 \leqslant x \leqslant 6, -6 \leqslant y \leqslant 6)$

    d $x^2 + y^2 = 4$ and $y = x + 1$ $(-5 \leqslant x \leqslant 5, -5 \leqslant y \leqslant 5)$

    e $y = x^2 - 3x + 1$ and $y = 2x - 1$ $(0 \leqslant x \leqslant 6, -4 \leqslant y \leqslant 12)$

    f $y = x^2 - 3$ and $y = x + 3$ $(-5 \leqslant x \leqslant 5, -4 \leqslant y \leqslant 8)$

    g $y = x^2 - 3x - 2$ and $y = 2x - 3$ $(-5 \leqslant x \leqslant 5, -5 \leqslant y \leqslant 10)$

    h $x^2 + y^2 = 9$ and $y = x - 1$ $[-5 \leqslant x \leqslant 5, -5 \leqslant y \leqslant 5)$

PS 2 **a** Solve the simultaneous equations $y = x^2 + 3x - 4$ and $y = 5x - 5$ $(-5 \leqslant x \leqslant 5, -8 \leqslant y \leqslant 8)$.

    b What is special about the intersection of these two graphs?

    c Show that $5x - 5 = x^2 + 3x - 4$ can be rearranged to $x^2 - 2x + 1 = 0$.

    d Factorise and solve $x^2 - 2x + 1 = 0$.

    e Explain how the solution in part **d** relates to the intersection of the graphs.

AU 3 **a** Solve the simultaneous equations $y = x^2 + 2x + 3$ and $y = x - 1$ $(-5 \leqslant x \leqslant 5, -5 \leqslant y \leqslant 8)$.

    b What is special about the intersection of these two graphs?

    c Rearrange $x - 1 = x^2 + 2x + 3$ into the general quadratic form $ax^2 + bx + c = 0$.

    d Work out the discriminant $b^2 - 4ac$ for the quadratic in part **c**.

    e Explain how the value of the discriminant relates to the intersection of the graphs.

Solving equations by the method of intersection

This section will show you how to:

- solve equations by the method of intersecting graphs

Many equations can be solved by drawing two intersecting graphs on the same axes and using the x-value(s) of their point(s) of intersection. (In the GCSE examination, you are likely to be presented with one drawn graph and asked to draw a straight line to solve a new equation.)

EXAMPLE 18

Show how each equation given below can be solved using the graph of $y = x^3 - 2x - 2$ and its intersection with another graph. In each case, give the equation of the other graph and the solution(s).

a $x^3 - 2x - 4 = 0$ **b** $x^3 - 3x - 1 = 0$

a This method will give the required graph.

Step 1: Write down the original (given) equation.

Step 2: Write down the (new) equation to be solved in reverse.

Step 3: Subtract these equations.

$$\begin{aligned} y &= x^3 - 2x - 2 \\ 0 &= x^3 - 2x - 4 \\ \hline y &= \qquad\qquad + 2 \end{aligned}$$

Step 4: Draw this line on the original graph to solve the new equation.

The graphs of $y = x^3 - 2x - 2$ and $y = 2$ are drawn on the same axes.

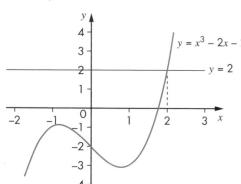

The intersection of these two graphs is the solution of

$$x^3 - 2x - 4 = 0.$$

The solution is $x = 2$.

This works because you are drawing a straight line on the same axes as the original graph, and solving for x and y where they intersect.

At the points of intersection the y-values will be the same and so will the x-values.

So you can say: original equation = straight line

Rearranging this gives: (original equation) − (straight line) = 0

You have been asked to solve: (new equation) = 0

So: (original equation) − (straight line) = (new equation)

Rearranging this again gives: (original equation) − (new equation) = straight line

Note: In GCSE exams the curve is always drawn already and you will only have to draw the straight line.

b Write down given graph: $y = x^3 - 2x - 2$

Write down new equation: $0 = x^3 - 3x - 1$

Subtract: $y = + x - 1$

The graphs of $y = x^3 - 2x - 2$ and $y = x - 1$ are then drawn on the same axes.

The intersection of the two graphs is the solution of $x^3 - 3x - 1 = 0$.

The solutions are $x = -1.5, -0.3$ and 1.9.

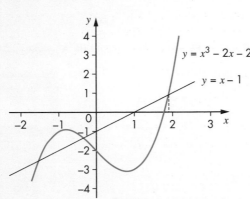

EXAMPLE 19

The graph shows the curve $y = x^2 + 3x - 2$.

By drawing a suitable straight line, solve these equations.

a $x^2 + 3x - 1 = 0$ **b** $x^2 + 2x - 3 = 0$

a Given graph: $y = x^2 + 3x - 2$

New equation: $0 = x^2 + 3x - 1$

Subtract: $y = - 1$

Draw: $y = -1$

Solutions: $x = 0.3, -3.3$

b Given graph: $y = x^2 + 3x - 2$

New equation: $0 = x^2 + 2x - 3$

Subtract: $y = + x + 1$

Draw: $y = x + 1$

Solutions: $x = 1, -3$

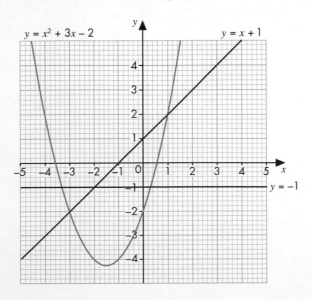

EXERCISE 11J

In questions **1** to **5**, use the graphs given here. Trace the graphs or place a ruler over them in the position of the line. Solution values only need to be given to 1 decimal place. In questions **6** to **10**, either draw the graphs yourself or use a graphics calculator to draw them.

A*

1 Below is the graph of $y = x^2 - 3x - 6$.

 a Solve these equations.

 i $x^2 - 3x - 6 = 0$ **ii** $x^2 - 3x - 6 = 4$ **iii** $x^2 - 3x - 2 = 0$

 b By drawing a suitable straight line solve $2x^2 - 6x + 2 = 0$.

> **HINTS AND TIPS**
>
> Cancel by 2 first.

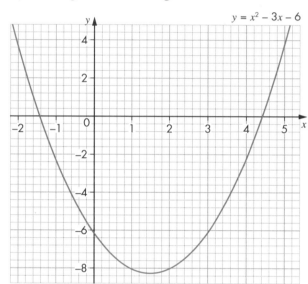

2 Below is the graph of

 $y = x^2 + 4x - 5$.

 a Solve $x^2 + 4x - 5 = 0$.

 b By drawing suitable straight lines solve these equations.

 i $x^2 + 4x - 5 = 2$

 ii $x^2 + 4x - 4 = 0$

 iii $3x^2 + 12x + 6 = 0$

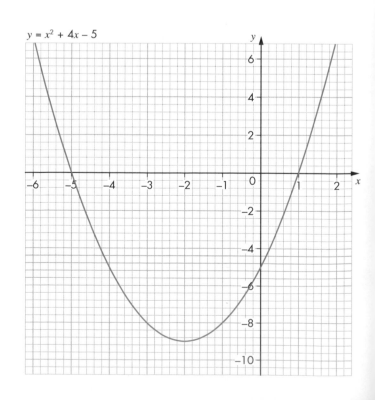

3 Below are the graphs of $y = x^2 - 5x + 3$ and $y = x + 3$.

    a Solve these equations.   **i** $x^2 - 6x = 0$ **ii** $x^2 - 5x + 3 = 0$

    b By drawing suitable straight lines solve these equations.

         i $x^2 - 5x + 3 = 2$ **ii** $x^2 - 5x - 2 = 0$

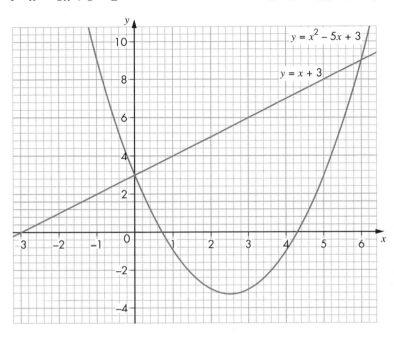

4 Below are the graphs of $y = x^2 - 2$ and $y = x + 2$.

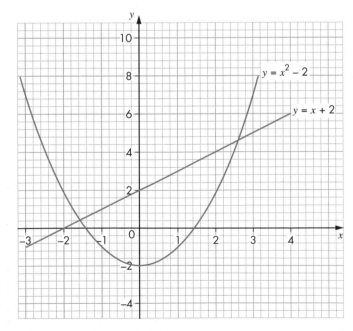

    a Solve these equations.   **i** $x^2 - x - 4 = 0$ **ii** $x^2 - 2 = 0$

    b By drawing suitable straight lines solve these equations.

         i $x^2 - 2 = 3$ **ii** $x^2 - 4 = 0$

A*

PS 5 Below are the graphs of $y = x^3 - 2x^2$, $y = 2x + 1$ and $y = x - 1$.

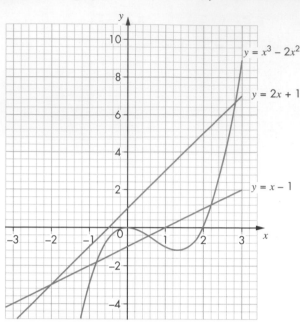

Solve these equations.

a $x^3 - 2x^2 = 0$ **b** $x^3 - 2x^2 = 3$ **c** $x^3 - 2x^2 + 1 = 0$

d $x^3 - 2x^2 - 2x - 1 = 0$ **e** $x^3 - 2x^2 - x + 1 = 0$

6 Draw the graph of $y = x^2 - 4x - 2$.

a Solve $x^2 - 4x - 2 = 0$.

b By drawing a suitable straight line solve $x^2 - 4x - 5 = 0$.

7 Draw the graph of $y = 2x^2 - 5$.

a Solve $2x^2 - 5 = 0$.

b By drawing a suitable straight line solve $2x^2 - 3 = 0$.

8 Draw the graphs of $y = x^2 - 3$ and $y = x + 2$ on the same axes. Use the graphs to solve these equations.

a $x^2 - 5 = 0$ **b** $x^2 - x - 5 = 0$

9 Draw the graphs of $y = x^2 - 3x - 2$ and $y = 2x - 3$ on the same axes. Use the graphs to solve these equations.

a $x^2 - 3x - 1 = 0$ **b** $x^2 - 5x + 1 = 0$

10 Draw the graphs of $y = x^3 - 2x^2 + 3x - 4$ and $y = 3x - 1$ on the same axes. Use the graphs to solve these equations.

a $x^3 - 2x^2 + 3x - 6 = 0$ **b** $x^3 - 2x^2 - 3 = 0$

AU 11 The graph shows the lines A: $y = x^2 + 3x - 2$; B: $y = x$; C: $y = x + 2$; D: $y + x = 3$
and E: $y + x + 1 = 0$.

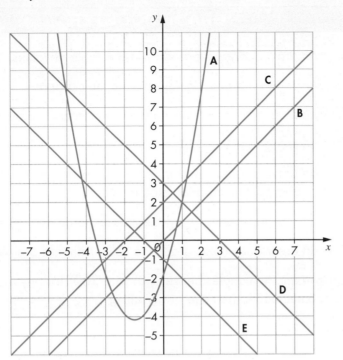

a Which pair of lines has a common solution of (0.5, 2.5)?

b Which pair of lines has the solutions of (1, 2) and (–5, 8)?

c What quadratic equation has an approximate solution of (–4.2, 3.2) and (0.2, –1.2)?

d The minimum point of the graph $y = x^2 + 3x - 2$ is at (–1.5, –4.25).

What is the minimum point of the graph $y = x^2 + 3x - 8$?

PS 12 Jamil was given a sketch of the graph $y = x^2 + 3x + 5$ and asked to draw an appropriate
straight line to solve $x^2 + x - 2 = 0$.

This is Jamil's working:

Original $\quad y = x^2 + 3x + 5$
New $\quad\quad\ 0 = x^2 + \ \ x - 2$
────────────────
$\quad\quad\quad y = \quad\quad 2x - 7$

When Jamil drew the line $y = 2x - 7$, it did not intersect with the parabola $y = x^2 + 3x + 5$.

He concluded that the equation $x^2 + x - 2 = 0$ did not have any solutions.

a Show by factorisation that the equation $x^2 + x - 2 = 0$ has solutions –2 and 1.

b Explain the error that Jamil made.

c What line should Jamil have drawn?

GRADE BOOSTER

C You can draw quadratic graphs, using a table of values

B You can solve quadratic equations from their graphs

B You can plot cubic graphs, using a table of values

B You can recognise the shapes of the graphs $y = x^3$ and $y = \frac{1}{x}$

A You can draw a variety of graphs, such as exponential graphs and reciprocal graphs using a table of values

A* You can solve equations, using the intersection of two graphs

A* You can use trigonometric graphs to solve sine and cosine problems

A* You can find two angles between 0° and 360° for any given value of a trigonometric ratio (positive or negative)

What you should know now

● How to draw non-linear graphs

● How to solve equations by finding the intersection points of the graphs of the equations with the x-axis or other related equations

1 a Copy and complete the table of values for
$y = x^2 - x - 5$. *(2 marks)*

x	-2	-1	0	1	2	3	4
y	1		-5	-5	-3	1	

b Draw, using x-axis range –2 to 4 and y-axis
–7 to 8, the graph of $y = x^2 - x - 5$ for
values of x from –2 to 4. *(2 marks)*

c An approximate solution of the equation
$x^2 - x - 5 = 0$ is $x = 2.8$.

Explain how you can find this from the
graph. *(1 mark)*

AQA, May 2008, Paper 1 Higher, Question 10

2 Match each of the sketch graphs to one of
these equations.

A $y = 2 - 2x$ **B** $y = 2x + 2$ **C** $y = 3 - x^2$

D $y = x^3 + 4$ **E** $y = \frac{2}{x}$

1
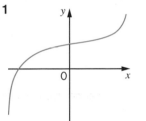

2
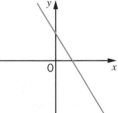

3
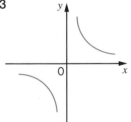

4
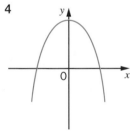

Graph 1 represents equation ......?   *(1 mark)*

Graph 2 represents equation ......?   *(1 mark)*

Graph 3 represents equation ......?   *(1 mark)*

Graph 4 represents equation ......?   *(1 mark)*

AQA, November 2005, Paper 1 Higher, Question 11

3 The sketch shows the graph of $y = \sin x$ for
$0° \leqslant x \leqslant 360°$.

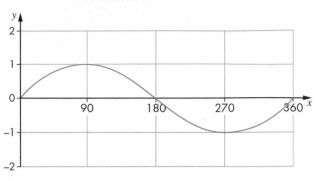

You are given that $\sin 70° = 0.9397$.

a Write down another solution of the equation
$\sin x = 0.9397$. *(1 mark)*

b Solve the equation
$\sin x = -0.9397$ for $0° \leqslant x \leqslant 360°$.
(2 marks)

c On a copy of the axes below, sketch the
graph of $y = \sin 2x$ for $0° \leqslant x \leqslant 360°$.

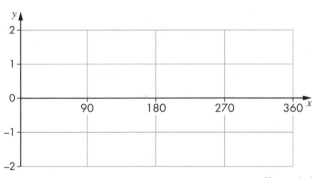

(2 marks)

d Hence write down the four solutions of the
equation $\sin 2x = 0.9397$. *(3 marks)*

AQA, June 2005, Paper 1 Higher, Question 18

A*   A   C

4 A straight line has the equation $y = 2x - 3$.
A curve has the equation $y^2 = 8x - 16$.

a Solve these simultaneous equations to find any points of intersection of the line and the curve.
You **must** show your working. *(5 marks)*

b Here are three sketches showing the curve $y^2 = 8x - 16$ and three possible positions of the line $y = 2x - 3$.

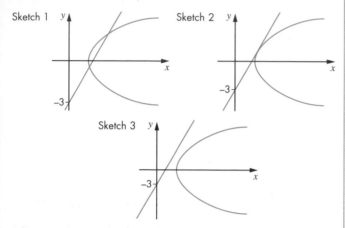

Which is the correct sketch?
You **must** explain your answer. *(2 marks)*

AQA, June 2005, Paper 1 Higher, Question 19

5 The grid below shows the graph of
$y = x^2 + 3x - 2$.

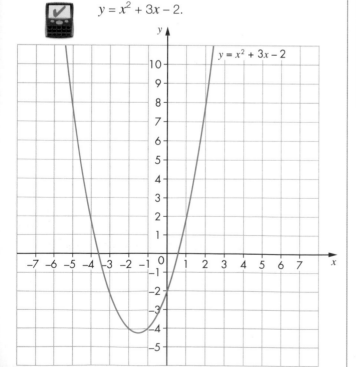

a By drawing an appropriate straight line on a copy of the graph, solve the equation:
$x^2 + 3x - 3 = 0$ *(2 marks)*

b By drawing an appropriate straight line on your copy of the graph, solve the equation:
$x^2 + 2x - 1 = 0$ *(3 marks)*

AQA, June 2005, Paper 2 Higher, Question 22

6 **a** Solve the simultaneous equations:
$$y = 2x - 5$$
$$x^2 + y^2 = 25$$

You **must** show your working. *(6 marks)*

b The graph of $y = 2x - 5$ is shown below.

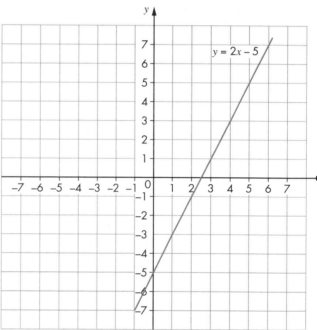

i On a copy of this graph, draw on the same axes the graph of $x^2 + y^2 = 25$. *(2 marks)*

ii Explain the connection between the two graphs and the answers you obtained in part **a**. *(1 mark)*

AQA, November 2005, Paper 1 Higher, Question 23

7 This is the graph of $y = \cos x$ for $0° \leqslant x \leqslant 360°$.

   a On a copy of the axes used for the graph above, draw the graph of $y = \cos(x - 90°)$ for $0° \leqslant x \leqslant 360°$. *(2 marks)*

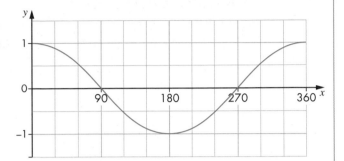

   b Write down a possible equation of the following graph. *(1 mark)*

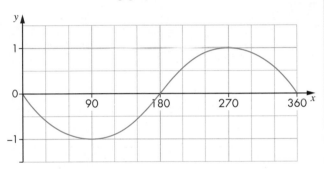

   AQA, November 2005, Paper 1 Higher, Question 22

8 The grid shows the graph of $y = x^2 + 2x - 5$.

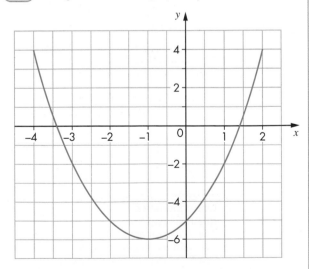

By drawing an appropriate straight line on a copy of this graph, solve the equation

$$x^2 + 2x - 5 = x - 1.$$ *(3 marks)*

   AQA, June 2006, Paper 1 Higher, Question 13

9 The diagram shows a quadratic graph and a straight line graph.

The two graphs intersect at the origin and at the point marked R.

The quadratic graph has equation $y = ax^2 + bx$, where a and b are integers.

Points P (–1, 10) and Q (4, 0) lie on this graph.

The straight line is $y = x$.

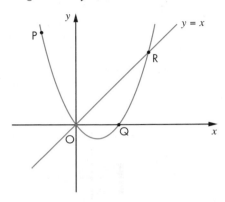

Find the coordinates of the point marked R.

You **must** show your working. *(6 marks)*

   AQA, June 2009, Paper 1 Higher, Question 22

10 The sketch shows the graph of $y = \cos x$ for $0° \leqslant x \leqslant 360°$.

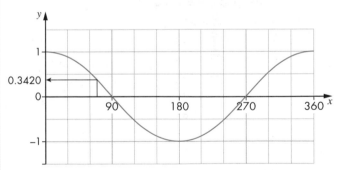

You are given that $\cos 70° = 0.3420$.

   a State another value of x, where $0° \leqslant x \leqslant 360°$, for which $\cos x = 0.3420$. *(1 mark)*

   b State a value of x, where $0° \leqslant x \leqslant 360°$, for which $\cos x = -0.3420$. *(1 mark)*

   AQA, June 2009, Paper 1 Higher, Question 24

Worked Examination Questions

1 a Complete the table of values for $y = (0.6)^x$.

b Copy the grid below and draw the graph of $y = 0.6^x$ for $0 \leqslant x \leqslant 4$.

c Use your graph to solve the equation $(0.6)^x = 0.2$.

x	0	1	2	3	4
y	1	0.6		0.22	

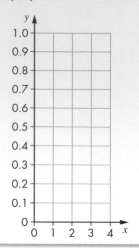

1 a *0.3, 0.13* ——————————— Use your power button to work these out. This scores 1 mark.

b

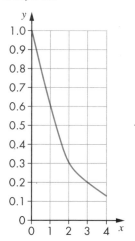

Plot the graph, use table of values above and also (2, 0–3) and (4, 0.13). This scores 1 mark.

c *3.1* ——————————— Draw a line from 0.2 on the y-axis across to the graph and down to the x-axis. This scores 1 mark.

Total: 3 marks

---

2 a Explain why the lines $y = 2x$ and $y = 2x + 1$ intersect at the point $(0, 1)$.

b Use trial and improvement to find another intersection point between $x = 2$ and $x = 3$ to 1 decimal place.

2 a *When $x = 0$, $2^0 = 1$ and $2 \times 0 + 1 = 1$* ——————

One important property of all exponential graphs is that they pass through $(0, 1)$. This question assesses that you know this, and the intersect of the linear graph is also 1. This scores 1 mark.

b *When $x = 2.6$, $2^{2.6} = 6.06$, $2 \times 2.6 + 1 = 6.2$*
When $x = 2.7$, $2^{2.7} = 6.49$, $2 \times 2.7 + 1 = 6.4$
When $x = 2.8$, $2^{2.8} = 6.96$, $2 \times 2.8 + 1 = 6.6$
  $x = 2.4$

Try 1 decimal place values between 2 and 3 until one gives values for both functions that are close to each other. This scores 1 mark for method and 1 mark for accuracy.

Total: 3 marks

Worked Examination Questions

3 The grid below shows the graph of $y = x^2 - x - 6$.

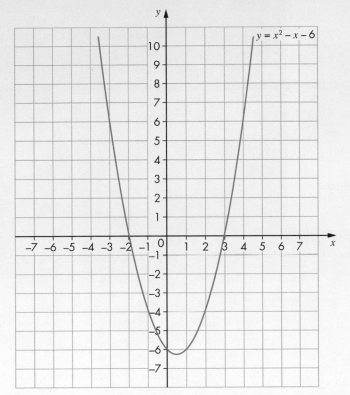

$y = x^2 - x - 6$

a Deduce the coordinates of the minimum point of the graph $y = x^2 - x - 12$.

b Use the graph to find the approximate solutions to the simultaneous equations
   $y = x^2 - x - 6$ and $y = x + 3$.

3 a (0.5, –12.25) ————————————

> The minimum point of the given graph is (0.5, –6.25) and the required graph is 6 lower than the given graph, as the constant terms have a difference of 6.

b (3.2, 6.2) and (–1.2, 2.2) ————

> Draw the line $y = x + 3$ and read off the points of intersection. This scores 1 mark each.

(**Total:** 3 marks)

The forms of many suspension bridges are based on quadratic functions. Their shape is a classic quadratic curve.

Quadratic curve

In this task you will investigate the quadratic functions that can be used to describe stable suspension bridges.

Getting started

Use these questions to familiarise yourself with how quadratic expressions can be used to represent bridges.

- What would you need to know, to be able to describe the shape of a bridge, in terms of a quadratic formula?
- Think about bridges and other landmarks in your local area. How many of these are based on quadratic equations and form parabolas. Use images to illustrate your findings.

Your task

Below you can see the dimensions of the Clifton Suspension Bridge. Use these dimensions to construct a diagram of the bridge.

Then, using your diagram, estimate the quadratic equation for the curve of the bridge. Represent this equation appropriately.

Write a report explaining the mathematical process that you used to solve this problem. State any assumptions that you made and explain whether you could have found different answers if you had changed your assumptions.

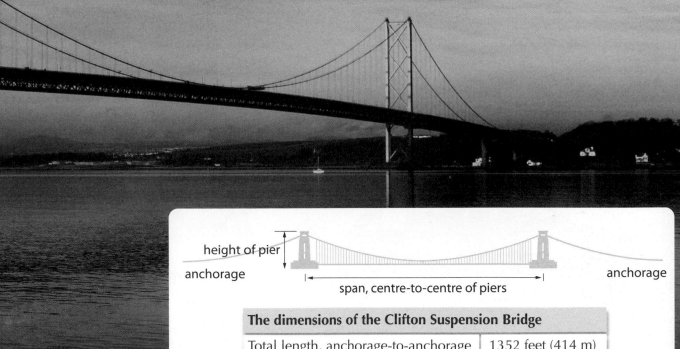

The dimensions of the Clifton Suspension Bridge	
Total length, anchorage-to-anchorage	1352 feet (414 m)
Total span, centre-to-centre of piers	702 feet (214 m)
Overall width	31 feet (9.5 m)
Width, centre-to-centre of chains	20 feet (6.1 m)
Height (deck level above high water)	245 feet (76 m)
Height of piers, including capping	86 feet (26.2 m)
Dip of chains	70 feet (21.3 m)

Why this chapter matters

In many real-life situations, variables are connected by a rule or relationship. It may be that as one variable increases the other increases. Alternatively, it may be that as one variable increases the other decreases.

This chapter looks at how quantities vary when they are related in some way.

As this plant gets older it becomes taller.

As the storm increases the number of sunbathers decreases.

As this car gets older it is worth less (and eventually it is worthless!).

As more songs are downloaded, there is less money left on the voucher.

Try to think of other variables that are connected in this way.

Number: Variation

 Direct variation

 Inverse variation

This chapter will show you ...

A how to solve problems where two variables are connected by a relationship that varies in direct or inverse proportion

Visual overview

Direct proportion ⟶ Inverse proportion

What you should already know

- Squares, square roots, cubes and cube roots of integers **(KS3 level 4–5, GCSE grade G–E)**
- How to substitute values into algebraic expressions **(KS3 level 5, GCSE grade E)**
- How to solve simple algebraic equations **(KS3 level 6, GCSE grade D)**

Quick check

1 Write down the value of each of the following.

a 5^2

b $\sqrt{81}$

c 3^3

d $\sqrt[3]{64}$

2 Calculate the value of y if $x = 4$.

a $y = 3x^2$

b $y = \dfrac{1}{\sqrt{x}}$

This section will show you how to:
- solve problems where two variables have a directly proportional relationship (direct variation)
- work out the constant of proportionality

Key words

constant of proportionality, k
direct proportion
direct variation

The term **direct variation** means the same as as **direct proportion**.

There is direct variation (or direct proportion) between two variables when one variable is a simple multiple of the other. That is, their ratio is a constant.

For example:

1 kilogram = 2.2 pounds   There is a multiplying factor of 2.2 between kilograms and pounds.

Area of a circle = πr^2 There is a multiplying factor of π between the area of a circle and the square of its radius.

An examination question involving direct variation usually requires you first to find this multiplying factor (called the **constant of proportionality**), then to use it to solve a problem.

The symbol for variation or proportion is $\propto$.

So the statement 'Pay is directly proportional to time' can be mathematically written as:

pay $\propto$ *time*

which implies that:

pay $= k \times$ *time*

where k is the constant of proportionality.

There are four steps to be followed when you are using proportionality to solve problems.

Step 1: Set up the statement, using the proportionality symbol (you may use symbols to represent the variables).

Step 2: Set up the equation, using a constant of proportionality.

Step 3: Use given information to work out the value of the constant of proportionality.

Step 4: Substitute the value of the constant of proportionality into the equation and use this equation to find unknown values.

EXAMPLE 1

The cost of an article is directly proportional to the time spent making it. An article taking 6 hours to make costs £30. Find:

a the cost of an article that takes 5 hours to make

b the length of time it takes to make an article costing £40.

Step 1: Let C be the cost of making an article and t the time it takes.

$C \propto t$

Step 2: Setting up the equation gives:

$C = kt$

where k is the constant of proportionality.

Note that you can 'replace' the proportionality sign $\propto$ with $= k$ to obtain the proportionality equation.

Step 3: Since $C = £30$ when $t = 6$ hours, then $30 = 6k$

$\Rightarrow \dfrac{30}{60} = k$

$\Rightarrow k = 5$

Step 4: So the formula is $C = 5t$.

a When $t = 5$ hours $C = 5 \times 5 = 25$

So the cost is £25.

b When $C = £40$ $40 = 5 \times t$

$\Rightarrow \dfrac{40}{5} = t \Rightarrow t = 8$

So the time spent making the article is 8 hours.

EXERCISE 12A

For questions **1** to **4**, first find k, the constant of proportionality, and then the formula connecting the variables.

1 T is directly proportional to M. If $T = 20$ when $M = 4$, find:

    a T when $M = 3$ **b** M when $T = 10$.

2 W is directly proportional to F. If $W = 45$ when $F = 3$, find:

    a W when $F = 5$ **b** F when $W = 90$.

3 Q varies directly with P. If $Q = 100$ when $P = 2$, find:

    a Q when $P = 3$ **b** P when $Q = 300$.

A

4 X varies directly with Y. If $X = 17.5$ when $Y = 7$, find:

   a X when $Y = 9$

   b Y when $X = 30$.

5 The distance covered by a train is directly proportional to the time taken for the journey. The train travels 105 miles in 3 hours.

   a What distance will the train cover in 5 hours?

   b How much time will it take for the train to cover 280 miles?

6 The cost of fuel delivered to your door is directly proportional to the weight received. When 250 kg is delivered, it costs £47.50.

   a How much will it cost to have 350 kg delivered?

   b How much would be delivered if the cost were £33.25?

FM 7 The number of children who can play safely in a playground is directly proportional to the area of the playground. A playground with an area of 210 m^2 is safe for 60 children.

   a How many children can safely play in a playground of area 154 m^2?

   b A playgroup has 24 children. What is the smallest playground area in which they could safely play?

8 The number of spaces in a car park is directly proportional to the area of the car park.

FM

   a A car park has 300 parking spaces in an area of 4500 m².

      It is decided to increase the area of the car park by 500 m² to make extra spaces.

      How many extra spaces will be made?

PS

   b The old part of the car park is redesigned so that the original area has 10% more parking spaces.

      How many more spaces than originally will there be altogether if the number of spaces in the new area is directly proportional to the number in the redesigned car park?

AU 9 The number of passengers in a bus queue is directly proportional to the time that the person at the front of the queue has spent waiting.

Karen is the first to arrive at a bus stop. When she has been waiting 5 minutes the queue has 20 passengers.

A bus has room for 70 passengers.

How long had Karen been in the queue if the bus fills up from empty when it arrives and all passengers get on?

Direct proportions involving squares, cubes, square roots and cube roots

The process is the same as for a linear direct variation, as the next example shows.

EXAMPLE 2

The cost of a circular badge is directly proportional to the square of its radius. The cost of a badge with a radius of 2 cm is 68p. Find:

a the cost of a badge of radius 2.4 cm   **b** the radius of a badge costing £1.53.

Step 1: Let C be the cost and r the radius of a badge.
$$C \propto r^2$$

Step 2: Setting up the equation gives:
$$C = kr^2$$
where k is the constant of proportionality.

Step 3: $C = 68$p when $r = 2$ cm. So:
$$68 = 4k$$
$$\Rightarrow \frac{68}{4} = k \Rightarrow k = 17$$

Step 4: So the formula is $C = 17r^2$.

a When $r = 2.4$ cm $C = 17 \times 2.4^2 p = 97.92$p
Rounding gives the cost as 98p.

b When $C = 153$p $153 = 17r^2$
$$\Rightarrow \frac{153}{7} = 9 = r^2$$
$$\Rightarrow r = \sqrt{9} = 3$$

Hence, the radius is 3 cm.

EXERCISE 12B

For questions **1** to **6**, first find k, the constant of proportionality, and then the formula connecting the variables.

1 T is directly proportional to x^2. If $T = 36$ when $x = 3$, find:

   a T when $x = 5$ **b** x when $T = 400$.

2 W is directly proportional to M^2. If $W = 12$ when $M = 2$, find:

   a W when $M = 3$ **b** M when $W = 75$.

A

3 E varies directly with $\sqrt{C}$. If $E = 40$ when $C = 25$, find:

   a E when $C = 49$ **b** C when $E = 10.4$.

4 X is directly proportional to $\sqrt{Y}$. If $X = 128$ when $Y = 16$, find:

   a X when $Y = 36$ **b** Y when $X = 48$.

5 P is directly proportional to f^3. If $P = 400$ when $f = 10$, find:

   a P when $f = 4$ **b** f when $P = 50$.

6 y is directly proportional to $\sqrt[3]{x}$. If $y = 100$ when $x = 125$, find:

   a y when $x = 64$ **b** x when $y = 40$.

7 The cost of serving tea and biscuits varies directly with the square root of the number of people at the buffet. It costs £25 to serve tea and biscuits to 100 people.

   a How much will it cost to serve tea and biscuits to 400 people?

   b For a cost of £37.50, how many could be served tea and biscuits?

8 In an experiment, the temperature, in °C, varied directly with the square of the pressure, in atmospheres (atm). The temperature was 20 °C when the pressure was 5 atm.

   a What will the temperature be at 2 atm?

   b What will the pressure be at 80 °C?

9 The mass, in grams, of ball bearings varies directly with the cube of the radius, measured in millimetres. A ball bearing of radius 4 mm has a mass of 115.2 g.

   a What will be the mass of a ball bearing of radius 6 mm?

   b A ball bearing has a mass of 48.6 g. What is its radius?

10 The energy, in J, of a particle varies directly with the square of its speed, in m/s. A particle moving at 20 m/s has 50 J of energy.

   a How much energy has a particle moving at 4 m/s?

   b At what speed is a particle moving if it has 200 J of energy?

11 The cost, in £, of a trip varies directly with the square root of the number of miles travelled. The cost of a 100-mile trip is £35.

   a What is the cost of a 500-mile trip (to the nearest £1)?

   b What is the distance of a trip costing £70?

FM 12 A sculptor is making statues.

The amount of clay used is directly proportional to the cube of the height of the statue.

A statue is 10 cm tall and uses 500 cm³ of clay.

How much clay will a similar statue use if it is twice as tall?

FM 13 The cost of making different-sized machines is proportional to the time taken.

A small machine costs £100 and takes two hours to make.

How much will a large machine cost that takes 5 hours to build?

PS 14 The sketch graphs show each of these proportion statements.

a $y \propto x^2$ **b** $y \propto x$ **c** $y \propto \sqrt{x}$

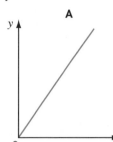 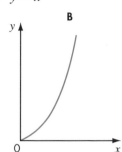 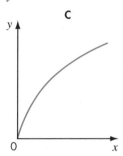

Match each statement to the correct sketch.

AU 15 Here are two tables.

Match each table to a graph in question **14**.

a

x	1	2	3
y	3	12	27

b

x	1	2	3
y	3	6	9

12.2 Inverse variation

This section will show you how to:
- solve problems where two variables have an inversely proportional relationship (inverse variation)
- work out the constant of proportionality

Key words
constant of proportionality, k
inverse proportion
inverse variation

The term **inverse variation** means the same as **inverse proportion**.

There is inverse variation between two variables when one variable is directly proportional to the *reciprocal* of the other. That is, the product of the two variables is constant. So, as one variable increases, the other decreases.

For example, the faster you travel over a given distance, the less time it takes. So there is an inverse variation between speed and time. Speed is inversely proportional to time.

$$S \propto \frac{1}{T} \text{ and so } S = \frac{k}{T}$$

which can be written as $ST = k$.

EXAMPLE 3

M is inversely proportional to R. If $M = 9$ when $R = 4$, find the value of:

a M when $R = 2$ **b** R when $M = 3$.

Step 1: $M \propto \dfrac{1}{R}$

Step 2: Setting up the equation gives:

$M = \dfrac{k}{R}$

where k is the **constant of proportionality**.

Step 3: $M = 9$ when $R = 4$. So $9 = \dfrac{k}{4}$

$\Rightarrow 9 \times 4 = k \Rightarrow k = 36$

Step 4: The formula is $M = \dfrac{36}{R}$

a When $R = 2$, then $M = \dfrac{36}{2} = 18$

b When $M = 3$, then $3 = \dfrac{36}{R} \Rightarrow 3R = 36 \Rightarrow R = 12$

EXERCISE 12C

For questions **1** to **6**, first find the formula connecting the variables.

A

1 T is inversely proportional to m. If $T = 6$ when $m = 2$, find:

   a T when $m = 4$ **b** m when $T = 4.8$.

2 W is inversely proportional to x. If $W = 5$ when $x = 12$, find:

   a W when $x = 3$ **b** x when $W = 10$.

3 Q varies inversely with $(5 - t)$. If $Q = 8$ when $t = 3$, find:

   a Q when $t = 10$ **b** t when $Q = 16$.

4 M varies inversely with t^2. If $M = 9$ when $t = 2$, find:

   a M when $t = 3$ **b** t when $M = 1.44$.

5 W is inversely proportional to $\sqrt{T}$. If $W = 6$ when $T = 16$, find:

   a W when $T = 25$ **b** T when $W = 2.4$.

6 y is inversely proportional to the cube of x. If $y = 4$ when $x = 2$, find:

   a y when $x = 1$ **b** x when $y = \frac{1}{2}$.

A

7 The grant available to a section of society was inversely proportional to the number of people needing the grant. When 30 people needed a grant, they received £60 each.

a What would the grant have been if 120 people had needed one?

b If the grant had been £50 each, how many people would have received it?

8 While doing underwater tests in one part of an ocean, a team of scientists noticed that the temperature, in °C, was inversely proportional to the depth, in kilometres. When the temperature was 6 °C, the scientists were at a depth of 4 km.

a What would the temperature have been at a depth of 8 km?

b To what depth would they have had to go to find the temperature at 2 °C?

9 A new engine was being tested, but it had serious problems. The distance it went, in kilometres, without breaking down was inversely proportional to the square of its speed in metres per second (m/s). When the speed was 12 m/s, the engine lasted 3 km.

a Find the distance covered before a breakdown, when the speed is 15 m/s.

b On one test, the engine broke down after 6.75 km. What was the speed?

10 In a balloon it was noticed that the pressure, in atmospheres (atm), was inversely proportional to the square root of the height, in metres. When the balloon was at a height of 25 m, the pressure was 1.44 atm.

a What was the pressure at a height of 9 m?

b What would the height have been if the pressure was 0.72 atm?

FM 11 The amount of waste which a firm produces, measured in tonnes per hour, is inversely proportional to the square root of the area of the filter beds, in square metres (m^2). The firm produces 1.25 tonnes of waste per hour, with filter beds of size 0.16 m^2.

a The filter beds used to be only 0.01 m^2. How much waste did the firm produce then?

b How much waste could be produced if the filter beds were 0.75 m^2?

PS 12 Which statement is represented by the graph?
Give a reason for your answer.

    A $y \propto x$ B $y \propto \dfrac{1}{x}$ C $y \sqrt{x}$

AU 13 In the table, y is inversely proportional to the cube root of x.

Complete the table, leaving your answers as fractions.

x	8	27	
y	1		$\frac{1}{2}$

FM 14 The fuel consumption, in miles per gallon (mpg) of a car is inversely proportional to its speed, in miles per hour (mph). When the car is travelling at 30 mph the fuel consumption is 60 mpg.

How much further would the car travel on 1 gallon of fuel by travelling at 60 mph instead of 70 mph on a motorway?

GRADE BOOSTER

A You can find formulae describing direct or inverse variation and use them to solve problems

---

What you should know now

- How to recognise direct and inverse variation
- What a constant of proportionality is, and how to find it
- How to find formulae describing inverse or direct variation
- How to solve problems involving direct or inverse variation

1 y is proportional to $\sqrt{x}$. Complete the table.

x	25		400
y	10	20	

2 The energy, E, of an object moving horizontally is directly proportional to the speed, v, of the object. When the speed is 10 m/s the energy is 40 000 joules.

  a Find an equation connecting E and v.

  b Find the speed of the object when the energy is 14 400 joules.

3 y is inversely proportional to the cube root of x. When $y = 8$, $x = \frac{1}{8}$.

  a Find an expression for y in terms of x.

  b Calculate:

   i the value of y when $x = \frac{1}{125}$,

   ii the value of x when $y = 2$.

4 The mass of a cube is directly proportional to the cube of its side. A cube with a side of 4 cm has a mass of 320 grams. Calculate the side length of a cube made of the same material with a mass of 36 450 grams

5 y is directly proportional to the cube of x.

  When $y = 16$, $x = 3$. Find the value of y when $x = 6$.

6 y is directly proportional to the square of x.

   a When $x = 10$, $y = 200$.

  Work out an equation connecting y and x.
  (3 marks)

  b Sketch a graph of y against x on a pair of axes. *(1 mark)*

  AQA, March 2008, Module 3, Question 9

7 Match each statement to a table.

  Statement 1 y is inversely proportional to x^2.
  Statement 2 y is proportional to x.
  Statement 3 y is proportional to x^2.

Table A

x	1	2	3	4
y	1	4	9	16

Table B

x	1	2	3	4
y	2	$\frac{1}{2}$	$\frac{2}{9}$	$\frac{1}{8}$

Table C

x	1	2	3	4
y	3	6	9	12

(2 marks)

AQA, November 2007, Module 3, Question 16

8 Two variables, x and y, are known to be proportional to each other. When $x = 10$, $y = 25$.

  Find the constant of proportionality, k, if:

  a $y \propto x$ **b** $y \propto x^2$ **c** $y \propto \frac{1}{x}$ **d** $\sqrt{y} \propto \frac{1}{x}$

9 y is directly proportional to the cube root of x. When $x = 27$, $y = 6$.

  a Find the value of y when $x = 125$.

  b Find the value of x when $y = 3$.

10 The surface area, A, of a solid is directly proportional to the square of the depth, d. When $d = 6$, $A = 12\pi$.

  a Find the value of A when $d = 12$. Give your answer in terms of π.

  b Find the value of d when $A = 27\pi$.

11 The frequency, f, of sound is inversely proportional to the wavelength, w. A sound with a frequency of 36 hertz has a wavelength of 20.25 metres.

  Calculate the frequency when the frequency and the wavelength have the same numerical value.

12 The volume, V cubic metres, of a hot-air balloon is proportional to the cube of its height, h metres.

   A balloon with a height of 10 metres has a volume of 500 cubic metres.

  a Find an equation connecting V and h.
  (3 marks)

  b Find the volume of a hot-air balloon which has a height of 30 metres. *(1 mark)*

  c Another hot-air balloon has a volume of 5000 cubic metres.
  Find its height. *(3 marks)*

  AQA, March 2005, Module 3, Question 7

13 P and Q are positive quantities. P is inversely proportional to Q^2. When $P = 160$, $Q = 20$. Find the value of P when $P = Q$.

A*   A

Worked Examination Questions

1 y is inversely proportional to the square of x. When y is 40, $x = 5$.

   a Find an equation connecting x and y.

   b Find the value of y when $x = 10$.

1 **a** $y \propto \dfrac{1}{x^2}$

First set up the proportionality relationship and replace the proportionality sign with $= k$.

This gets 1 method mark for stating first or second line or both.

$y = \dfrac{k}{x^2}$

$40 = \dfrac{k}{25}$

Substitute the given values of y and x into the proportionality equation to find the value of k.

This gets 1 accuracy mark for finding k.

$\Rightarrow k = 40 \times 25 = 1000$

$y = \dfrac{1000}{x^2}$

Substitute the value of k to get the final equation connecting y and x.

This gets 1 mark for accuracy.

or $yx^2 = 1000$

b When $x = 10$, $y = \dfrac{1000}{10^2} = \dfrac{1000}{100} = 10$

Substitute the value of x into the equation to find y.

This gets 1 method mark for substitution of $x = 10$ and 1 accuracy mark for correct answer.

Total: 5 marks

Worked Examination Questions

PS **2** The mass of a solid, M, is directly proportional to the cube of its height, h.
When $h = 10$, $M = 4000$.

The surface area, A, of the solid is directly proportional to the square of the
height, h. When $h = 10$, $A = 50$.

Find A, when $M = 32\,000$.

2 $M \propto h^3$

> First set up the proportionality statement.
> This gets 1 method mark for writing either the proportionality
> statement or the proportionality equation.

$M = kh^3$

$4000 = k \times 1000 \Rightarrow k = 4$

> First, find the relationship between M and h using the given
> information.
> This gets 1 accuracy mark for obtaining the correct value of k.

So, $M = 4h^3$

> This gets 1 accuracy mark for writing out the equation with the
> value of k substituted.

$A = ph^2$

> Be careful when using the second equation to use a different
> letter for the constant of proportionality to avoid confusion.
> As setting up the second equation is the same technique as in
> the first part of the question the marks for method are only
> awarded in one part.

$50 = p \times 100 \Rightarrow p = \dfrac{1}{2}$

So, $A = \dfrac{1}{2}h^2$

> Next, find the relationship between A and h using the given
> information, $h = 10$ and $A = 50$

$32\,000 = 4h^3$

> This gets 1 mark for accuracy.

$h^3 = 8000 \Rightarrow h = 20$

> Find the value of h when $M = 32\,000$.

$A = \dfrac{1}{2}(20)^2 = \dfrac{400}{2} = 200$

> Now find the value of A for that value of h. This gets 1 mark
> for accuracy.

Total: 5 marks

The Council of the European Union is the main decision-making body for Europe. One minister from each of the EU's national governments attends Council meetings and decisions are taken by voting. The bigger the country's population, the more votes it has, but numbers are currently weighted in favour of the less populous countries.

Getting started

In June 2007, Poland argued for a change to the rules for the voting in the Council of the European Union. The Polish suggested that each country's voting strength should be directly proportional to the square root of its population. This idea is known as **Pensore's rule**.

Let V be the voting strength (that is the number of votes a country gets) and P be the country's population.

- Write down a mathematical statement for Pensore's rule, using the symbol of variation, $\propto$.

- Write a proportionality equation for Pensore's rule, using a constant of proportionality, k.

Country	Population	Current number of votes in the Council of the European Union
UK	61 600 835	29
Poland	38 125 478	27
Romania	21 398 181	14
The Netherlands	16 518 199	13
Belgium	10 574 595	12
Sweden	9 290 113	10
Ireland	4 434 925	7
Luxembourg	472 569	4
Malta	408 009	3

Your task

1 Suppose that Pensore's rule was introduced and Poland gained an additional vote, making its voting strength 28. Your task is to determine how Pensore's rule would affect other countries' votes.

2 Now, suppose another member, such as the UK, proposed that each member's voting strength should be directly proportional to its country's population, making its voting strength 40. Your task is to determine how this suggested voting system would affect other countries' votes.

3 Imagine you are an advisor to the President of the European Union. How would you advise on Council voting? Write a letter setting out what you think of Poland's and the UK's suggestions, explaining the advantages and disadvantages. As an independent advisor, can you propose an alternative voting system that may be fairer to all countries?

Why this chapter matters

Vectors are used to represent any quantity that has both magnitude and direction. The velocity of a speeding car may be described in terms of its direction and its speed. The speed is the magnitude, but when it has direction it becomes the velocity – a vector.

To understand how a force acts on an object, you need to know the magnitude of the force and the direction in which it moves – the two bits of information that define a vector.

And when you watch the weather report, you are told which way the wind will blow tomorrow, and how strongly – again, a direction and a magnitude together making up a vector.

Vectors are used to describe many quantities in science, such as displacement, acceleration and momentum.

But are vectors used in real life? Yes! Here are some examples.

In the 1950s, a group of talented Brazilian footballers invented the **swerving free kick**. By kicking the ball in just the right place, they managed to make it curl around the wall of defending players and, quite often, go straight into the back of the net. When a ball is in flight, it is acted upon by various forces. Some of these depend on the way the ball is spinning. The forces at work here can be described by vectors.

Formula 1 teams always employ physicists and mathematicians to help them build the perfect racing car. **Aerodynamics** is the study of how the air moves. Since vectors describe movements and forces, they are used as the basis of a car's design.

Pilots have to consider wind speed and direction when they plan to land an aircraft at an airport. Vectors are an integral part of the computerised landing system.

The science of aerodynamics is used in the design of aircraft; vectors play a key role in the design of wings, where an upward force or lift is needed to enable the aircraft to fly.

Meteorologists or weather forecasters use vectors to map out weather patterns. Wind speeds can be represented by vectors of different lengths to indicate the intensity of the wind.

Vectors are used extensively in computer graphics. Software designed to give the viewer the impression that an object or person is moving around a scene makes extensive use of the mathematics of vectors.

13 Geometry: Vectors

1 Properties of vectors

2 Vectors in geometry

3 Geometric proof

This chapter will show you ...

A how to add and subtract vectors

to A / A* the properties of vectors

A* how to use vectors to solve geometrical problems

A* how to prove geometric results using rigorous and logical mathematical arguments

Visual overview

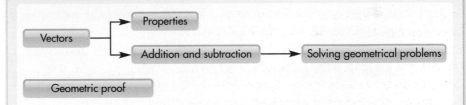

What you should already know

● Vectors are used to describe translations (KS3 level 7, GCSE grade C)

Quick check

Use column vectors to describe these translations.

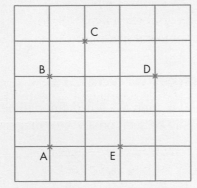

a A to C
b B to D
c C to D
d D to E

This section will show you how to:
● add and subtract vectors

Key words
direction
magnitude
vector

A vector is a quantity which has both **magnitude** and **direction**. It can be represented by a straight line which is drawn in the direction of the vector and whose length represents the magnitude of the vector. Usually, the line includes an arrowhead.

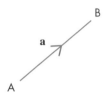

The translation or movement from A to B is represented by the vector **a**.

a is always printed in bold type, but is written as <u>a</u>.

a can also be written as $\overrightarrow{AB}$.

A quantity which is completely described by its magnitude, and has no direction associated with it, is called a scalar. The mass of a bus (10 tonnes) is an example of a scalar. Another example is a linear measure, such as 25.4 mm.

Multiplying a vector by a number (scalar) alters its magnitude (length) but not its direction. For example, the vector 2**a** is twice as long as the vector **a**, but in the same direction.

A negative vector, for example –**b**, has the same magnitude as the vector **b**, but is in the opposite direction.

Addition and subtraction of vectors

Take two non-parallel vectors **a** and **b**, then **a** + **b** is defined to be the translation of **a** followed by the translation of **b**. This can easily be seen on a vector diagram.

FM Functional Maths **AU** (AO2) Assessing Understanding **PS** (AO3) Problem Solving

Similarly, **a** – **b** is defined to be the translation of **a** followed by the translation of –**b**.

Look at the parallelogram grid below. **a** and **b** are two independent vectors that form the basis of this grid. It is possible to define the position, with reference to O, of any point on this grid by a vector expressed in terms of **a** and **b**. Such a vector is called a position vector.

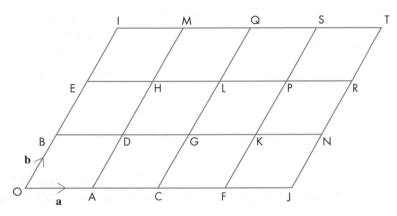

For example, the position vector of K is $\overrightarrow{OK}$ or **k** = 3**a** + **b**, the position vector of E is $\overrightarrow{OE}$ or **e** = 2**b**. The vector $\overrightarrow{HT}$ = 3**a** + **b**, the vector $\overrightarrow{PN}$ = **a** – **b**, the vector $\overrightarrow{MK}$ = 2**a** – 2**b**, and the vector $\overrightarrow{TP}$ = –**a** – **b**.

Note $\overrightarrow{OK}$ and $\overrightarrow{HT}$ are called equal vectors because they have exactly the same length and are in the same direction. $\overrightarrow{MK}$ and $\overrightarrow{PN}$ are parallel vectors but $\overrightarrow{MK}$ is twice the magnitude of $\overrightarrow{PN}$.

EXAMPLE 1

a Using the grid above, write down the following vectors in terms of **a** and **b**.

   i $\overrightarrow{BH}$ **ii** $\overrightarrow{HP}$ **iii** $\overrightarrow{GT}$

   iv $\overrightarrow{TI}$ **v** $\overrightarrow{FH}$ **vi** $\overrightarrow{BQ}$

b What is the relationship between the following vectors?

   i $\overrightarrow{BH}$ and $\overrightarrow{GT}$ **ii** $\overrightarrow{BQ}$ and $\overrightarrow{GT}$ **iii** $\overrightarrow{HP}$ and $\overrightarrow{TI}$

c Show that B, H and Q lie on the same straight line.

a **i** **a** + **b**   **ii** 2**a**   **iii** 2**a** + 2**b**   **iv** –4**a**   **v** –2**a** + 2**b**   **vi** 2**a** + 2**b**

b **i** $\overrightarrow{BH}$ and $\overrightarrow{GT}$ are parallel and $\overrightarrow{GT}$ is twice the length of $\overrightarrow{BH}$.

   ii $\overrightarrow{BQ}$ and $\overrightarrow{GT}$ are equal.

   iii $\overrightarrow{HP}$ and $\overrightarrow{TI}$ are in opposite directions and $\overrightarrow{TI}$ is twice the length of $\overrightarrow{HP}$.

c $\overrightarrow{BH}$ and $\overrightarrow{BQ}$ are parallel and start at the same point B. Therefore, B, H and Q must lie on the same straight line.

EXAMPLE 2

Use a vector diagram to show that **a** + **b** = **b** + **a**.

Take two independent vectors **a** and **b**:

a + **b** and **b** + **a** have the same magnitude and direction and are therefore equal.

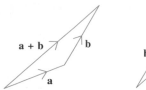

EXERCISE 13A

1 On this grid, $\overrightarrow{OA}$ is **a** and $\overrightarrow{OB}$ is **b**.

    a Name three other vectors equivalent to **a**.

    b Name three other vectors equivalent to **b**.

    c Name three vectors equivalent to –**a**.

    d Name three vectors equivalent to –**b**.

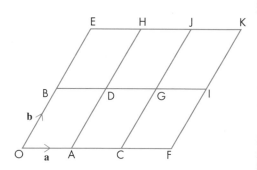

2 Using the same grid as in question **1**, give the following vectors in terms of **a** and **b**.

    a $\overrightarrow{OC}$ **b** $\overrightarrow{OE}$ **c** $\overrightarrow{OD}$ **d** $\overrightarrow{OG}$ **e** $\overrightarrow{OJ}$

    f $\overrightarrow{OH}$ **g** $\overrightarrow{AG}$ **h** $\overrightarrow{AK}$ **i** $\overrightarrow{BK}$ **j** $\overrightarrow{DI}$

    k $\overrightarrow{GJ}$ **l** $\overrightarrow{DK}$

3 **a** What do the answers to parts **2c** and **2g** tell you about the vectors $\overrightarrow{OD}$ and $\overrightarrow{AG}$?

    b On the grid in question **1**, there are three vectors equivalent to $\overrightarrow{OG}$. Name all three.

4 **a** What do the answers to parts **2c** and **2e** tell you about vectors $\overrightarrow{OD}$ and $\overrightarrow{OJ}$?

    b On the grid in question **1**, there is one other vector that is twice the size of $\overrightarrow{OD}$. Which is it?

    c On the grid in question **1**, there are three vectors that are three times the size of $\overrightarrow{OA}$. Name all three.

5 On a copy of this grid, mark on the points C to P to show the following.

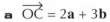

a $\overrightarrow{OC} = 2\mathbf{a} + 3\mathbf{b}$ **b** $\overrightarrow{OD} = 2\mathbf{a} + \mathbf{b}$

c $\overrightarrow{OE} = \mathbf{a} + 2\mathbf{b}$ **d** $\overrightarrow{OF} = 3\mathbf{b}$

e $\overrightarrow{OG} = 4\mathbf{a}$ **f** $\overrightarrow{OH} = 4\mathbf{a} + 2\mathbf{b}$

g $\overrightarrow{OI} = 3\mathbf{a} + 3\mathbf{b}$ **h** $\overrightarrow{OJ} = \mathbf{a} + \mathbf{b}$

i $\overrightarrow{OK} = 2\mathbf{a} + 2\mathbf{b}$ **j** $\overrightarrow{OM} = 2\mathbf{a} + \frac{3}{2}\mathbf{b}$ **k** $\overrightarrow{ON} = \frac{1}{2}\mathbf{a} + 2\mathbf{b}$ **l** $\overrightarrow{OP} = \frac{5}{2}\mathbf{a} + \frac{3}{2}\mathbf{b}$

6 **a** Look at the diagram in question **5**. What can you say about the points O, J, K and I?

b How could you tell this by looking at the vectors for parts **5g**, **5h** and **5i**?

c There is another point on the same straight line as O and D. Which is it?

d Copy and complete these statements and then mark the appropriate points on the diagram you drew for question **5**.

   i The point Q is on the straight line ODH. The vector $\overrightarrow{OQ}$ is given by:

   $\overrightarrow{OQ} = \mathbf{a} + \ldots\ldots \mathbf{b}$

   ii The point R is on the straight line ODH. The vector $\overrightarrow{OR}$ is given by:

   $\overrightarrow{OR} = 3\mathbf{a} + \ldots\ldots \mathbf{b}$

e Copy and complete the following statement.

   Any point on the line ODH has a vector $n\mathbf{a} + \ldots\ldots \mathbf{b}$, where n is any number.

7 On this grid, $\overrightarrow{OA}$ is **a** and $\overrightarrow{OB}$ is **b**.

Give the following vectors in terms of **a** and **b**.

a $\overrightarrow{OH}$ **b** $\overrightarrow{OK}$

c $\overrightarrow{OJ}$ **d** $\overrightarrow{OI}$

e $\overrightarrow{OC}$ **f** $\overrightarrow{CO}$

g $\overrightarrow{AK}$ **h** $\overrightarrow{DI}$

i $\overrightarrow{JE}$ **j** $\overrightarrow{AB}$ **k** $\overrightarrow{CK}$ **l** $\overrightarrow{DK}$

8 **a** What do the answers to parts **7e** and **7f** tell you about the vectors $\overrightarrow{OC}$ and $\overrightarrow{CO}$?

b On the grid in question **7**, there are five other vectors opposite to $\overrightarrow{OC}$. Name at least three.

9 **a** What do the answers to parts **7j** and **7k** tell you about vectors $\overrightarrow{AB}$ and $\overrightarrow{CK}$?

b On the grid in question **7**, there are two vectors that are twice the size of $\overrightarrow{AB}$ and in the opposite direction. Name both of them.

c On the grid in question **7**, there are three vectors that are three times the size of $\overrightarrow{OA}$ and in the opposite direction. Name all three.

10 On a copy of this grid, mark on the points C to P to show the following.

a $\overrightarrow{OC} = 2\mathbf{a} - \mathbf{b}$

b $\overrightarrow{OD} = 2\mathbf{a} + \mathbf{b}$

c $\overrightarrow{OE} = \mathbf{a} - 2\mathbf{b}$

d $\overrightarrow{OF} = \mathbf{b} - 2\mathbf{a}$

e $\overrightarrow{OG} = -\mathbf{a}$

f $\overrightarrow{OH} = -\mathbf{a} - 2\mathbf{b}$

g $\overrightarrow{OI} = 2\mathbf{a} - 2\mathbf{b}$

h $\overrightarrow{OJ} = -\mathbf{a} + \mathbf{b}$

i $\overrightarrow{OK} = -\mathbf{a} - \mathbf{b}$

j $\overrightarrow{OM} = -\mathbf{a} - \frac{3}{2}\mathbf{b}$

k $\overrightarrow{ON} = -\frac{1}{2}\mathbf{a} - 2\mathbf{b}$

l $\overrightarrow{OP} = \frac{3}{2}\mathbf{a} - \frac{3}{2}\mathbf{b}$

AU 11 The diagram shows two sets of parallel lines.

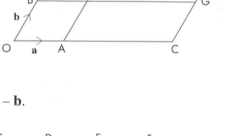

$\overrightarrow{OA} = \mathbf{a}$ and $\overrightarrow{OB} = \mathbf{b}$

$\overrightarrow{OC} = 3\overrightarrow{OA}$ and $\overrightarrow{OD} = 2\overrightarrow{OB}$

a Write down the following vectors in terms of **a** and **b**.

   i $\overrightarrow{OF}$ **ii** $\overrightarrow{OG}$ **iii** $\overrightarrow{EG}$ **iv** $\overrightarrow{CE}$

b Write down two vectors that can be written as $3\mathbf{a} - \mathbf{b}$.

12 This grid shows the vectors $\overrightarrow{OA} = \mathbf{a}$ and $\overrightarrow{OB} = \mathbf{b}$.

a Name three vectors equivalent to $\mathbf{a} + \mathbf{b}$.

b Name three vectors equivalent to $\mathbf{a} - \mathbf{b}$.

c Name three vectors equivalent to $\mathbf{b} - \mathbf{a}$.

d Name three vectors equivalent to $-\mathbf{a} - \mathbf{b}$.

e Name three vectors equivalent to $2\mathbf{a} - \mathbf{b}$.

f Name three vectors equivalent to $2\mathbf{b} - \mathbf{a}$.

g For each of these, name one equivalent vector.

   i $3\mathbf{a} - \mathbf{b}$ **ii** $2(\mathbf{a} + \mathbf{b})$ **iii** $3\mathbf{a} - 2\mathbf{b}$

   iv $3(\mathbf{a} - \mathbf{b})$ **v** $3(\mathbf{b} - \mathbf{a})$ **vi** $3(\mathbf{a} + \mathbf{b})$

   vii $-3(\mathbf{a} + \mathbf{b})$ **viii** $2\mathbf{a} + \mathbf{b} - 3\mathbf{a} - 2\mathbf{b}$ **ix** $2(2\mathbf{a} - \mathbf{b}) - 3(\mathbf{a} - \mathbf{b})$

13 The points P, Q and R lie on a straight line. The vector $\overrightarrow{PQ}$ is $2\mathbf{a} + \mathbf{b}$, where **a** and **b** are vectors. Which of the following vectors could be the vector $\overrightarrow{PR}$ and which could not be the vector $\overrightarrow{PR}$ (two of each).

a $2\mathbf{a} + 2\mathbf{b}$ **b** $4\mathbf{a} + 2\mathbf{b}$ **c** $2\mathbf{a} - \mathbf{b}$ **d** $-6\mathbf{a} - 3\mathbf{b}$

14 The points P, Q and R lie on a straight line. The vector $\overrightarrow{PQ}$ is $3\mathbf{a} - \mathbf{b}$, where **a** and **b** are vectors.

a Write down any other vector that could represent $\overrightarrow{PR}$.

b How can you tell from the vector $\overrightarrow{PS}$ that S lies on the same straight line as P, Q and R?

15 Use a vector diagram to prove that $\mathbf{a} + (\mathbf{b} + \mathbf{c}) = (\mathbf{a} + \mathbf{b}) + \mathbf{c}$.

AU 16 OABC is a quadrilateral.

P, Q, R and S are the midpoints of OA, AB, BC and OC respectively.

$$\overrightarrow{OA} = 2\mathbf{a}, \overrightarrow{OB} = 2\mathbf{b} \text{ and } \overrightarrow{OC} = 2\mathbf{c}$$

a Find the following vectors in terms of $\mathbf{a}$, $\mathbf{b}$ and $\mathbf{c}$.

Give your answers in their simplest form.

  i $\overrightarrow{AB}$ **ii** $\overrightarrow{SP}$ **iii** $\overrightarrow{BC}$ **iv** $\overrightarrow{PR}$

b Use vectors to prove that PQRS is a parallelogram.

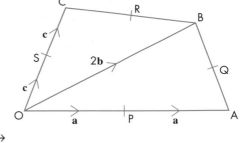

13.2   Vectors in geometry

This section will show you how to:
- use vectors to solve geometrical problems

Key words

vector

Vectors can be used to prove many results in geometry, as the following examples show.

EXAMPLE 3

In the diagram, $\overrightarrow{OA} = \mathbf{a}$, $\overrightarrow{OB} = \mathbf{b}$, and $\overrightarrow{BC} = 1.5\mathbf{a}$. M is the midpoint of BC, N is the midpoint of AC and P is the midpoint of OB.

a Find these vectors in terms of $\mathbf{a}$ and $\mathbf{b}$.

  i $\overrightarrow{AC}$ **ii** $\overrightarrow{OM}$ **iii** $\overrightarrow{BN}$

b Prove that $\overrightarrow{PN}$ is parallel to $\overrightarrow{OA}$.

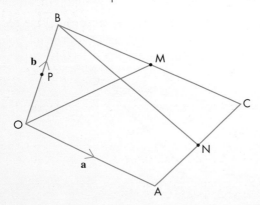

EXAMPLE 3 (continued)

a i You have to get from A to C in terms of vectors that you know.

$$\overrightarrow{AC} = \overrightarrow{AO} + \overrightarrow{OB} + \overrightarrow{BC}$$

Now $\overrightarrow{AO} = -\overrightarrow{OA}$, so you can write,

$$\overrightarrow{AC} = -\mathbf{a} + \mathbf{b} + \tfrac{3}{2}\mathbf{a}$$

$$= \tfrac{1}{2}\mathbf{a} + \mathbf{b}$$

Note that the letters 'connect up' as we go from A to C, and that the negative of a vector represented by any pair of letters is formed by reversing the letters.

ii In the same way:

$$\overrightarrow{OM} = \overrightarrow{OB} + \overrightarrow{BM} = \overrightarrow{OB} + \tfrac{1}{2}\overrightarrow{BC}$$

$$= \mathbf{b} + \tfrac{1}{2}\left(\tfrac{3}{2}\mathbf{a}\right)$$

$$\overrightarrow{OM} = \tfrac{3}{4}\mathbf{a} + \mathbf{b}$$

iii $\overrightarrow{BN} = \overrightarrow{BC} + \overrightarrow{CN} = \overrightarrow{BC} - \tfrac{1}{2}\overrightarrow{AC}$

$$= \tfrac{3}{2}\mathbf{a} - \tfrac{1}{2}\left(\tfrac{1}{2}\mathbf{a} + \mathbf{b}\right)$$

$$= \tfrac{3}{2}\mathbf{a} - \tfrac{1}{4}\mathbf{a} - \tfrac{1}{2}\mathbf{b}$$

$$= \tfrac{5}{4}\mathbf{a} - \tfrac{1}{2}\mathbf{b}$$

Note that if you did this as $\overrightarrow{BN} = \overrightarrow{BO} + \overrightarrow{OA} + \overrightarrow{AN}$, you would get the same result.

b $\overrightarrow{PN} = \overrightarrow{PO} + \overrightarrow{OA} + \overrightarrow{AN}$

$$= \tfrac{1}{2}(-\mathbf{b}) + \mathbf{a} + \tfrac{1}{2}\left(\tfrac{1}{2}\mathbf{a} + \mathbf{b}\right)$$

$$= -\tfrac{1}{2}\mathbf{b} + \mathbf{a} + \tfrac{1}{4}\mathbf{a} + \tfrac{1}{2}\mathbf{b}$$

$$= \tfrac{5}{4}\mathbf{a}$$

$\overrightarrow{PN}$ is a multiple of $\mathbf{a}$ only, so must be parallel to $\overrightarrow{OA}$.

EXAMPLE 4

OACB is a parallelogram. $\overrightarrow{OA}$ is represented by the vector $\mathbf{a}$. $\overrightarrow{OB}$ is represented by the vector $\mathbf{b}$. P is a point $\tfrac{2}{3}$ the distance from O to C, and M is the midpoint of AC. Show that B, P and M lie on the same straight line.

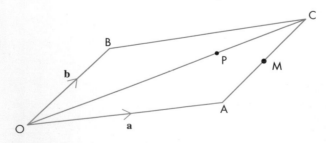

$$\overrightarrow{OC} = \overrightarrow{OA} + \overrightarrow{AC} = \mathbf{a} + \mathbf{b}$$

$$\overrightarrow{OP} = \tfrac{2}{3}\overrightarrow{OC} = \tfrac{2}{3}\mathbf{a} + \tfrac{2}{3}\mathbf{b}$$

$$\overrightarrow{OM} = \overrightarrow{OA} + \overrightarrow{AM} = \overrightarrow{OA} + \tfrac{1}{2}\overrightarrow{AC} = \mathbf{a} + \tfrac{1}{2}\mathbf{b}$$

$$\overrightarrow{BP} = \overrightarrow{BO} + \overrightarrow{OP} = -\mathbf{b} + \tfrac{2}{3}\mathbf{a} + \tfrac{2}{3}\mathbf{b} = \tfrac{2}{3}\mathbf{a} - \tfrac{1}{3}\mathbf{b} = \tfrac{1}{3}(2\mathbf{a} - \mathbf{b})$$

$$\overrightarrow{BM} = \overrightarrow{BO} + \overrightarrow{OM} = -\mathbf{b} + \mathbf{a} + \tfrac{1}{2}\mathbf{b} = \mathbf{a} - \tfrac{1}{2}\mathbf{b} = \tfrac{1}{2}(2\mathbf{a} - \mathbf{b})$$

Therefore, $\overrightarrow{BM}$ is a multiple of $\overrightarrow{BP}$ ($\overrightarrow{BM} = \tfrac{3}{2}\overrightarrow{BP}$).

Therefore, $\overrightarrow{BP}$ and $\overrightarrow{BM}$ are parallel and as they have a common point, B, they must lie on the same straight line.

EXERCISE 13B

1 The diagram shows the vectors $\overrightarrow{OA} = \mathbf{a}$ and $\overrightarrow{OB} = \mathbf{b}$. M is the midpoint of AB.

a **i** Work out the vector $\overrightarrow{AB}$.

    ii Work out the vector $\overrightarrow{AM}$.

    iii Explain why $\overrightarrow{OM} = \overrightarrow{OA} + \overrightarrow{AM}$.

    iv Using your answers to parts **ii** and **iii**, work out $\overrightarrow{OM}$ in terms of **a** and **b**.

b **i** Work out the vector $\overrightarrow{BA}$.

    ii Work out the vector $\overrightarrow{BM}$.

    iii Explain why $\overrightarrow{OM} = \overrightarrow{OB} + \overrightarrow{BM}$.

    iv Using your answers to parts **ii** and **iii**, work out $\overrightarrow{OM}$ in terms of **a** and **b**.

c Copy the diagram and show on it the vector $\overrightarrow{OC}$ which is equal to **a** + **b**.

d Describe in geometrical terms the position of M in relation to O, A, B and C.

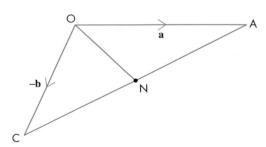

2 The diagram shows the vectors $\overrightarrow{OA} = \mathbf{a}$ and $\overrightarrow{OC} = -\mathbf{b}$. N is the midpoint of AC.

a **i** Work out the vector $\overrightarrow{AC}$.

    ii Work out the vector $\overrightarrow{AN}$.

    iii Explain why
$$\overrightarrow{ON} = \overrightarrow{OA} + \overrightarrow{AN}.$$

    iv Using your answers to parts **ii** and **iii**, work out $\overrightarrow{ON}$ in terms of **a** and **b**.

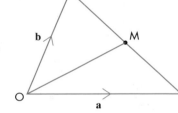

b i Work out the vector $\overrightarrow{CA}$.

   ii Work out the vector $\overrightarrow{CN}$.

   iii Explain why $\overrightarrow{ON} = \overrightarrow{OC} + \overrightarrow{CN}$.

   iv Using your answers to parts **ii** and **iii**, work out $\overrightarrow{ON}$ in terms of **a** and **b**.

c Copy the diagram above and show on it the vector $\overrightarrow{OD}$ which is equal to **a** − **b**.

d Describe in geometrical terms the position of N in relation to O, A, C and D.

3 The diagram shows the vectors $\overrightarrow{OA} = $ **a** and $\overrightarrow{OB} = $ **b**.
The point C divides the line AB in the ratio 1:2.

> **HINTS AND TIPS**
>
> AC is $\frac{1}{3}$ the distance from A to B.

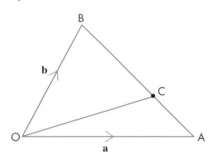

a i Work out the vector $\overrightarrow{AB}$.   **ii** Work out the vector $\overrightarrow{AC}$.

   iii Work out the vector $\overrightarrow{OC}$ in terms of **a** and **b**.

b If C now divides the line AB in the ratio 1:3, write down the vector that represents $\overrightarrow{OC}$.

> **HINTS AND TIPS**
>
> AC is now $\frac{1}{4}$ the distance from A to B.

4 The diagram shows the vectors $\overrightarrow{OA} = $ **a** and $\overrightarrow{OB} = $ **b**.

> **HINTS AND TIPS**
>
> OC is $\frac{2}{3}$ the distance from O to B.

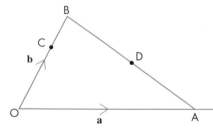

The point C divides OB in the ratio 2:1. The point E is such that $\overrightarrow{OE} = 2\overrightarrow{OA}$. D is the midpoint of AB.

a Write down (or work out) these vectors in terms of **a** and **b**.

   i $\overrightarrow{OC}$ **ii** $\overrightarrow{OD}$ **iii** $\overrightarrow{CO}$

b The vector $\overrightarrow{CD}$ can be written as $\overrightarrow{CD} = \overrightarrow{CO} + \overrightarrow{OD}$. Use this fact to work out $\overrightarrow{CD}$ in terms of **a** and **b**.

c Write down a similar rule to that in part **b** for the vector $\overrightarrow{DE}$. Use this rule to work out $\overrightarrow{DE}$ in terms of **a** and **b**.

d Explain why C, D and E lie on the same straight line.

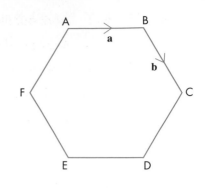

5 ABCDEF is a regular hexagon. $\overrightarrow{AB}$ is represented by the vector **a** and $\overrightarrow{BC}$ by the vector **b**.

a By means of a diagram, or otherwise, explain why $\overrightarrow{CD} = \mathbf{b} - \mathbf{a}$.

b Express these vectors in terms of **a** and **b**.
  i $\overrightarrow{DE}$ ii $\overrightarrow{EF}$ iii $\overrightarrow{FA}$

c Work out the answer to:
  $\overrightarrow{AB} + \overrightarrow{BC} + \overrightarrow{CD} + \overrightarrow{DE} + \overrightarrow{EF} + \overrightarrow{FA}$

  Explain your answer.

d Express these vectors in terms of **a** and **b**.
  i $\overrightarrow{AD}$ ii $\overrightarrow{BE}$ iii $\overrightarrow{CF}$ iv $\overrightarrow{AE}$ v $\overrightarrow{DF}$

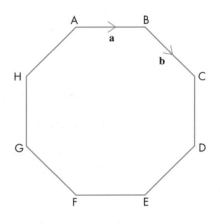

6 ABCDEFGH is a regular octagon. $\overrightarrow{AB}$ is represented by the vector **a**, and $\overrightarrow{BC}$ by the vector **b**.

a By means of a diagram, or otherwise, explain why $\overrightarrow{CD} = \sqrt{2}\mathbf{b} - \mathbf{a}$.

b By means of a diagram, or otherwise, explain why $\overrightarrow{DE} = \mathbf{b} - \sqrt{2}\mathbf{a}$.

c Express the following vectors in terms of **a** and **b**.
  i $\overrightarrow{EF}$ ii $\overrightarrow{FG}$ iii $\overrightarrow{GH}$ iv $\overrightarrow{HA}$
  v $\overrightarrow{HC}$ vi $\overrightarrow{AD}$ vii $\overrightarrow{BE}$ viii $\overrightarrow{BF}$

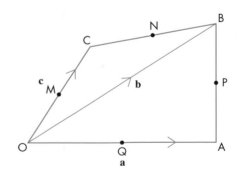

7 In the quadrilateral OABC, M, N, P and Q are the midpoints of the sides as shown. $\overrightarrow{OA}$ is represented by the vector **a**, and $\overrightarrow{OC}$ by the vector **c**. The diagonal $\overrightarrow{OB}$ is represented by the vector **b**.

a Express these vectors in terms of **a**, **b** and **c**.
  i $\overrightarrow{AB}$ ii $\overrightarrow{AP}$ iii $\overrightarrow{OP}$

  Give your answers as simply as possible.

b i Express the vector $\overrightarrow{ON}$ in terms of **b** and **c**.

  ii Hence express the vector $\overrightarrow{PN}$ in terms of **a** and **c**.

c i Express the vector $\overrightarrow{QM}$ in terms of **a** and **c**.

  ii What relationship is there between $\overrightarrow{PN}$ and $\overrightarrow{QM}$?

  iii What sort of quadrilateral is PNMQ?

d Prove that $\overrightarrow{AC} = 2\overrightarrow{QM}$.

A*

8 L, M, N, P, Q, R are the midpoints of the line segments, as shown.

$\overrightarrow{OA} = \mathbf{a}$, $\overrightarrow{OB} = \mathbf{b}$ and $\overrightarrow{OC} = \mathbf{c}$

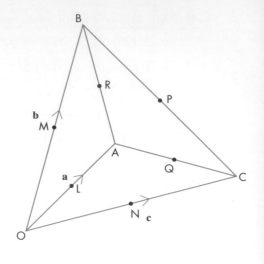

a Express these vectors in terms of **a** and **c**.

   i $\overrightarrow{OL}$

   ii $\overrightarrow{AC}$

   iii $\overrightarrow{OQ}$

   iv $\overrightarrow{LQ}$

b Express these vectors in terms of **a** and **b**.

   i $\overrightarrow{LM}$

   ii $\overrightarrow{QP}$

c Prove that the quadrilateral LMPQ is a parallelogram.

d Find two other sets of four points that form parallelograms.

AU 9 In the triangle OAB, M is the midpoint of AB.

$\overrightarrow{OA} = \mathbf{a}$ and $\overrightarrow{OB} = \mathbf{b}$

a Find $\overrightarrow{AM}$ in terms of **a** and **b**.

Give your answer in its simplest form.

b $\overrightarrow{OC} = \mathbf{a} + \mathbf{b}$

The length of OA is equal to the length of OB.

   i Write down the name of the shape OACB.

   ii Write down one fact about the points O, M and C.

Give a reason for your answer.

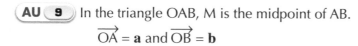

AU 10 ABCD is a trapezium with AB parallel to DC.

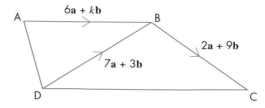

$\overrightarrow{AB} = 6\mathbf{a} + k\mathbf{b}$, $\overrightarrow{BC} = 2\mathbf{a} + 9\mathbf{b}$ and $\overrightarrow{DB} = 7\mathbf{a} + 3\mathbf{b}$, where k is a number.

Work out the value of k.

Geometric proof

This section will show you how to:	Key words
● understand the difference between a proof and a demonstration	demonstration proof prove

You should already know these.

● The angle sum of the interior angles in a triangle (180°)

● The circle theorems

● Pythagoras' theorem

Can you **prove** them?

For a mathematical **proof**, you must proceed in logical steps, establishing a series of mathematical statements by using facts that are already known to be true.

Below are three standard proofs: *the sum of the interior angles of a triangle is 180°, Pythagoras' theorem* and *congruency*. Read through them, following the arguments carefully. Make sure you understand each step in the process.

Proof that the sum of the interior angles of a triangle is 180°

One of your earlier activities in geometry may have been to draw a triangle, to cut off its corners and to stick them down to *show that* they make a straight line.

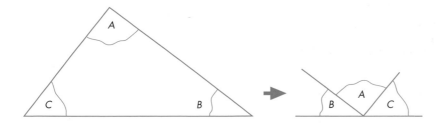

Does this prove that the interior angles make 180° or were you just lucky and picked a triangle that worked? Was the fact that everyone else in the class managed to pick a triangle that worked also a lucky coincidence?

Of course not! However, this was a **demonstration**, not a proof. You would have to show that this method worked for *all* possible triangles (there is an infinite number!) to say that you have proved this result.

Your proof must establish that the result is true for *all* triangles.

Look at the following proof.

Start with triangle ABC with angles α, β and γ (figure **i**).

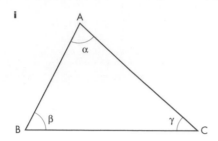 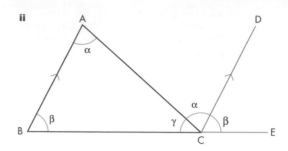

On figure **i** draw a line CD parallel to side AB and extend BC to E, to give figure **ii**.

Since AB is parallel to CD:

$\angle$ACD = $\angle$BAC = α (alternate angles) $\angle$DCE = $\angle$ABC = β (corresponding angles)

BCE is a straight line, so γ + α + β = 180°. Therefore the interior angles of a triangle = 180°.

This proof assumes that alternate angles are equal and that corresponding angles are equal. Strictly speaking, we should prove these results, but we have to accept certain results as true. These are based on Euclid's axioms from which all geometric proofs are derived.

Proof of Pythagoras' theorem

Draw a square of side c inside a square of side $(a + b)$, as shown.

The area of the exterior square is $(a + b)^2 = a^2 + 2ab + b^2$.

The area of each small triangle around the shaded square is $\frac{1}{2}ab$.

The total area of all four triangles is $4 \times \frac{1}{2}ab = 2ab$.

Subtracting the total area of the four triangles from the area of the large square gives the area of the shaded square:

$$a^2 + 2ab + b^2 - 2ab = a^2 + b^2$$

But the area of the shaded square is c^2, so

$$c^2 = a^2 + b^2$$

which is Pythagoras' theorem.

Congruency proof

There are four conditions to prove congruency. These are commonly known as SSS (three sides the same), SAS (two sides and the included angle the same), ASA (or AAS) (two angles and one side the same) and RHS (right-angled triangle, hypotenuse, and one short side the same). **Note:** AAA (three angles the same) is not a condition for congruency.

When you prove a result, you must explain or justify every statement or line. Proofs have to be rigorous and logical.

EXAMPLE 5

ABCD is a parallelogram. X is the point where the diagonals meet.

Prove that triangles AXB and CXD are congruent.

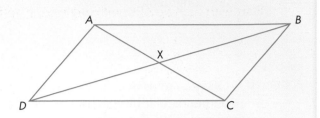

$\angle BAX = \angle DCX$ (alternate angles)

$\angle ABX = \angle CDX$ (alternate angles)

$AB = CD$ (opposite sides in a parallelogram)

Hence $\triangle AXB$ is congruent to $\triangle CXD$ (ASA).

Note that you could have used $\angle AXB = \angle CXD$ (vertically opposite angles) as the second line but whichever approach is used you *must* give a reason for each statement.

EXERCISE 13C

PS 1 **a** Show that the triangle ABC is isosceles.

b Prove that the triangle DEF with one angle of $x°$ and an exterior angle of $90° + \dfrac{x°}{2}$ is isosceles.

i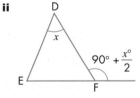

ii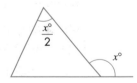

PS 2 Prove that a triangle with an interior angle of $\dfrac{x°}{2}$ and an exterior angle of $x°$ is isosceles.

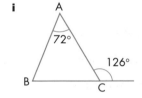

PS 3 **a** Using the theorem that the angle subtended by an arc at the centre of a circle is twice the angle subtended by the same arc at the circumference, find the values of angles DAB and DCB in the circle shown in figure **i**.

b Prove that the sum of the opposite angles of a cyclic quadrilateral is 180°. (You may find figure **ii** useful.)

i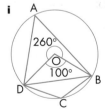

ii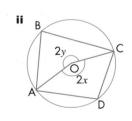

PS 4 **a** The triangle ABC is isosceles. BCD and AED are straight lines. Find the value of the angle CED, marked x, in figure **i**.

b Prove that angle ACB = angle CED in figure **ii**.

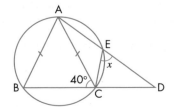

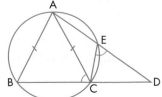

PS 5 PQRS is a parallelogram. Prove that triangles PQS and RQS are congruent.

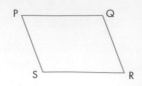

PS 6 OB is a radius of a circle, centre O. C is the point where the perpendicular bisector of OB meets the circumference. Prove that triangle OBC is equilateral.

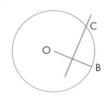

PS 7 The grid is made up of identical parallelograms.
In the grid, $\overrightarrow{OA} = \mathbf{a}$ and $\overrightarrow{OB} = \mathbf{b}$.
Prove that AB is parallel to EF.

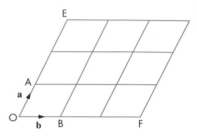

PS 8 **a** Prove the alternate segment theorem.

b Two circles touch internally at T. The common tangent at T is drawn. Two lines TAB and TXY are drawn from T. Prove that AX is parallel to BY.

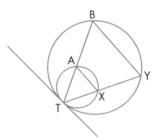

PS 9 Two circles touch externally at T. A line ATB is drawn through T. The common tangent at T and the tangents at A and B meet at P and Q. Prove that PB is parallel to AQ.

10 **a** and **b** are vectors.

$$\overrightarrow{XY} = \mathbf{a} + \mathbf{b} \qquad \overrightarrow{YZ} = 2\mathbf{a} + \mathbf{b} \qquad \overrightarrow{ZW} = \mathbf{a} + 2\mathbf{b}$$

a Show that $\overrightarrow{YW}$ is parallel to $\overrightarrow{XY}$.

b Write down the ratio YW : XY.

c What do your answers to **a** and **b** tell you about the points X, Y and W?

d O is the origin.

A, B and C are three points such that:

$$\overrightarrow{OA} = \begin{pmatrix} 6 \\ 2 \end{pmatrix} \qquad \overrightarrow{OB} = \begin{pmatrix} 1 \\ 1 \end{pmatrix} \qquad \overrightarrow{OC} = \begin{pmatrix} 2 \\ -4 \end{pmatrix}$$

Prove that angle ABC is a right angle.

GRADE BOOSTER

A You can solve problems, using addition and subtraction of vectors

A* You can solve complex geometrical problems, using vectors

A* You can use proof in geometrical problems

What you should know now

- How to add and subtract vectors
- How to apply vector methods to solve geometrical problems

1 In triangle ABC, M lies on BC such that $BM = \frac{3}{4}BC$.

$\overrightarrow{AB} = \mathbf{s}$ and $\overrightarrow{AC} = \mathbf{t}$.

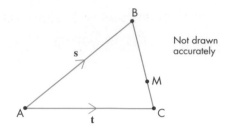

Not drawn accurately

Find $\overrightarrow{AM}$ in terms of $\mathbf{s}$ and $\mathbf{t}$.

Give your answer in its simplest form. *(3 marks)*

AQA, June 2005, Paper 1, Question 17

2 OABC is a quadrilateral.

D, E, F and G are midpoints of OA, AB, BC and OC respectively.

$\overrightarrow{OA} = 2\mathbf{a}$, $\overrightarrow{OB} = 2\mathbf{b}$ and $\overrightarrow{OC} = 2\mathbf{c}$

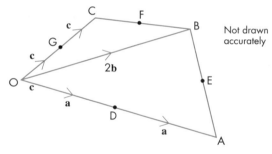

Not drawn accurately

Find the following vectors in terms of $\mathbf{a}$, $\mathbf{b}$ and $\mathbf{c}$.

For example, $\overrightarrow{DG} = \mathbf{c} - \mathbf{a}$

a $\overrightarrow{AB}$ *(1 mark)*

b $\overrightarrow{BC}$ *(1 mark)*

c Use your answers to parts **a** and **b** to show that $\overrightarrow{EF} = \mathbf{c} - \mathbf{a}$. *(1 mark)*

d Explain how you can tell that DEFG is a parallelogram. *(1 mark)*

AQA, May 2009, Module 5, Paper 1, Question 14

3 In the diagram $\overrightarrow{OP} = 4\mathbf{a}$, $\overrightarrow{PA} = \mathbf{a}$, $\overrightarrow{OB} = 5\mathbf{b}$, $\overrightarrow{BR} = 3\mathbf{b}$ and $\overrightarrow{AQ} = \frac{2}{5}\overrightarrow{AB}$.

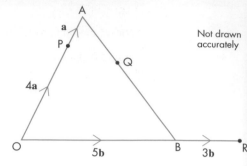

Not drawn accurately

a Find, in terms of $\mathbf{a}$ and $\mathbf{b}$, simplifying your answers,

i $\overrightarrow{AB}$ *(1 mark)*

ii $\overrightarrow{PQ}$ *(2 marks)*

b Show clearly that points P, Q and R lie on a straight line. *(3 marks)*

AQA, November 2005, Paper 1, Question 21

4 OAB is a triangle with P the midpoint of OA and M the midpoint of AB.

$\overrightarrow{OP} = \mathbf{a}$, $\overrightarrow{PA} = \mathbf{a}$ and $\overrightarrow{OB} = 2\mathbf{b}$.

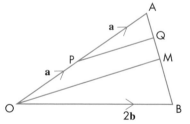

Not drawn accurately

a Write down an expression for $\overrightarrow{AB}$ in terms of $\mathbf{a}$ and $\mathbf{b}$. *(1 mark)*

b Q lies on AB such that $\overrightarrow{AQ} = \frac{1}{4}\overrightarrow{AB}$.

Show that $PQ = \frac{1}{2}\mathbf{a} + \frac{1}{2}\mathbf{b}$.

Explain your answer. *(2 marks)*

c Write down, and simplify, an expression for $\overrightarrow{OM}$ in terms of $\mathbf{a}$ and $\mathbf{b}$. *(2 marks)*

d Explain why the answers for part **b** and part **c** show that OPQM is a trapezium. *(1 mark)*

AQA, November 2008, Paper 1, Question 24

A* A

5 The diagram shows a square OAPB.

M is the midpoint of AP.

N is the midpoint of BM.

AP is extended to Q where $AQ = 1\frac{1}{2}AP$.

$\overrightarrow{OA} = \mathbf{a}$ and $\overrightarrow{OB} = \mathbf{b}$

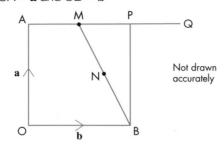

Not drawn accurately

a Write down these vectors in terms of **a** and **b**.

Give your answers in their simplest form.

i $\overrightarrow{OQ}$ (1 mark)

ii $\overrightarrow{BM}$ (1 mark)

iii $\overrightarrow{BN}$ (1 mark)

iv $\overrightarrow{ON}$ (2 marks)

b What can you deduce about points O, N and Q? (2 marks)

AQA, June 2007, Paper 1, Question 17

6 OAB is a triangle.

X is the midpoint of AB.

Y is the midpoint of OB.

Z is the point on OX such that OZ : ZX = 2 : 1.

$\overrightarrow{OA} = 3\mathbf{a}$, $\overrightarrow{OB} = 3\mathbf{b}$.

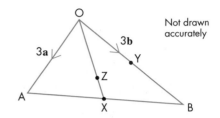

Not drawn accurately

a Find, in terms of **a** and **b**, the vectors

i $\overrightarrow{AY}$ (1 mark)

ii $\overrightarrow{OX}$ (2 marks)

iii $\overrightarrow{AZ}$ (2 marks)

b A, Z and Y are on a straight line.

Find the ratio AZ : ZY. (2 marks)

AQA, November 2006, Paper 2, Question 23

Worked Examination Questions

1 The diagram shows triangle OAB. M is the midpoint of OA.
P lies on BM and $BP = \frac{2}{3}BM$.

$\overrightarrow{OA} = 2\mathbf{a}$ and $\overrightarrow{OB} = 2\mathbf{b}$

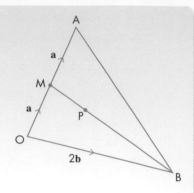

  a Find expressions, in terms of **a** and **b**, for **i** $\overrightarrow{BM}$ and **ii** $\overrightarrow{OP}$.
  Write each answer in its simplest form.

  b N is the midpoint of OB. Q lies on AN and $AQ = \frac{2}{3}AN$.
   i Find an expression for $\overrightarrow{OQ}$, in terms of **a** and **b**.
   Write your answer in its simplest form.
   ii What do your answers for $\overrightarrow{OP}$ and $\overrightarrow{OQ}$ tell you about the
   points P and Q?

1 **a** **i** $\overrightarrow{BM} = \mathbf{a} - 2\mathbf{b}$ ——————————————

> Find a route from B to M in terms of known vectors. $\overrightarrow{BM} = \overrightarrow{BO} + \overrightarrow{OM}$
>
> This scores 1 mark for accuracy.

  ii $\overrightarrow{OP} = \overrightarrow{OB} + \frac{2}{3}\overrightarrow{BM} = 2\mathbf{b} + \frac{2}{3}\mathbf{a} - \frac{4}{3}\mathbf{b} = \frac{2}{3}\mathbf{a} + \frac{2}{3}\mathbf{b}$ ——

> Find a route from O to P in terms of known vectors. $\overrightarrow{OP} = \overrightarrow{OB} + \overrightarrow{BP}$
>
> This scores 1 mark each for accuracy and method.

  b **i** $\overrightarrow{OQ} = \overrightarrow{OA} + \overrightarrow{AQ} = \overrightarrow{OA} + \frac{2}{3}\overrightarrow{AN}$ with $\overrightarrow{AN} = \mathbf{b} - 2\mathbf{a}$ ——

> Find a route from O to Q in terms of known vectors. $\overrightarrow{OQ} = \overrightarrow{OA} + \overrightarrow{AQ}$
>
> This scores 1 mark each for accuracy and method.

  So $\overrightarrow{OQ} = 2\mathbf{a} + \frac{2}{3}(\mathbf{b} - 2\mathbf{a}) = 2\mathbf{a} + \frac{2}{3}\mathbf{b} - \frac{4}{3}\mathbf{a} = \frac{2}{3}\mathbf{a} + \frac{2}{3}\mathbf{b}$ ——

> This scores 1 mark for accuracy.

  ii $\overrightarrow{OP} = \overrightarrow{OQ}$, so P and Q are the same point. ——

> This statement scores 1 mark.

Total: 7 marks

Worked Examination Questions

AU **2** OABC is a parallelogram.

M is the midpoint of the diagonal OB.

$\overrightarrow{OA}$ = 2**a** and $\overrightarrow{OC}$ = 2**c**

  a Express $\overrightarrow{OM}$ in terms of **a** and **c**.

  b Use vectors to prove that M is also the midpoint of the diagonal AC.

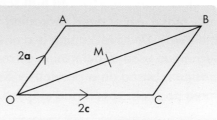

2 **a** $\overrightarrow{OB}$ = 2a + 2c and $\overrightarrow{OM}$ = $\frac{1}{2}\overrightarrow{OB}$, so $\overrightarrow{OM}$ = a + c.

> The correct answer scores 1 mark for accuracy.

  b $\overrightarrow{AC}$ = 2c – 2a and $\overrightarrow{AM}$ = $\overrightarrow{AO}$ + $\overrightarrow{OM}$ = –2a + a + c = c – a.

> This scores 1 method mark for 2c – 2a and 1 method mark for c – a.

    So $\overrightarrow{AM}$ = $\frac{1}{2}\overrightarrow{AC}$, hence M is the midpoint of AC.

> This statement scores 1 mark for accuracy.

(**Total:** 4 marks)

PS **3** In the diagram the lines VX and WY intersect at Z. VW and YX are parallel and VW = XY.

Prove that triangles VWZ and XYZ are congruent.

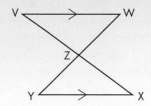

3 ∠VWZ = ∠ZYX (Alternate angles)

∠WVZ = ∠ZXY (Alternate angles)

∠VZW = ∠YZX (Vertically opposite)

> State which angles are equal and give a reason. You only need two angles. It doesn't matter which two. You can state all three but there will still only be two marks available.
> This scores 2 marks.

VW = YZ (Given)

> Even though this information is given in the question, do not assume that the examiner knows you know it. If information given in the question is needed in the answer, restate it.
> This scores 1 mark.

Hence the triangles are congruent, ASA.

> State the reason for congruency.
> This scores 1 mark.

(**Total:** 4 marks)

Scientists have discovered that some desert ants make use of dead reckoning to find their way. Dead reckoning is a navigational technique used to determine current position, based on a previously determined fixed position, speed and elapsed time.

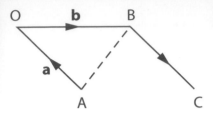

The diagram uses the vectors $\overrightarrow{OA} = -\mathbf{a}$ and $\overrightarrow{OB} = \mathbf{b}$.

Describe in terms of $\mathbf{a}$ and $\mathbf{b}$:

- the route the ant took, from its nest to its end point after it had been moved, if it was using dead reckoning
- the route the ant would have taken from its nest to its end point, if it had navigated by scent rather than by dead reckoning.

Getting started

Scientists conducted an experiment to prove that Tunisian desert ants navigate using dead reckoning rather than other means such as laying down scents.

They conducted the following experiment:

The Tunisian desert ant set out from its nest at A. As soon as it found food at O, the scientists moved it to an alternative position at B. The ant then headed in exactly the direction it should have taken to find its nest, had it been returning from O to A, as if it had not been moved, and so ending up at C. If the ant had used scent it would have gone from B straight back to A.

Your task

Look at the diagram below. An ant's nest is at O. Each time the ant sets off it finds food at a different location: D, E, F, G, H, I or J.

1 Suggest possible vectors for its route to food at each of these points, writing them in terms of **a** and **b**.

2 Now imagine you are a scientist researching colonies of ants in the jungle and the desert. The position of the ants' nest, in each case, is again described as O. Choose one location for food at K, L, M, N or P. As soon as an ant finds food, you move it to point C.

Use vectors to describe the route the ant takes:

- from its nest to the food
- then when it is moved to C
- back to its nest, assuming it is an ant that lives in the jungle and relies on scent
- to its end point, assuming it is a desert ant and relies on dead reckoning.

Write a scientific report, with three sections, describing the method, results and conclusion, and using a vector diagram to explain your theory.

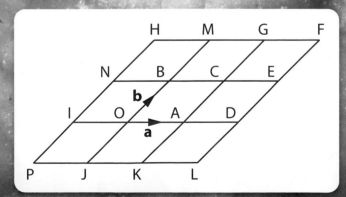

Why this chapter matters

By transforming graphs into other shapes, it is possible to change a circle into an aerofoil. This enables aeroplane engineers to do much simpler calculations when designing wings. This chapter will not help you to design aeroplane wings, but everyone has to start somewhere!

So far you have met four transformations:

- Translation
- Rotation
- Reflection
- Enlargement

Can you remember how to describe each of these?

Enlargement

Reflection

Original

Rotation

Translation

There are many other transformations, but one that you will need here is the 'stretch'. It is exactly what it says it is.

The stretch can be in any direction, but in GCSE mathematics the stretch will be in the *x*- and *y*-directions.

A stretch is defined by a direction and a scale factor.

Original

Stretch scale factor 1.5 in the *y*-direction

Stretch scale factor 0.5 in the *x*-direction

Stretch scale factor 3 in the *x*-direction and 0.5 in the *y*-direction

14 Algebra: Transformation of graphs

1 Transformations of the graph $y = f(x)$

This chapter will show you ...

- **A*** how to transform a graph
- **A*** how to recognise the relationships between graphs and their equations

Visual overview

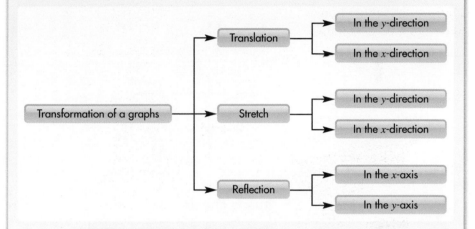

What you should already know

- How to transform a shape by a translation and a reflection
  (KS3 level 6, GCSE grade D)

- A translation is described by a column vector
  (KS3 level 7, GCSE grade C)

- A reflection is described by a mirror line
  (KS3 level 5, GCSE grade E)

continued

● The graphs of $y = x^2$, $y = x^3$, $y = \dfrac{1}{x}$, $y = \sin x$, $y = \cos x$ and $y = \tan x$

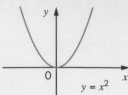

$y = x^2$

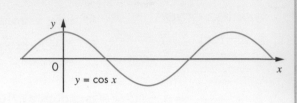

$y = \sin x$

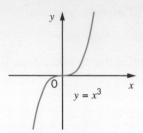

$y = x^3$

$y = \cos x$

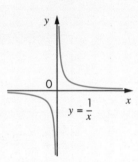

$y = \dfrac{1}{x}$

Quick check

Starting with the shaded triangle every time, do the following transformations.

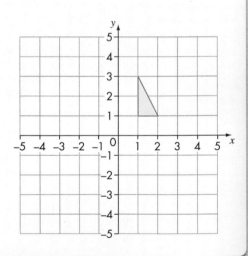

a Translation

  i $\begin{pmatrix} 3 \\ 0 \end{pmatrix}$ **ii** $\begin{pmatrix} 0 \\ -2 \end{pmatrix}$

b Reflection in the

  i y-axis   **ii** x-axis

c Rotation of 180° about the origin

This section will show you how to:
- transform a graph

Key words

function	transform
reflection	translation
scale factor	vector
stretch	

The notation $f(x)$ is used to represent a **function** of x. A function of x is any algebraic expression in which x is the only variable. Examples of functions are: $f(x) = x + 3$, $f(x) = 5x$, $f(x) = 2x - 7$, $f(x) = x^2$, $f(x) = x^3 + 2x - 1$, $f(x) = \sin x$ and $f(x) = \dfrac{1}{x}$.

On this page and the next are six general statements or rules about **transforming** graphs.

This work is much easier to understand if you can use to a graphics calculator or a graph-drawing computer program.

The graph on the right represents any function $y = f(x)$.

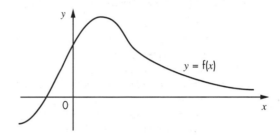

Rule 1 The graph of $y = f(x) + a$ is a **translation** of the graph of $y = f(x)$ by a **vector** $\begin{pmatrix} 0 \\ a \end{pmatrix}$.

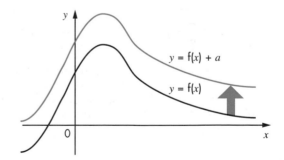

Rule 2 The graph of $y = f(x - a)$ is a translation of the graph of $y = f(x)$ by a vector $\begin{pmatrix} a \\ 0 \end{pmatrix}$.

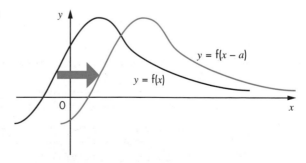

Note: The sign in front of a in the bracket is negative, but the translation is in the positive direction. $f(x + a)$ would translate $f(x)$ by the vector $\begin{pmatrix} -a \\ 0 \end{pmatrix}$.

A **stretch** is an enlargement that takes place in one direction only. It is described by a **scale factor** and the direction of the stretch.

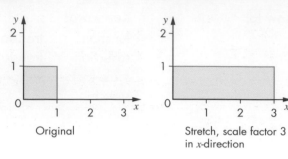

| Original | Stretch, scale factor 3 in x-direction | Stretch, scale factor 2 in y-direction |

Rule 3 The graph of $y = af(x)$ is a stretch of the graph $y = f(x)$ by a scale factor of a in the y-direction.

Note: Points on the x-axis do not move. These are called invariant points.

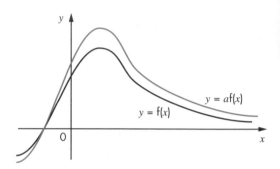

Rule 4 The graph of $y = f(ax)$ is a stretch of the graph $y = f(x)$ by a scale factor of $\dfrac{1}{a}$ in the x-direction.

Note: Points on the y-axis do not move and the scale factor of the stretch is the reciprocal of the constant multiplier inside the bracket.

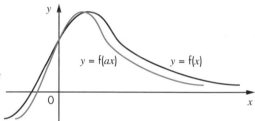

Rule 5 The graph of $y = -f(x)$ is the **reflection** of the graph $y = f(x)$ in the x-axis.

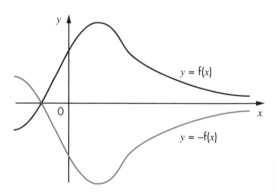

Rule 6 The graph of $y = f(-x)$ is the reflection of the graph $y = f(x)$ in the y-axis.

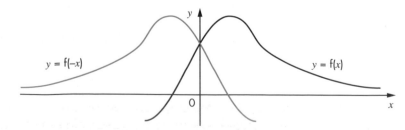

EXAMPLE 1

Sketch the following graphs.

a $y = x^2$ b $y = 5x^2$ c $y = x^2 - 5$

d $y = -x^2$ e $y = (x - 5)^2$ f $y = 2x^2 + 3$

Describe the transformation(s) that change(s) graph **a** to each of the other graphs.

Graph **a** is the basic graph to which you will apply the rules to make the necessary transformations: graph **b** uses Rule 3, graph **c** uses Rule 1, graph **d** uses Rule 5, graph **e** uses Rule 2, and graph **f** uses Rules 3 and 1.

The graphs are:

a
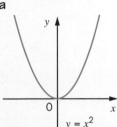

b
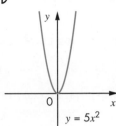

c
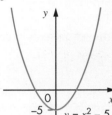

d
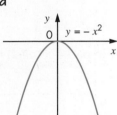

e
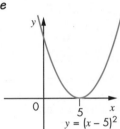

f
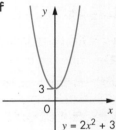

The transformations are:

graph **b** is a stretch of scale factor 5 in the y-direction,

graph **c** is a translation of $\begin{pmatrix} 0 \\ -5 \end{pmatrix}$,

graph **d** is a reflection in the x-axis,

graph **e** is a translation of $\begin{pmatrix} 5 \\ 0 \end{pmatrix}$,

graph **f** is a stretch of scale factor 2 in the y-direction,

followed by a translation of $\begin{pmatrix} 0 \\ 3 \end{pmatrix}$.

Note that two of the transformations cause problems because they seem to do the opposite of what is expected. These are:

$y = f(x + a)$ (Rule 2)

The translation is $\begin{pmatrix} -a \\ 0 \end{pmatrix}$, so the sign of the constant inside the bracket changes in the vector (see part **e** in Example 1).

$y = f(ax)$ (Rule 4)

This does not look like a stretch. It actually closes the graph up. Just like an enlargement (see Chapter 7) can make something smaller, a stretch can make it squeeze closer to the axes.

EXERCISE 14A

1 On the same axes sketch the following graphs.

    a $y = x^2$ **b** $y = 3x^2$ **c** $y = \frac{1}{2}x^2$ **d** $y = 10x^2$

    e Describe the transformation(s) that take(s) the graph in part **a** to each of the graphs in parts **b** to **d**.

2 On the same axes sketch the following graphs.

    a $y = x^2$ **b** $y = x^2 + 3$ **c** $y = x^2 - 1$ **d** $y = 2x^2 + 1$

    e Describe the transformation(s) that take(s) the graph in part **a** to each of the graphs in parts **b** to **d**.

3 On the same axes sketch the following graphs.

    a $y = x^2$ **b** $y = (x + 3)^2$ **c** $y = (x - 1)^2$ **d** $y = 2(x - 2)^2$

    e Describe the transformation(s) that take(s) the graph in part **a** to each of the graphs in parts **b** to **d**.

4 On the same axes sketch the following graphs.

    a $y = x^2$ **b** $y = (x + 3)^2 - 1$ **c** $y = 4(x - 1)^2 + 3$

    d Describe the transformation(s) that take(s) the graph in part **a** to each of the graphs in parts **b** and **c**.

5 On the same axes sketch the following graphs.

    a $y = x^2$ **b** $y = -x^2 + 3$ **c** $y = -3x^2$ **d** $y = -2x^2 + 1$

    e Describe the transformation(s) that take(s) the graph in part **a** to each of the graphs in parts **b** to **d**.

6 On the same axes sketch the following graphs.

    a $y = \sin x$ **b** $y = 2\sin x$ **c** $y = \frac{1}{2}\sin x$ **d** $y = 10\sin x$

    e Describe the transformation(s) that take(s) the graph in part **a** to each of the graphs in parts **b** to **d**.

7 On the same axes sketch the following graphs.

    a $y = \sin x$ **b** $y = \sin 3x$ **c** $y = \sin \dfrac{x}{2}$ **d** $y = 5\sin 2x$

    e Describe the transformation(s) that take(s) the graph in part **a** to each of the graphs in parts **b** to **d**.

8 On the same axes sketch the following graphs.

    a $y = \sin x$ **b** $y = \sin (x + 90°)$ **c** $y = \sin (x - 45°)$ **d** $y = 2\sin (x - 90°)$

    e Describe the transformation(s) that take(s) the graph in part **a** to the graphs in parts **b** to **d**.

9 On the same axes sketch the following graphs.

  a $y = \sin x$ **b** $y = \sin x + 2$ **c** $y = \sin x - 3$ **d** $y = 2\sin x + 1$

  e Describe the transformation(s) that take(s) the graph in part **a** to the graphs parts **b** to **d**.

10 On the same axes sketch the following graphs.

  a $y = \sin x$ **b** $y = -\sin x$ **c** $y = \sin (-x)$ **d** $y = -\sin (-x)$

  e Describe the transformation(s) that take(s) the graph in part **a** to the graphs in parts **b** to **d**.

11 On the same axes sketch the following graphs.

  a $y = \cos x$ **b** $y = 2\cos x$ **c** $y = \cos (x - 60°)$ **d** $y = \cos x + 2$

  e Describe the transformation(s) that take(s) the graph in part **a** to the graphs in parts **b** to **d**.

AU 12 Which of the equations below represents the graph shown?

  A: $y = \sin x$

  B: $y = \cos (x - 90°)$

  C: $y = -\sin (-x)$

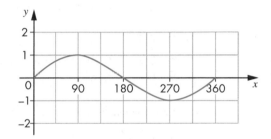

13 **a** Describe the transformations of the graph of $y = x^2$ needed to obtain these graphs.

  i $y = 4x^2$ **ii** $y = 9x^2$ **iii** $y = 16x^2$

  b Describe the transformations of the graph of $y = x^2$ needed to obtain these graphs.

  i $y = (2x)^2$ **ii** $y = (3x)^2$ **iii** $y = (4x)^2$

  c Describe two different transformations that take the graph of $y = x^2$ to the graph of $y = (ax)^2$, where a is a positive number.

14 On the right is a sketch of the function $y = f(x)$. Use this to sketch the following.

  a $y = f(x) + 2$ **b** $y = 2f(x)$ **c** $y = f(x - 3)$

  d $y = -f(x)$ **e** $y = 2f(x) + 3$ **f** $y = -f(x) - 2$

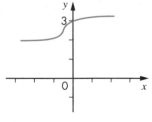

15 What is the equation of the graph obtained when the following transformations are performed on the graph of $y = x^2$?

  a Stretch by a factor of 5 in the y-direction

  b Translation of $\begin{pmatrix} 0 \\ 7 \end{pmatrix}$ **c** Translation of $\begin{pmatrix} -3 \\ 0 \end{pmatrix}$ **d** Translation of $\begin{pmatrix} -2 \\ -3 \end{pmatrix}$

  e Stretch by a factor of 3 in the y-direction followed by a translation of $\begin{pmatrix} 0 \\ 4 \end{pmatrix}$

  f Reflection in the x-axis, followed by a stretch, scale factor 3, in the y-direction

16 What is the equation of the graph obtained when the following transformations are performed on the graph of $y = \cos x$?

a Stretch by a factor of 6 in the y-direction

b Translation of $\begin{pmatrix} 0 \\ 3 \end{pmatrix}$

c Translation of $\begin{pmatrix} -30 \\ 0 \end{pmatrix}$

d Translation of $\begin{pmatrix} 45 \\ -2 \end{pmatrix}$

e Stretch by a factor of 3 in the y-direction followed by a translation of $\begin{pmatrix} 0 \\ -2 \end{pmatrix}$

17 a Sketch the graph $y = x^3$.

b Use your sketch in part **a** to draw the graphs obtained after $y = x^3$ is transformed as follows.

   i Reflection in the x-axis

   ii Translation of $\begin{pmatrix} 0 \\ -2 \end{pmatrix}$

   iii Stretch by a scale factor of 3 in the y-direction

   iv Translation of $\begin{pmatrix} -2 \\ 0 \end{pmatrix}$

c Give the equation of each of the graphs obtained in part **b**.

18 a Sketch the graph of $y = \dfrac{1}{x}$.

b Use your sketch in part **a** to draw the graphs obtained after $y = \dfrac{1}{x}$ is transformed as follows.

   i Translation of $\begin{pmatrix} 0 \\ 4 \end{pmatrix}$

   ii Translation of $\begin{pmatrix} 4 \\ 0 \end{pmatrix}$

   iii Stretch, scale factor 3 in the y-direction

   iv Stretch, scale factor $\frac{1}{2}$ in the x-direction

c Give the equation of each of the graphs obtained in part **b**.

PS 19 A teacher asked her class to apply the following transformations to the function $f(x) = x^2$.

   a $f(-x)$

   b $-f(x)$

Martyn said that they must be the same as $-x^2 = x^2$.

Is Martyn correct? Explain your answer.

20 The graphs below are all transformations of $y = x^2$. Two points through which each graph passes are indicated. Use this information to work out the equation of each graph.

a
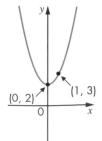

b
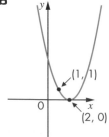

c
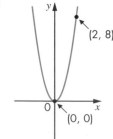

d
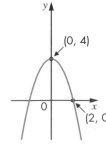

21 The graphs below are all transformations of $y = \sin x$. Two points through which each graph passes are indicated. Use this information to work out the equation of each graph.

a
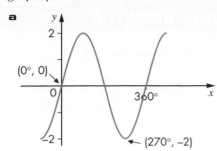

b
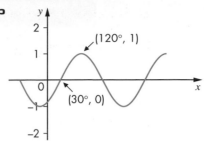

c
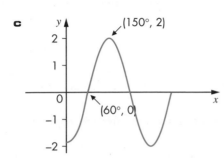

d
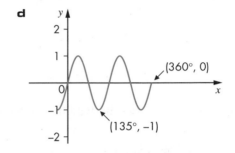

22 Below are the graphs of $y = \sin x$ and $y = \cos x$.

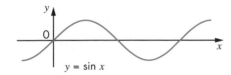
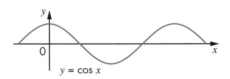

a Describe a series of transformations that would take the first graph to the second.

b Which of these is equivalent to $y = \cos x$?

  i $y = \sin (x + 90°)$ **ii** $y = -\sin (x - 90°)$ **iii** $y = 2\cos \dfrac{x}{2}$

23 **A**
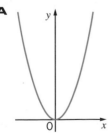

B
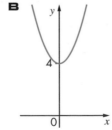

C
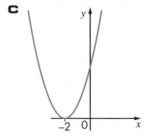

D
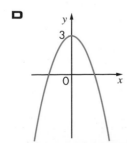

E
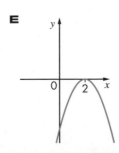

Match each of the graphs **A**, **B**, **C**, **D** and **E** to one of these equations.

  i $y = x^2$ **ii** $y = -x^2 + 3$ **iii** $y = -(x - 2)^2$ **iv** $y = (x + 2)^2$ **v** $y = x^2 + 4$

GRADE BOOSTER

A* You can transform the graph of a given function

A* You can identify the equation of a function from its graph, which has been formed by a transformation on a known function

What you should know now

- How to sketch the graphs of functions such as $y = f(ax)$ and $y = f(x + a)$ from the known graph of $y = f(x)$

- How to describe from their graphs the transformation of one function into another

- How to identify equations from the graphs of transformations of known graphs

1 This is the graph of $y = \cos x$ for $0° \leqslant x \leqslant 360°$.

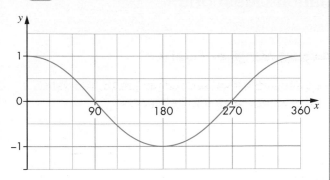

a On a copy of the axes used for the above graph, draw the graph of $y = \cos(x - 90)$ for $0° \leqslant x \leqslant 360°$.

b Write down a possible equation for the following graph.

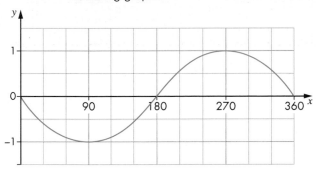

AQA, November 2005, Paper 1, Question 22

2 This is the graph of $y = \cos x$ for $0° \leqslant x \leqslant 360°$.

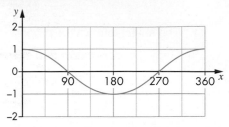

Write the equation of each of the transformed graphs below.

In each case, the graph of $y = \cos x$ is shown dotted to help you.

a

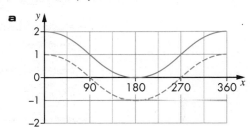

b

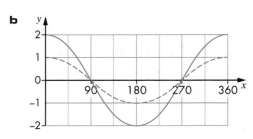

c

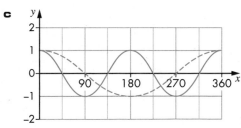

d

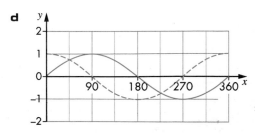

AQA, June 2006, Paper 2, Question 19

A*

Worked Examination Questions

1 The sketch shows the graph $y = x^3$.

Copy the axes below and sketch the graphs indicated.

p is a positive integer greater than 1.
(The graph $y = x^3$ is shown dotted to help you.)

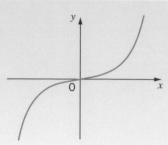

a $4 = x^3 - p$

b $y = (x + p)^3$

c $y = \dfrac{x^3}{p}$

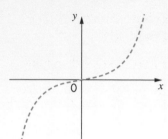

1 a This is a translation of $y = x^3$ by the vector $\begin{pmatrix} 0 \\ -p \end{pmatrix}$.

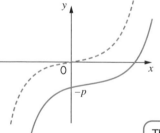

This gets 1 mark.

b This is a translation of $y = x^3$ by the vector $\begin{pmatrix} 0 \\ -p \end{pmatrix}$.

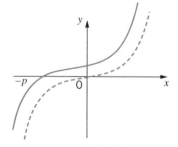

You do not know what the actual value of p is so make sure that the translation is clear. Alternatively, make a value for p up, say 2. This gets 1 mark.

c This is a stretch of $y = x^3$ by a scale factor of $\dfrac{1}{p}$ in the y-direction.

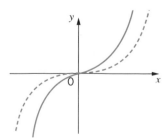

This gets 1 mark.

Total: 3 marks

Worked Examination Questions

PS **2** The sketch shows the graph of $y = x^2 - 6x + 5$.

The minimum point of the graph is $(3, -4)$.

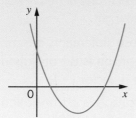

   a Describe what happens to the graph of $f(x) = x^2$ under the transformation $f(x - 3)$.

   b Describe what happens to the graph of $f(x) = x^2$ under the transformation $f(x) - 4$.

   c Explain how the answers to **a** and **b** connect with the equation $y = x^2 - 6x + 5$ and the minimum point $(3, -4)$.

2 **a** A translation of $\begin{pmatrix} 3 \\ 0 \end{pmatrix}$

  b A translation of $\begin{pmatrix} 0 \\ -4 \end{pmatrix}$

  c $x^2 - 6x + 5 = (x - 3)^2 - 4$,

   so the graph is a translation of $\begin{pmatrix} 3 \\ -4 \end{pmatrix}$,

   which takes the original minimum point

   $(0, 0)$ to $(3, -4)$.

> The answers to parts **b** and **c** give the clue to link with the minimum point. Remember that writing the equation in 'completing the square' form $(x - a)^2 - b$ gives the minimum point $(a, -b)$. This gets 1 mark for method and 1 mark for accuracy.

(Total: 2 marks)

In preparation for the Olympics, sportsmen and women across the world dedicate a lot of time and effort to training. Their coaches analyse every action that may contribute to their performance. The smallest detail can make the difference between winning or missing out on an Olympic medal.

Getting started

The graph shows the mean boat speed against time at the beginning of a race for two female Olympic rowers: one a heavyweight and the other a lightweight.

Which of these statements describes the graphs?

- The blue graph is a translation of the red graph by a vector $\begin{pmatrix} 0 \\ a \end{pmatrix}$.
- The blue graph is a translation of the red graph by a vector $\begin{pmatrix} a \\ 0 \end{pmatrix}$.
- The blue graph is a stretch of the red graph in the vertical or y-direction.
- The blue graph is a reflection of the red graph in the horizontal or x-axis.

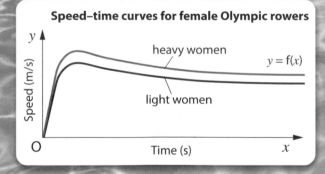

Speed–time curves for female Olympic rowers

heavy women

$y = f(x)$

light women

Speed (m/s)

Time (s)

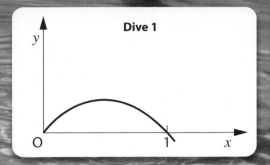

Dive 1

Your task

An Olympic diver begins her training for the day by performing a warm-up dive from the side of the pool. Her coach analyses the path of the dive and describes it as

$$y = -x^2 + x \qquad \text{(dive 1)}$$

where y represents the distance from the surface of the water and x represents the distance from the side of the pool. The graph to the left shows how this looks.

The diver performs a second dive from the side of the pool. Its graph is like the one for dive 1 but with a stretch in the y-direction (dive 2).

Then the diver climbs to the first diving platform, arches her back with arms outstretched and performs a swan dive (dive 3). The graph for this third dive is a transformation of the graph for dive 2.

Finally, the diver is joined by a team-mate to practise for the synchronised diving event. They dive, in unison, from two adjacent platforms along the side of the pool, both at the height of the second diving platform. The coach calls this dive 4.

Read the description of each dive above carefully.

Then write an appropriate equation and an accurate description for each of the transformations for dive 2 and dive 3.

Now consider dive 4. Describe the transformation for this graph.

Write the coach's end-of-day diving team report, sketching some graphs to show the shapes of the dives.

ANSWERS

Quick check

1 **a** 137 **b** 65 **c** 161 **d** 42
e 6.5 **f** 4.6 **g** 13.5 **h** 1.3
2 **a** **i** $\frac{12}{5}$ **ii** $\frac{13}{4}$ **iii** $\frac{16}{9}$
b **i** $1\frac{5}{6}$ **ii** $2\frac{1}{3}$ **iii** $3\frac{2}{7}$

3 **a** 14 **b** 20 **c** 1 **d** 7
4 **a** $1\frac{5}{12}$ **b** $\frac{17}{35}$ **c** $\frac{11}{20}$ **d** $\frac{14}{15}$

1.1 Basic calculations and using brackets

Exercise 1A

1 **a** 144 **b** 108
2 **a** 12.54 **b** 27.45
3 **a** 26.7 **b** 24.5 **c** 145.3 **d** 1.5
4 Sovereign is 102.47p per litre, Bridge is 102.73p per litre so Sovereign is cheaper.
5 Abby 1.247, Bobby 2.942, Col 5.333, Donna 6.538
Col is correct.

6 $31 \times 3600 \div 1610 = 69.31677 \approx 70$
7 **a** 167.552 **b** 196.48
8 **a** 2.77 **b** 6
9 **a** 497.952 **b** 110.978625

1.2 Adding and subtracting fractions with a calculator

Exercise 1B

1 **a** $6\frac{11}{20}$ **b** $8\frac{8}{15}$ **c** $16\frac{1}{4}$ **d** $11\frac{147}{200}$
e $7\frac{43}{80}$ **f** $11\frac{63}{80}$ **g** $3\frac{11}{30}$ **h** $2\frac{29}{48}$
i $3\frac{17}{96}$ **j** $7\frac{167}{240}$ **k** $7\frac{61}{80}$ **l** $4\frac{277}{396}$

2 $\frac{1}{12}$

3 **a** $12\frac{1}{4}$ **b** $3\frac{1}{4}$

4 Use the fraction key ▦ to input $\frac{3}{25}$, then key in ➕ and then use the fraction key again to input $\frac{7}{10}$.

▦ 3 ▼ 2 5 ▶ ➕ ▦ 7 ▼ 1 0 ▶ =

5 $\frac{47}{120}$

6 **a** $-\frac{77}{1591}$ **b** Answer negative
7 **a** $\frac{223}{224}$ **b** $\frac{97}{1248}$ **c** $-\frac{97}{273}$
d One negative and one positive so $\frac{5}{7} > \frac{14}{39} > \frac{9}{32}$.
8 **a** Answers will vary
b Yes, always true, unless fractions are equivalent then answer is also equivalent.
9 $18\frac{11}{12}$ cm
10 $\frac{5}{12}$ (anticlockwise) or $\frac{7}{12}$ (clockwise)

1.3 Multiplying and dividing fractions with a calculator

Exercise 1C

1 **a** $\frac{3}{5}$ **b** $\frac{7}{12}$ **c** $\frac{9}{25}$ **d** $\frac{27}{200}$
e $\frac{21}{320}$ **f** $\frac{27}{128}$ **g** $5\frac{2}{5}$ **h** $5\frac{1}{7}$
i $2\frac{1}{16}$ **j** $\frac{27}{40}$ **k** $3\frac{9}{32}$ **l** $\frac{11}{18}$

2 $\frac{1}{6}$ m²

3 15

4 **a** $\frac{27}{64}$ **b** $\frac{27}{64}$

5 **a** $\frac{4}{5}$ **b** $\frac{4}{5}$ **c** $\frac{16}{21}$ **d** $\frac{16}{21}$

6 **a** $8\frac{11}{20}$ **b** $18\frac{1}{60}$ **c** $65\frac{91}{100}$ **d** $22\frac{1}{8}$
e $7\frac{173}{320}$ **f** $52\frac{59}{160}$ **g** $2\frac{17}{185}$ **h** $2\frac{22}{103}$
i $1\frac{305}{496}$ **j** $5\frac{17}{65}$ **k** $7\frac{881}{4512}$ **l** $5\frac{547}{1215}$

7 $18\frac{5}{12}$ m²

8 $3\frac{11}{32}$ cm³

9 $90\frac{5}{8}$ miles

10 3
11 3

Examination questions

1 $\frac{14}{3} = 4\frac{2}{3}$ litres milk

So three bottles needed.

2 $73\frac{13}{19}$ or 73.7 mph

3 16

4 $20\frac{5}{12}$ cm²

5 a $\frac{3}{4}$ m

 b 100 strides

 c 2250 m = 2.25 km

6 a $56\frac{1}{4}$ cm² **b** $10\frac{1}{4}$ cm

7 a 19.854 545 45... **b** 19.9

8 a 23.761 536 42... **b** 23.8 or 24

9 a 30.946 944 26... **b** 30.95

10 a 3.586 440 678... **b** 3.59

11 a 77 cm³

 b Two numbers with a product of 20, for example 5 cm and 4 cm

12 $12\frac{1}{4}$ cm². He has calculated 3×3 and $\frac{1}{2} \times \frac{1}{2}$

13 4 cm

Answers to Chapter 2

Quick check

1 a $3x - 15$ **b** $2x + 14$ **c** $14x - 21$
2 a $6y$ **b** $7x - 3$ **c** $x + 5$
3 a $8x$ **b** $18y^2$ **c** $3x^3$
4 a 4 **b** 6 **c** 64
 d -1 **e** 4 **f** 33

2.1 Basic algebra

Exercise 2A

1 a All of them

 b $\frac{1}{2}$

2 a $15 - 5m$ **b** $6x + 21$
 c $x^2 + 2x$ **d** $10m - 2m^2$
 e $5s^2 + 15s$ **f** $3nm - 3np$

3 a $3(6 - m)$ **b** $6(x + 2)$
 c $x(x + 5)$ **d** $m(10 - m)$
 e $3(5s^2 + 1)$ **f** $n(3 - p)$

4 a $-3x - 8y$ **b** $-2a + 4b$

5 a Side AF − side DE = $4x - 1 - x$
   $= 3x - 1$
 b $14x$
 c 84 cm

6 4 cm × 12 cm

7 a 4.1 **b** 8 **c** 4.525

8 Any values that work, e.g. $x = 8$, $b = 4$, $h = 32$

9 a £767.50
 b £107.50 in debit

10 a x must be 2, y can be any other prime number
 b x must be an odd prime, y can be any other prime number

11 a $6 + 3 \times 9 - 5 \times 3 = 18$
 b $2 \times 6 - 9 + 3 \times 3 = 12$

12 a $\frac{450}{5n}$ **b** £390

13 a $12p^3 - 4p^2q$ **b** $10t^4 + 35t^2$
 c $10x^2 + 35xy$ **d** $10m^2 - 2m^5$
 e $8s^4 + 24s^3t$ **f** $6nm^3 - 6n^2m^2$

14 a $4(t - 2)$ and $4t - 8$ **b** £26

15 a $23x + 11$ **b** $9y + 7$
 c $2x - 8$ **d** $22x + 9$
 e $14x^2 - 10x$ **f** $2x^3 + 17x^2 - 9$

16 a $3p(3p + 2t)$
 b $4m(3p - 2m)$
 c $4ab(4a + 1)$
 d $2(2a^2 - 3a + 1) = 2(2a - 1)(a - 1)$
 e $5xy(4y + 2x + 1)$
 f $4mt(2t - m)$

17 Darren has added 2 and 3 instead of multiplying, and has added 2 and -5 instead of multiplying. The correct answer is $6x - 10$.

18 a $4(2y + 4)$
 b $3(2z + 1)$

19 Number off each day continues 81, 243, 729, 2187
Total number off continues 121, 364, 1093, 3280
So by the 8th day there are no students left in school.

20 a $21f + 21s$
 b $315f + 504s$
 c £240

21 $6(3x + 5) - 2(x - 2) = 18x + 30 - 2x + 4 = 16x + 34$

22 a Both calculations give the cost of 5 meals and 5 desserts
 b Easier to work out as bracketed term evaluates to 10
 c £50

23 a Aimee
 b They do not take out the highest common factor

24 No common factors

25 a $3 \times (5 + 1) = 3 \times 6 = 18$, $3 \times 5 + 3 = 15 + 3 = 18$
 b $3 \times (n + 2 + 1) = 3 \times (n + 3) = 3n + 9$, $3 \times (n + 2) + 3$
  $= 3n + 6 + 3 = 3n + 9$

2.2 Solving linear equations

Exercise 2B

1 a 13 **b** 19 **c** −1 **d** 41
2 a −3 **b** $2\frac{1}{2}$ **c** 0 **d** $5\frac{1}{2}$

3 a 2 **b** 15 **c** 7 **d** 1
4 a −12 **b** 5 **c** −1 **d** 1
5 $a = b - c$

6 a 2nd term is $2a + 3$, 3rd term is $2(2a + 3) + 3 = 4a + 9$, 4th term is $2(4a + 9) + 3 = 41$
b 2.5

2.3 Setting up equations

Exercise 2C

1 90p
2 a 1.5 **b** 2
3 a 1.5 cm **b** 6.75 cm^2
4 17
5 8
6 a $8c - 10 = 56$
b £8.25
7 a B: 450 cars, C: 450 cars, D: 300 cars
b 800
c 750

8 Length is 5.5 m, width is 2.5 m and area is 13.75 m^2. Carpet costs £123.75
9 3 years
10 9 years
11 3 cm
12 5
13 a $4x + 40 = 180$
b $x = 35°$
14 a $\frac{x + 10}{5} = 9.50$
b £37.50

15 a 15
b −1
c $2(n + 3)$, $2(n + 3) - 5$
d $2(n + 3) - 5 = n$, $2n + 6 - 5 = n$, $2n + 1 = n$, $n = -1$
16 No, as $x + x + 2 + x + 4 + x + 6 = 360$ gives $x = 87°$ so the consecutive numbers (87, 89, 91, 93) are not even but odd
17 $4x + 18 = 3x + 1 + 50$, $x = 33$ Large bottle 1.5 litres, small bottle 1 litre

2.4 Trial and improvement

Exercise 2D

1 a 4 and 5 **b** 4 and 5
c 2 and 3
2 $x = 3.5$
3 $x = 3.7$
4 $x = 2.5$
5 $x = 1.5$
6 a $x = 2.4$ **b** $x = 2.8$
c $x = 3.2$

7 a Area $= x(x + 5) = 100$
b width = 7.8 cm, length = 12.8 cm
8 $x = 5.8$
9 Volume $= x \times 2x(x + 8) = 500$, $x^3 + 8x^2 = 250$, $4 \Rightarrow 192$, $5 \Rightarrow 325$, $4.4 \Rightarrow 240.064$, $4.5 \Rightarrow 253.125$, $4.45 \Rightarrow 246.541125$, so dimensions are 4.5 cm, 9 cm and 12.5 cm

10 a Cube is x^3, hole is $\frac{x}{2} \times \frac{x}{2} \times 8 = 2x^2$
Cube minus hole is 1500
b $12 \Rightarrow 1440$, $13 \Rightarrow 1859$, $12.1 \Rightarrow 1478.741$, $12.2 \Rightarrow 1518.168$, $12.15 \Rightarrow 1498.368375$ so the value of $x = 12.2$ (to 1 dp)
11 2.76 and 7.24

2.5 Solving simultaneous equations

Exercise 2E

1 $x = 2.5$, $y = -1.25$
2 $x = 1.5$, $y = 3.5$
3 $x = 3$, $y = 2$
4 $x = 7$, $y = -1$
5 $x = 5$, $y = -2$

6 $x = 6$, $y = -4$
7 $x = 2$, $y = -3$
8 $x = 2$, $y = 1$
9 $x = 2$, $y = -1$
10 $x = -1$, $y = 3$

11 $x = 5$, $y = -2$
12 $x = 3.5$, $y = 1.5$
13 $x = -2.5$, $y = -3.5$
14 $x = 4$, $y = -2$
15 $x = 4.25$, $y = 3.75$

2.6 Solving problems with simultaneous equations

Exercise 2F

1 Amul £7.20, Kim £3.50
2 a $10x + 5y = 420$, $8x + 10y = 540$
b £2.11
3 a $6x + 3y = 435$, $11x + 7y = 880$
b £5.55
4 a My age minus 6 equals $2 \times$ (my son's age minus 6)
b $x = 46$ and $y = 26$
5 a $3t + 5b = 810$, $3t + 3b = 630$
b £10.20

6 84p
7 10.3 kg
8 £4.40
9 £62
10 £195
11 2 hr 10 min
12 $p = 36$, $c = 22$. Total weight for Baz is 428 pounds so he can carry the load safely on his trailer

13 b = £3.50, p = £1.75. Camilla needs £35 so she will not have enough money
14 When Carmen worked out (2) − (3), she should have got $y = 6$
When Jeff rearranged $2x + 8 - x = 10$, he should have got $x = 2$
They also misunderstood 'two, six' as this means $x = 2$ and $y = 6$, not the other way round

2.7 Solving quadratic equations

Exercise 2G

1 $-1, -4$

2 $3, -8$

3 $6, -1$

4 $15, -2$

5 $5, 2$

6 $3, -3$

7 $\pm\sqrt{\frac{5}{2}}$

8 $5, -5$

9 $\pm\frac{2}{3}$

10 $0, 5$

11 $0, -\frac{7}{3}$

12 $\frac{2}{3}, -\frac{1}{4}$

13 $2, \frac{1}{5}$

14 -3

15 $\frac{1}{3}, -2$

16 $-2\frac{1}{2}$

17 $\frac{4}{3}, 4$

18 $\frac{1}{3}, -2\frac{1}{2}$

19 $\frac{1}{2}, -1\frac{1}{2}$

20 $\frac{1}{4}, -1\frac{1}{3}$

21 **a** $x^2 - 2x + 1 = 0$
  b $4x^2 - 9 = 0$

22 $(-1.5, -2.25)$

2.8 The quadratic formula

Exercise 2H

1 $1.77, -2.27$

2 $-0.23, -1.43$

3 $3.70, -2.70$

4 $0.29, -0.69$

5 $-0.19, -1.53$

6 $-1.23, -2.43$

7 $-0.41, -1.84$

8 $-1.39, -2.27$

9 $1.37, -4.37$

10 $2.18, 0.15$

11 $-0.39, -5.11$

12 $0.44, -1.69$

13 $1.64, 0.61$

14 $0.36, -0.79$

15 $1.89, 0.11$

16 13

17 $x^2 - 3x - 7 = 0$

18 Terry gets $x = \frac{4 + \sqrt{0}}{8}$ and June gets $(2x - 1)^2 = 0$ which only give one solution $x = \frac{1}{2}$

2.9 Solving problems with quadratic equations

Exercise 2I

1 52, two

2 65, two

3 24, two

4 85, two

5 145, two

6 68, two

7 -35, none

8 -23, none

9 41, two

10 40, two

11 -135, none

12 37, two

13 $x^2 + 3x - 1 = 0$; $x^2 - 3x - 1 = 0$; $x^2 + x - 3 = 0$; $x^2 - x - 3 = 0$

Exercise 2J

1 15 m, 20 m

2 29

3 6.54, 0.46

4 5, 0.5

5 16 m by 14 m

6 48 km/h

7 45, 47

8 2.54 m, 3.54 m

9 30 km/h

10 10p

11 1.25, 0.8

12 10

13 5 h

14 0.75 m

15 Area = 22.75, width = 3.5 m

Examination questions

1 **a** $6x - 18 = 270$ or $6x + 72 = 360$
  b $x = 48$, largest $= 132°$

2 **a** $(0, -8)$
  b 2.5

3 **a** $4a + 3 = 2b + 5$, $4a - 2b = 2$, $2a - b = 1$
  b $a = 2.25$, $b = 3.5$

4 **a** $2y + x + 1 + 11 = 11 + 2x + 2y + y$, $x + 1 = 2x + y$, $1 = x + y$
  b $2y + x + 1 + 11 = x + 1 + 2x + y$, $2y + 11 = 2x + y$, $2x - y = 11$
  c $x = 4, y = -3$
  d Clockwise from 11: (11), 2, -3, 8, 5, -6

5 $x = 1.27, -2.77$

6 $3.65, -1.65$

7 **a** $(8 - x)(10 - x) = 0.6 \times 80$, $80 - 18x + x^2 = 48$, $x^2 - 18x + 32 = 0$
  b $x = 2$ or 16 (reject 16), so path is 2 m wide

Answers to Chapter 3

Quick check

1 **a** $\frac{3}{5}$ **b** $\frac{1}{5}$ **c** $\frac{1}{3}$ **d** $\frac{16}{25}$ **e** $\frac{2}{5}$ **f** $\frac{3}{4}$ **g** $\frac{1}{3}$

2 **a** £12   **b** £33   **c** 175 litres   **d** 15 kg   **e** 40 m   **f** £35   **g** 135 g   **h** 1.05 litres

3.1   Speed, time and distance

Exercise 3A

1 18 mph
2 280 miles
3 52.5 mph
4 11.50 am
5 500 seconds
6 **a** 75 mph   **b** 6.5 hours
   c 175 miles   **d** 240 km
   e 64 km/h   **f** 325 km
   g 4.3 h (4 h 18 min)

7 **a** 7.75 h   **b** 52.9 mph
8 **a** 2.25 h   **b** 99 miles
9 **a** 1.25 h   **b** 1 h 15 min
10 **a** 48 mph   **b** 6 h 40 min
11 **a** 120 km   **b** 48 km/h
12 **a** 30 min   **b** 6 mph
13 **a** 10 m/s   **b** 3.3 m/s
   c 16.7 m/s   **d** 41.7 m/s
   e 20.8 m/s

14 **a** 90 km/h   **b** 43.2 km/h
   c 14.4 km/h   **d** 108 km/h
   e 1.8 km/h
15 **a** 64.8 km/h   **b** 28 s
   c 8.07
16 **a** 6.7 m/s   **b** 66 km
   c 5 minutes   **d** 133.3
17 7 minutes
18 **a** 20 mph   **b** 07.30

3.2   Direct proportion problems

Exercise 3B

1 60 g
2 £5.22
3 45
4 £6.72
5 **a** £312.50   **b** 8
6 **a** 56 litres   **b** 350 miles
7 **a** 300 kg   **b** 9 weeks
8 40 seconds
9 **a** **i** 100 g, 200 g, 250 g, 150 g
    ii 150 g, 300 g, 375 g, 225 g
    iii 250 g, 500 g, 625 g, 375 g
   b 24

10 Peter: £2.30 ÷ 6 = 38.33p each; I can buy four packs (24 sausages) from him (£9.20)
Paul: £3.50 ÷ 10 = 35p each; I can only buy two packs (20 sausages) from him (£7)
I should use Peter's shop to get the most sausages for £10
11 11 minutes 40 seconds + 12 minutes = 23 minutes 40 seconds
12 Possible answer:
30 g plain flour (rounding to nearest 10 g)
60 ml whole milk (rounding to nearest 10 ml)
1 egg (need an egg)
1 g salt (nearest whole number)
10 ml beef dripping or lard (rounding to nearest 10 ml)
13 30 litres

3.3   Best buys

Exercise 3C

1 **a** £4.50 for a 10-pack
   b £1.08 for 6
   c £2.45 for 1 litre
   d Same value
   e 29p for 250 g
   f £1.39 for a pack of 6
   g £4 for 3

2 **a** Large jar as more g per £
   b 600 g tin as more g per p
   c 5 kg bag as more kg per £
   d 75 ml tube as more ml per £
   e Large box as more g per £
   f Large box as more g per £
   g 400 ml bottle as more ml per £

3 **a** £5.11
   b Large tin (small £5.11/l, medium £4.80/l, large £4.47/l)
4 **a** 95p   **b** Family size
5 Bashir's
6 Mary
7 Kelly

3.4   Density

Exercise 3D

1 0.75 g/cm^3
2 $8\frac{1}{3}$ g/cm^3
3 32 g
4 120 cm^3

5 156.8 g
6 3200 cm^3
7 2.72 g/cm^3
8 36 800 kg
9 1.79 g/cm^3 (3 sf)

10 1.6 g/cm^3
11 First statue is the fake as density is approximately 26 g/cm^3
12 Second piece by 1 cm^3
13 0.339 m^3

Examination questions

1 4 minutes
2 a 75%
   b 36 000 litres
3 8 mph

4 a £105
   b 70%
5 4.17 kg

6 a 140 km
   b 100 km/h

Answers to Chapter 4

Quick check

1 a 90 mm^2 **b** 40 cm^2 **c** 21 m^2 **2** 120 cm^3

4.1 Circumference and area of a circle

Exercise 4A

1 a 8 cm, 25.1 cm, 50.3 cm^2
   b 5.2 m, 16.3 m, 21.2 m^2
   c 6 cm, 37.7 cm, 113 cm^2
   d 1.6 m, 10.1 m, 8.04 m^2
2 a 5π cm **b** 8π cm
   c 18π m **d** 12π cm
3 a 25π cm^2 **b** 36π cm^2
   c 100π cm^2 **d** 0.25π m^2

4 8.80 m
5 4 complete revolutions
6 1p : 3.1 cm^2, 2p : 5.3 cm^2,
   5p : 2.3 cm^2, 10p : 4.5 cm^2
7 0.83 m
8 38.6 cm
9 Claim is correct (ratio of the areas is
   just over 1.5 : 1)

10 a 18π cm^2 **b** 4π cm^2
11 9π cm^2
12 28.3 m^2
13 Diameter of tree is 9.96 m
14 45 complete revolutions

4.2 Area of a trapezium

Exercise 4B

1 a 30 cm^2 **b** 77 cm^2
   c 24 cm^2 **d** 42 cm^2
   e 40 m^2 **f** 6 cm
   g 3 cm **h** 10 cm
2 a 27.5 cm, 36.25 cm^2
   b 33.4 cm, 61.2 cm^2
   c 38.5 m, 90 m^2

3 The area of the parallelogram is $\frac{(a + b)}{h}$.
   This is the same as two trapezia
4 Two of 20 cm^2 and two of 16 cm^2
5 a 57 m^2
   b 702.5 cm^2
   c 84 m^2

6 47 m^2
7 4, because the total area doubled is
   about 32 m^2
8 80.2%
9 1 100 000 km^2
10 160 cm^2

4.3 Sectors

Exercise 4C

1 a i 5.59 cm **ii** 22.3 cm^2
   b i 8.29 cm **ii** 20.7 cm^2
   c i 16.3 cm **ii** 98.0 cm^2
   d i 15.9 cm **ii** 55.6 cm^2
2 2π cm, 6π cm^2
3 a 73.8 cm **b** 20.3 cm
4 a 107 cm^2
   b 173 cm^2

5 43.6 cm
6 a $\frac{180}{\pi}$
   b If arc length is 10 cm, distance
   along chord joining the two points of
   the sector on the circumference will
   be less than 10 cm, so angle at
   centre will be less than 60°

7 (36π − 72) cm^2
8 36.5 cm^2
9 16 cm (15.7)
10 a 13.9 cm
   b 7.07 cm^2

4.4 Volume of a prism

Exercise 4D

1 a i 21 cm^2 **ii** 63 cm^3
   b i 48 cm^2 **ii** 432 cm^3
   c i 36 m^2 **ii** 324 m^3
2 a 432 m^3 **b** 225 m^3 **c** 1332 m^3
3 a A cross-section parallel to the side of
   the pool always has the same shape

   b About 3$\frac{1}{2}$ hours

4 7.65 m^3
5 a 21 cm^3, 210 cm^3
   b 54 cm^2, 270 cm^3
6 146 cm^3

7 78 m^3 (78.3 m^3)
8 327 litres
9 1.02 tonnes
10 672 cm^2

4.5   Cylinders

Exercise 4E

1 **a** **i** 226 cm^3
      ii 207 cm^2
   b **i** 14.9 cm^3
      ii 61.3 cm^2
   c **i** 346 cm^3
      ii 275 cm^2
   d **i** 1060 cm^3
      ii 636 cm^2
2 **a** **i** 72π cm^3
      ii 48π cm^2
   b **i** 112π cm^3
      ii 56π cm^2

   c **i** 180π cm^3
      ii 60π cm^2
   d **i** 600π m^3
      ii 120π m^2
3 £80
4 1.23 tonnes
5 665 cm^3
6 Label should be less than 10.5 cm wide
   so that it fits the can and does not
   overlap the rim and more than 23.3 cm
   long to allow an overlap
7 332 litres

8 There is no right answer. Students
   could start with the dimensions of a
   real can. Often drinks cans are not
   exactly cylindrical. One possible
   answer is height of 6.6 cm and
   diameter of 8 cm
9 1.71 g/cm^3
10 7.78 g/cm^3
11 About 127 cm
12 A diameter of 10 cm and a length of
   5 cm give a volume close to 400 cm^3
   (0.4 litres)

4.6   Volume of a pyramid

Exercise 4F

1 **a** 56 cm^3 **b** 168 cm^3
   c 1040 cm^3 **d** 84 cm^3
   e 160 cm^3
2 270 cm^3
3 **a** Put the apexes of the pyramids
      together. The 6 square bases will
      then form a cube

   b If the side of the base is a then the
      height will be $\frac{1}{2}a$.
      Total volume of the 6 pyramids is a^3.
      Volume of one pyramid is $\frac{1}{6}a^3 =$
      $\frac{1}{3} \times \frac{1}{2} \times a \times a^2 =$
      $\frac{1}{3} \times$ height $\times$ base area

4 6.9 m ($\frac{1}{3}$ height of pyramid)
5 **a** 73.3 m^3 **b** 45 m^3
   c 3250 cm^3
6 208 g
7 1.5 g
8 6.0 cm
9 14.4 cm
10 260 cm^3

4.7   Cones

Exercise 4G

1 **a** **i** 3560 cm^3
      ii 1430 cm^2
   b **i** 314 cm^3
      ii 283 cm^2
   c **i** 1020 cm^3
      ii 679 cm^2
2 935 g

3 24π cm^2
4 **a** 816π cm^3 **b** 720π mm^3
5 **a** 4 cm
   b 6 cm
   c Various answers, e.g. 60° gives
      2 cm, 240° gives 8 cm
6 24π cm^2

7 If radius of base is r, slant height is $2r$.
   Area of curved surface $= \pi r \times 2r =$
   $2\pi r^2$, area of base $= \pi r^2$
8 140 g
9 2.81 cm

4.8   Spheres

Exercise 4H

1 **a** 36π cm^3 **b** 288π cm^3
   c 1330π cm^3
2 **a** 36π cm^2 **b** 100π cm^2
   c 196π cm^2
3 65 400 cm^3, 7850 cm^2
4 **a** 1960 cm^2 **b** 8180 cm^3
5 125 cm
6 6231

7 **a** The surface area, because this is the
      amount of material (leather or
      plastic) needed to make the ball
   b Surface area can vary from about
      1470 cm^2 to 1560 cm^2, difference
      of about 90 cm^2. This seems
      surprisingly large
8 7.8 cm

9 48%
10 Radius of sphere = base radius of
   cylinder = r, height of cylinder = $2r$
   Curved surface area of cylinder =
   circumference $\times$ height $= 2\pi r \times 2r =$
   $4\pi r^2 =$ surface area of sphere

Examination questions

1 **a** 66.5 cm^2 **b** 855.5 cm^2
2 **a** 320π cm^3 **b** 4
3 11 777 cm^3
4 9.08 cm
5 480π cm^3
6 $\frac{3}{8}$

Answers to Chapter 5

Quick check

1	5.3	**3**	0.6	**5**	16.1
2	246.5	**4**	2.8	**6**	0.7

5.1 Pythagoras' theorem

Exercise 5A

1 10.3 cm
2 5.9 cm
3 8.5 cm
4 20.6 cm

5 18.6 cm
6 17.5 cm
7 5 cm
8 13 cm

9 10 cm
10 The square in the first diagram and the two squares in the second have the same area

5.2 Finding a shorter side

Exercise 5B

1 a 15 cm   **b** 14.7 cm
   c 6.3 cm   **d** 18.3 cm
2 a 20.8 m   **b** 15.5 cm
   c 15.5 m   **d** 12.4 cm

3 a 5 m   **b** 6 m
   c 3 m   **d** 50 cm

4 There are infinite possibilities, e.g. any multiple of 3, 4, 5 such as 6, 8, 10; 9, 12, 15; 12, 16, 20; multiples of 5, 12, 13 and of 8, 15, 17
5 42.6 cm

5.3 Applying Pythagoras' theorem in real situations

Exercise 5C

1 No. The foot of the ladder is about 6.6 m from the wall
2 2.06 m
3 11.3 m
4 About 17 minutes, assuming it travels at the same speed.
5 127 m − 99.6 m = 27.4 m
6 4.58 m

7 a 3.87 m
   b 1.74 m
8 3.16 m
9 13 units
10 a 4.85 m
   b 4.83 m (There is only a small difference.)

11 Yes, because $24^2 + 7^2 = 25^2$
12 6 cm
13 Greater than 20 cm (no width) and less than 28.3 cm (a square)

Exercise 5D

1 a 32.2 cm^2
   b 2.83 cm^2
   c 50.0 cm^2
2 22.2 cm^2
3 15.6 cm^2
4 a

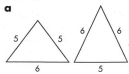

   b The areas are 12 cm^2 and 13.6 cm^2 respectively, so triangle with 6 cm, 6 cm, 5 cm sides has the greater area
5 a

   b 166.3 cm^2

6 259.8 cm^2

7 a No, areas vary from 24.5 cm^2 to 27.7 cm^2
   b No, equilateral triangle gives the largest area
   c The closer the isosceles triangle gets to an equilateral triangle the larger its area becomes
8 19.8 or 20 m^2
9 48 cm^2
10 a 10 cm   **b** 26 cm   **c** 9.6 cm

5.4 Pythagoras' theorem in three dimensions

Exercise 5E

1 a i 14.4 cm **ii** 13 cm **iii** 9.4 cm
   b 15.2 cm
2 No, 6.6 m is longest length
3 a 20.6 cm   **b** 15.0 cm

4 21.3 cm
5 a 8.49 m   **b** 9 m
6 17.3 cm
7 20.6 cm

8 a 11.3 cm   **b** 7 cm
   c 8.06 cm
9 a 50.0 cm   **b** 54.8 cm
   c 48.3 cm   **d** 27.0 cm

5.5   Trigonometric ratios

Exercise 5F

1 **a** 0.682 **b** 0.829 **c** 0.922
   d 1   **e** 0.707 **f** 0.342
   g 0.375 **h** 0
2 **a** 0.731 **b** 0.559 **c** 0.388
   d 0   **e** 0.707 **f** 0.940
   g 0.927 **h** 1
3 45°
4 **a** **i** 0.574 **ii** 0.574
   b **i** 0.208 **ii** 0.208
   c **i** 0.391 **ii** 0.391
   d Same
   e **i** sin 15° is the same as cos 75°
     ii cos 82° is the same as sin 8°
     iii sin x is the same as cos (90° − x)

5 **a** 0.933 **b** 1.48 **c** 2.38
   d Infinite **e** 1 **f** 0.364
   g 0.404 **h** 0
6 **a** 0.956 **b** 0.899 **c** 2.16
   d 0.999 **e** 0.819 **f** 0.577
   g 0.469 **h** 0.996
7 Has values > 1
8 **a** 4.53 **b** 4.46 **c** 6   **d** 0
9 **a** 10.7 **b** 5.40 **c** Infinite **d** 0
10 **a** 3.56 **b** 8.96 **c** 28.4 **d** 8.91
11 **a** 5.61 **b** 11.3 **c** 6   **d** 10
12 **a** 1.46 **b** 7.77 **c** 0.087 **d** 7.15
13 **a** 7.73 **b** 48.6 **c** 2.28 **d** 15.2

14 **a** 29.9 **b** 44.8
   c 20.3 **d** 2.38
15 **a** $\frac{4}{5}, \frac{3}{5}, \frac{4}{3}$
   b $\frac{5}{13}, \frac{12}{13}, \frac{5}{12}$
   c $\frac{7}{25}, \frac{24}{25}, \frac{7}{24}$

5.6   Calculating angles

Exercise 5G

1 **a** 30°   **b** 51.7° **c** 39.8°
   d 61.3° **e** 87.4° **f** 45.0°
2 **a** 60°   **b** 50.2° **c** 2.6°
   d 45.0 **e** 78.5° **f** 45.6°
3 **a** 31.0° **b** 20.8° **c** 41.8°
   d 46.4° **e** 69.5° **f** 77.1°

4 **a** 53.1° **b** 41.8° **c** 44.4°
   d 56.4° **e** 2.4°   **f** 22.6°
5 **a** 36.9° **b** 48.2° **c** 45.6°
   d 33.6° **e** 87.6° **f** 67.4°
6 **a** 31.0° **b** 37.9° **c** 15.9°
   d 60.9° **e** 57.5° **f** 50.2°

7 Error message, largest value 1,
   smallest value −1
8 **a** **i** 17.5° **ii** 72.5° **iii** 90°
   b Yes

5.7   Using the sine and cosine functions

Exercise 5H

1 **a** 17.5° **b** 22.0°
   c 32.2°
2 **a** 5.29 cm **b** 5.75 cm
   c 13.2 cm

3 **a** 4.57 cm **b** 6.86 cm
   c 100 cm
4 **a** 5.12 cm **b** 9.77 cm
   c 11.7 cm **d** 15.5 cm

5 **a** 47.2° **b** 5.42 cm
   c 13.7 cm **d** 38.0°
6 **a** 6   **b** 15
   c 30

Exercise 5I

1 **a** 51.3° **b** 75.5°
   c 51.3°
2 **a** 6.47 cm **b** 32.6 cm
   c 137 cm

3 **a** 7.32 cm **b** 39.1 cm
   c 135 cm
4 **a** 5.35 cm **b** 14.8 cm
   c 12.0 cm **d** 8.62 cm

5 **a** 5.59 cm **b** 46.6°
   c 9.91 cm **d** 40.1°
6 **a** 10   **b** 39
   c 2.5

5.8   Using the tangent function

Exercise 5J

1 **a** 33.7° **b** 36.9° **c** 52.1°
2 **a** 5.09 cm   **b** 30.4 cm
   c 1120 cm

3 **a** 8.24 cm   **b** 62.0 cm
   c 72.8 cm
4 **a** 9.02 cm   **b** 7.51 cm
   c 7.14 cm   **d** 8.90 cm

5 **a** 13.7 cm   **b** 48.4°
   c 7.03 cm   **d** 41.2°
6 12, 12, 2

5.9   Which ratio to use

Exercise 5K

1 **a** 12.6 **b** 59.6 **c** 74.7
   d 16.0 **e** 67.9 **f** 20.1
2 **a** 44.4° **b** 39.8° **c** 44.4°
   d 49.5° **e** 58.7° **f** 38.7°

3 **a** 67.4° **b** 11.3 **c** 134
   d 28.1° **e** 39.7 **f** 263
   g 50.2° **h** 51.3° **i** 138
   j 22.8

4 **a** Sides of right-hand triangle are sine
     and cosine
   b Pythagoras' theorem
   c Students should check the formulae

5.10 Solving problems using trigonometry 1

Exercise 5L

1 65°
2 The safe limits are between 1.04 m and 2.05 m. The ladder will reach between 5.63 m and 5.90 m up the wall
3 44°
4 6.82 m
5 31°

6 a 25°
  b 2.10 m
  c Thickness of wood has been ignored
7 a 20° **b** 4.78 m
8 She would calculate 100 tan 23°. The answer is about 42.4 m
9 21.1 m

10 One way is stand opposite a feature, such as a tree, on the opposite bank, move a measured distance, x, along your bank and measure the angle, θ, between your bank and the feature. Width of river is x tan θ. This of course requires measuring equipment! An alternative is to walk along the bank until the angle is 45° (if that is possible). This angle is easily found by folding a sheet of paper. This way an angle measurer is not required

Exercise 5M

1 10.1 km
2 22°
3 429 m
4 a 156 m

b No. The new angle of depression is $\tan^{-1}\left(\frac{200}{312}\right)$ = 33° and half of 52° is 26°

5 a 222 m **b** 42°
6 a 21.5 m **b** 17.8 m
7 13.4 m
8 19°

9 The angle is 16° so Cara is not quite correct

5.11 Solving problems using trigonometry 2

Exercise 5N

1 a 73.4 km   **b** 15.6 km
2 a 14.7 miles **b** 8.5 miles
3 120°
4 a 59.4 km   **b** 8.4 km

5 a 15.9 km   **b** 24.1 km
  c 31.2 km   **d** 052°
6 2.28 km
7 235°

8 a 66.2 km   **b** 11.7 km
  c 13.1 km   **d** 170°
9 48.4 km, 100°

Exercise 5P

1 a 5.79 cm   **b** 48.2°
  c 7.42 cm   **d** 81.6 cm

2 9.86 m
3 a 36.4 cm^2 **b** 115 cm^2

c 90.6 cm^2 **d** 160 cm^2
4 473 cm^2

Examination questions

1 13.6 cm
2 12 cm^2

3 64°
4 a 24.1 cm   **b** 14.7 cm

5 20.3°
6 a 15.3 cm   **b** 19.1°

Answers to Chapter 6

Quick check

1 $a = 50°$
2 $b = 140°$
3 $c = d = 65°$

6.1 Special triangles and quadrilaterals

Exercise 6A

1 $a = b = 70°$, $c = 50°$, $d = 80°$, $e = 55°$, $f = 70°$, $g = h = 57.5°$
2

3 a $a = 110°$, $b = 55°$
  b $c = e = 105°$, $d = 75°$
  c $f = 135°$, $g = 25°$
  d $e = f = 94°$
  e $j = l = 105°$, $k = 75°$
  f $m = o = 49°$, $n = 131°$
4 40°, 40°, 100°

5 $a = b = 65°$, $c = d = 115°$, $e = f = 65°$, $g = 80°$, $h = 60°$, $i = 60°$, $j = 60°$, $k = 20°$
6 a $x = 25°$, $y = 15°$
  b $x = 7°$, $y = 31°$
  c $x = 60°$, $y = 30°$
7 a $x = 50°$: 60°, 70°, 120°, 110° – possibly trapezium
  b $x = 60°$: 50°, 130°, 50°, 130° – parallelogram or isosceles trapezium
  c $x = 30°$: 20°, 60°, 140°, 140° – possibly kite
  d $x = 20°$: 90°, 90°, 90°, 90° – square or rectangle

8 52°
9 Both 129°
10 $y = 360° - 4x$
11 a 65°
  b Trapezium, angle A + angle D = 180° and angle B + angle C = 180°

6.2　Angles in polygons

Exercise 6B

1 a 1440°　　**b** 2340°
　c 17 640°　　**d** 7740°
2 a 150°　**b** 162°
　c 140°　**d** 174°
3 a 9　　**b** 15　　**c** 102　　**d** 50
4 a 15　　**b** 36　　**c** 24　　**d** 72
5 a 12　　**b** 9　　**c** 20　　**d** 40
6 a 130°　**b** 95°　**c** 130°
7 a 50°　**b** 40°　**c** 59°

8 Hexagon
9 a Octagon　　**b** 89°
10 a i 71°　　**ii** 109°　　**iii** Equal
　b If S = sum of the two opposite
　interior angles, then $S + I = 180°$
　(angles in a triangle), and we know
　$E + I = 180°$ (angles on a straight
　line), so $S + I = E + I$, therefore
　$S = E$

11 $a = 144°$
12 Three angles are 135° and two angles
　are 67.5°.
13 88°; $\dfrac{1440° - 5 \times 200}{5}$
14 a 36°　　**b** 10

6.3　Circle theorems

Exercise 6C

1 a 56°　　**b** 62°　　**c** 105°
　d 55°　　**e** 45°　　**f** 30°
　g 60°　　**h** 145°
2 a 55°　　**b** 52°　　**c** 50°
　d 24°　　**e** 39°　　**f** 80°
　g 34°　　**h** 30°
3 a 41°　　**b** 49°　　**c** 41°
4 a 72°　　**b** 37°　　**c** 72°
5 $\angle$AZY = 40° (angles in a triangle),
　$a = 50°$ (angle in a semicircle = 90°)

6 a $x = y = 40°$
　b $x = 131°, y = 111°$
　c $x = 134°, y = 23°$
　d $x = 32°, y = 19°$
　e $x = 59°, y = 121°$
　f $x = 155°, y = 12.5°$
7 68°

8 $\angle$ABC = $180° - x$ (angles on a line),
　$\angle$AOC = $360° - 2x$ (angle at centre
　is twice angle at circumference), reflex
　$\angle$AOC = $360° - (360° - 2x) = 2x$
　(angles at a point)
9 a x
　b $2x$
　c $\angle$ABC = $(x + y)$ and $\angle$AOC =
　$2(x + y)$

6.4　Cyclic quadrilaterals

Exercise 6D

1 a $a = 50°, b = 95°$
　b $c = 92°, x = 90°$
　c $d = 110°, e = 110°, f = 70°$
　d $g = 105°, h = 99°$
　e $j = 89°, k = 89°, l = 91°$
　f $m = 120°, n = 40°$
　g $p = 44°, q = 68°$
　h $x = 40°, y = 34°$
2 a $x = 26°, y = 128°$
　b $x = 48°, y = 78°$
　c $x = 133°, y = 47°$
　d $x = 36°, y = 72°$
　e $x = 55°, y = 125°$
　f $x = 35°$
　g $x = 48°, y = 45°$
　h $x = 66°, y = 52°$

3 a $x = 49°, y = 49°$
　b $x = 70°, y = 20°$
　c $x = 80°, y = 100°$
　d $x = 100°, y = 75°$
4 a $x = 50°, y = 62°$
　b $x = 92°, y = 88°$
　c $x = 93°, y = 42°$
　d $x = 55°, y = 75°$
5 a $x = 95°, y = 138°$
　b $x = 14°, y = 62°$
　c $x = 32°, y = 48°$
　d 52°
6 a 71°　　**b** 125.5°　**c** 54.5°
7 a $x + 2x - 30° = 180°$ (opposite
　angles in a cyclic quadrilateral), so
　$3x - 30° = 180°$

　b $x = 70°$, so $2x - 30° = 110°$
　$\angle$DOB = 140° (angle at centre
　equals twice angle at
　circumference), $y = 60°$ (angles in a
　quadrilateral)
8 a x
　b $360° - 2x$
　c $\angle$ADC = $\frac{1}{2}$ reflex $\angle$AOC = $180° -$
　x, so $\angle$ADC + $\angle$ABC = $180°$
9 Let $\angle$AED = x, then $\angle$ABC = x
　(opposite angles are equal in a
　parallelogram), $\angle$ADC = $180° - x$
　(opposite angles in a cyclic
　quadrilateral), so $\angle$ADE = x (angles
　on a line)

6.5　Tangents and chords

Exercise 6E

1 a 38°　**b** 110°　**c** 15°　**d** 45°
2 a 6 cm　　**b** 10.8 cm
　c 3.21 cm　　**d** 8 cm
3 a $x = 12°, y = 156°$
　b $x = 100°, y = 50°$
　c $x = 62°, y = 28°$
　d $x = 30°, y = 60°$
4 a 62°　**b** 66°　**c** 19°　**d** 20°

5 19.5 cm
6 5.77 cm
7 $\angle$OCD = 58° (triangle OCD is
　isosceles), $\angle$OCB = 90°
　(tangent/radius theorem), so $\angle$DCB =
　32°, hence triangle BCD is isosceles (2
　equal angles)

8 a $\angle$AOB = $\cos^{-1}\dfrac{OA}{OB} = \cos^{-1}\dfrac{OC}{OB} =$
　$\angle$COB
　b As $\angle$AOB = $\angle$COB, so $\angle$ABO =
　$\angle$CBO, so OB bisects $\angle$ABC

6.6 Alternate segment theorem

Exercise 6F

1 a $a = 65°$, $b = 75°$, $c = 40°$
b $d = 79°$, $e = 58°$, $f = 43°$
c $g = 41°$, $h = 76°$, $i = 76°$
d $k = 80°$, $m = 52°$, $n = 80°$
2 a $a = 75°$, $b = 75°$, $c = 75°$, $d = 30°$
b $a = 47°$, $b = 86°$, $c = 86°$, $d = 47°$
c $a = 53°$, $b = 53°$
d $a = 55°$
3 a $36°$ **b** $70°$

4 a $x = 25°$
b $x = 46°$, $y = 69°$, $z = 65°$
c $x = 38°$, $y = 70°$, $z = 20°$
d $x = 48°$, $y = 42°$
5 $\angle ACB = 64°$ (angle in alternate segment), $\angle ACX = 116°$ (angles on a line), $\angle CAX = 32°$ (angles in a triangle), so triangle ACX is isosceles (two equal angles)

6 $\angle AXY = 69°$ (tangents equal and so triangle AXY is isosceles), $\angle XZY = 69°$ (alternate segment), $\angle XYZ = 55°$ (angles in a triangle)
7 a $2x$
b $90° - x$
c OPT = $90°$, so APT = x

Examination questions

1 a
$2 \times 180° = 360°$

b i $6x - 18 = 270$ **ii** $x = 48°$, largest angle is $132°$
2 a A **b** $36°$
3 a $45°$ **b** $53°$ **c** $90°$ **d** $80°$
4 a $140°$ **b** $70°$
5 a $124°$ **b** $48°$
6 $\angle DCB = 104°$ (cyclic quadrilateral), $\angle CBD = 38°$ (isosceles triangle), $\angle ADB = 38°$ (alternate segment), so AD is parallel to BC (alternate angles)
7 a $75°$ (cyclic quadrilateral)
b $42°$
8 Let $\angle ABC = x$, $\angle ADC = 180° - x$ (cyclic quadrilateral), $\angle ADE = 180° - (180° - x) = x$ (angles on a line), so $\angle ABC = \angle ADE$

Answers to Chapter 7

Quick check

Trace shape **a** and check whether it fits exactly on top of the others.
You should find that shape **b** is not congruent to the others.

7.1 Congruent triangles

Exercise 7A

1 a SAS **b** SSS **c** ASA
d RHS **e** SSS **f** ASA
2 a SSS. A to R, B to P, C to Q
b SAS. A to R, B to Q, C to P
3 a $60°$ **b** $80°$ **c** $40°$ **d** 5 cm
4 a $110°$ **b** $55°$ **c** $85°$ **d** $110°$ **e** 4 cm
5 SSS or RHS

6 SSS or SAS or RHS
7 For example, use $\triangle ADE$ and $\triangle CDG$. AD = CD (sides of large square), DE = DG (sides of small square), $\angle ADE = \angle CDG$ (angles sum to $90°$ with $\angle ADG$), so $\triangle ADE \equiv \triangle CDG$ (SAS), so AE = CG
8 AB and PQ are the corresponding sides to the $42°$ angle, but they are not equal in length

7.2 Translations

Exercise 7B

1 a i $\begin{pmatrix}1\\3\end{pmatrix}$ **ii** $\begin{pmatrix}4\\2\end{pmatrix}$ **iii** $\begin{pmatrix}2\\-1\end{pmatrix}$
iv $\begin{pmatrix}5\\1\end{pmatrix}$ **v** $\begin{pmatrix}-1\\6\end{pmatrix}$ **vi** $\begin{pmatrix}4\\6\end{pmatrix}$
b i $\begin{pmatrix}-1\\-3\end{pmatrix}$ **ii** $\begin{pmatrix}3\\-1\end{pmatrix}$ **iii** $\begin{pmatrix}1\\-4\end{pmatrix}$
iv $\begin{pmatrix}4\\-2\end{pmatrix}$ **v** $\begin{pmatrix}-2\\3\end{pmatrix}$ **vi** $\begin{pmatrix}3\\3\end{pmatrix}$

c i $\begin{pmatrix}-4\\-2\end{pmatrix}$ **ii** $\begin{pmatrix}-3\\1\end{pmatrix}$ **iii** $\begin{pmatrix}-2\\-3\end{pmatrix}$
iv $\begin{pmatrix}1\\-1\end{pmatrix}$ **v** $\begin{pmatrix}-5\\4\end{pmatrix}$ **vi** $\begin{pmatrix}0\\4\end{pmatrix}$
d i $\begin{pmatrix}3\\2\end{pmatrix}$ **ii** $\begin{pmatrix}-4\\2\end{pmatrix}$ **iii** $\begin{pmatrix}5\\-4\end{pmatrix}$
iv $\begin{pmatrix}-2\\-7\end{pmatrix}$ **v** $\begin{pmatrix}5\\0\end{pmatrix}$ **vi** $\begin{pmatrix}1\\-5\end{pmatrix}$

2

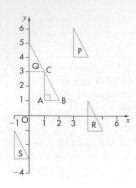

3 a $\begin{pmatrix} -3 \\ -1 \end{pmatrix}$ **b** $\begin{pmatrix} 4 \\ -4 \end{pmatrix}$ **c** $\begin{pmatrix} -5 \\ -2 \end{pmatrix}$

d $\begin{pmatrix} 4 \\ 7 \end{pmatrix}$ **e** $\begin{pmatrix} -1 \\ 5 \end{pmatrix}$ **f** $\begin{pmatrix} 1 \\ 6 \end{pmatrix}$

g $\begin{pmatrix} -4 \\ 4 \end{pmatrix}$ **h** $\begin{pmatrix} -4 \\ -7 \end{pmatrix}$

4 $10 \times 10 = 100$ (including $\begin{pmatrix} 0 \\ 0 \end{pmatrix}$)

5 Check students' designs for a *Snakes and ladders* board.

6 $\begin{pmatrix} -x \\ -y \end{pmatrix}$

7 $\begin{pmatrix} -300 \\ -500 \end{pmatrix}$

8 $\begin{pmatrix} -1 \\ 4 \end{pmatrix}$

7.3 Reflections

Exercise 7C

1

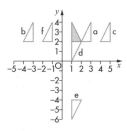

c x-value changes sign

d $(-a, b)$

5 Possible answer: Take the centre square as ABCD then reflect this square each time in the line, AB, then BC, then CD and finally AD

6 $x = -1$

7 Possible answer:

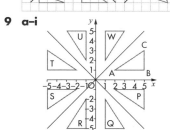

8

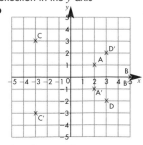

9 a–i

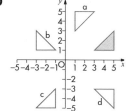

j A reflection in $y = x$

10

2 a–e

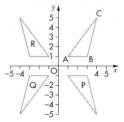

f Reflection in the y-axis

3 a–b

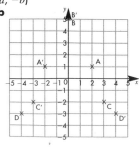

c y-value changes sign

d $(a, -b)$

4 a–b

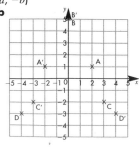

11 a–c

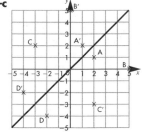

d Coordinates are reversed: x becomes y and y becomes x

e (b, a)

12 a–c

d

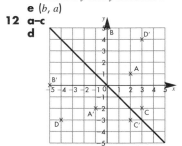

Coordinates are reversed and change sign, x becomes $-y$ and y becomes $-x$

e $(-b, -a)$

7.4 Rotations

Exercise 7D

1 a

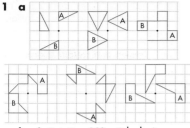

b i Rotation 90°anticlockwise
ii Rotation 180°

2

3 Possible answer: If ABCD is the centre square, rotate about A 90° anticlockwise, rotate about new B 180°, now rotate about new C 180°, and finally rotate about new D 180°

4

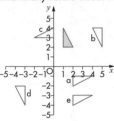

5 a 90° anticlockwise
b 270° anticlockwise
c 300° clockwise
d 260° clockwise

6 a b c i

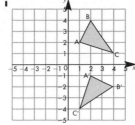

ii A'(2, −1), B'(4, −2), C'(1, −4)
iii Original coordinates (x, y) become (y, −x)
iv Yes

7 i

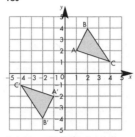

ii A'(−1, −2), B'(−2, −4), C'(−4, −1)
iii Original coordinates (x, y) become (−x, −y)
iv Yes

8 i

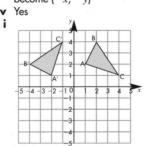

ii A'(−2, 1), B'(−4, 2), C'(−1, 4)
iii Original coordinates (x, y) become (−y, x)
iv Yes

9 Show by drawing a shape or use the fact that (a, b) becomes (a, −b) after reflection in the x-axis, and (a, −b) becomes (−a, −b) after reflection in the y-axis, which is equivalent to a single rotation of 180°.

10 Show by drawing a shape or use the fact that (a, b) becomes (b, a) after reflection in the line y = x, and (b, a) becomes (−a, −b) after reflection in the line y = −x, which is equivalent to a single rotation of 180°.

11 a

b i Rotation 60°clockwise about O
ii Rotation 120°clockwise about O
iii Rotation 180°about O
iv Rotation 240°clockwise about O
c i Rotation 60°clockwise about O
ii Rotation 180°about O

12 Rotation 90° anticlockwise about (3, −2)

7.5 Enlargements

Exercise 7E

1

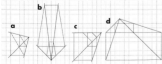

2 a

b

c

3 a

b

4

5

6 a

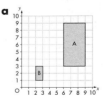

b 3 : 1
c 3 : 1
d 9 : 1

7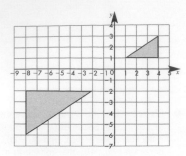

8 a–c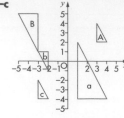

d Scale factor $-\frac{1}{2}$, centre (1, 3)

e Scale factor -2, centre (1, 3)

f Scale factor -1, centre $(-2.5, -1.5)$

g Scale factor -1, centre $(-2.5, -1.5)$

h Same centres, and the scale factors are reciprocals of each other

9 Enlargement, scale factor -2, about (1, 3)

7.6 Combined transformations

Exercise 7F

1 $(-4, -3)$

2 a $(-5, 2)$
b Reflection in y-axis

3 A: translation $\begin{pmatrix} 1 \\ -2 \end{pmatrix}$, B: reflection in y-axis, C: rotation 90°clockwise about (0, 0), D: reflection in $x = 3$, E: reflection in $y = 4$, F: enlargement by scale factor 2, centre (0, 1)

4 a T_1 to T_2: rotation 90°clockwise about (0, 0)
b T_1 to T_6: rotation 90°anticlockwise about (0, 0)
c T_2 to T_3: translation $\begin{pmatrix} 2 \\ 2 \end{pmatrix}$
d T_6 to T_2: rotation 180°about (0, 0)
e T_6 to T_5: reflection in y-axis
f T_5 to T_4: translation $\begin{pmatrix} 4 \\ 0 \end{pmatrix}$

5 a–d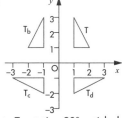

e T_d to T: rotation 90° anticlockwise about (0, 0)

6 Reflection in x-axis, translation $\begin{pmatrix} 0 \\ -5 \end{pmatrix}$, rotation 90°clockwise about (0, 0)

7 Translation $\begin{pmatrix} 0 \\ -8 \end{pmatrix}$, reflection in x-axis, rotation 90°clockwise about (0, 0)

8 a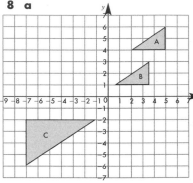

b Enlargement of scale factor $-\frac{1}{2}$ about (1, 2)

Examination questions

1

2 a Rotation 90° clockwise about (0, 0)
b $\begin{pmatrix} -5 \\ -4 \end{pmatrix}$

3 a $x = 5$
b $\begin{pmatrix} 5 \\ 0 \end{pmatrix}$
c 180° about (5, 2.5)

4 a, b

5 a Enlargement scale factor of $\frac{1}{3}$ about $(-4, 5)$
b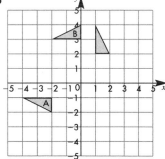

6 a Reflection in the line $y = x$
b Rotation of 90° anticlockwise about (1, 1)
c Enlargement scale factor of -2 about (0, 0)

7 For example, AB = BC (isosceles triangle), AM = MC (M is midpoint of AC), BM is common, so $\triangle$ABM $\equiv$ $\triangle$CBM (SSS)

8 For example, $\angle$MYZ = $\angle$NZY (given), YZ is common, MY = NZ (symmetry of isosceles triangle), so $\triangle$YMZ $\equiv$ $\triangle$ZNY (SAS)

Answers to Chapter 8

Quick check

1 a 6 cm **b** 7.5 cm **c** 11 cm   **2 a** 30° **b** 135°

8.1   Constructing triangles

Exercise 8A

1 a BC = 2.9 cm, ∠B = 53°, ∠C = 92°
   b EF = 7.4 cm, ED = 6.8 cm,
     ∠E = 50°
   c ∠G = 105°, ∠H = 29°, ∠I = 46°
   d ∠J = 48°, ∠L = 32°, JK = 4.3 cm
   e ∠N = 55°, ON = OM = 7 cm
   f ∠P = 51°, ∠R = 39°, QP = 5.7 cm
2 a Students can check one another's
   triangles

   b ∠ABC = 44°, ∠BCA = 79°,
     ∠CAB = 57°
3 a 5.9 cm
   b 18.8 cm^2
4 BC = 2.6 cm, 7.8 cm
5 a 4.5
   b 11.25 cm^2
6 a 4.3 cm
   b 34.5 cm^2

7 a Right-angled triangle constructed
   with sides 3, 4, 5 and 4.5, 6, 7.5,
   and scale marked 1 cm : 1 m
   b Right-angled triangle constructed
   with 12 equally-spaced dots
8 An equilateral triangle of side 4 cm
9 Even with all three angles, you need to
   know at least one length

8.2   Bisectors

Exercise 8B

1–9 Practical work; check students'
   constructions
10 Leicester
11 The centre of the circle

12 Start with a base line AB; then
   construct a perpendicular to the line
   from point A. At point B, construct an
   angle of 60°. Ensure that the line for
   this 60° angle crosses the
   perpendicular line; where they meet
   will be the final point C

13–15 Practical work; check students'
   constructions

8.3   Defining a locus

Exercise 8C

1 Circle with radius:
   a 2 cm **b** 4 cm **c** 5 cm
2 a   **b**   **c**

3 a Circle with radius 4 m
   b

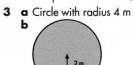

   2 m

4 a   **b**   **c**
   d   **e**   **f**

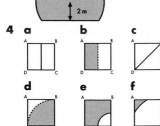

5

6

7 Construct the bisector of
   angle BAC and the
   perpendicular bisector of
   the line AC

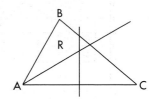

8

8.4 Loci problems

Exercise 8D

1

2

3

4

5

6
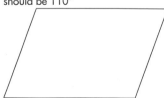

7

8 a Sketch should show a circle of radius 6 cm around London and one of radius 4 cm around Glasgow
   b No
   c Yes

9 a Yes
   b Sketch should show a circle of radius 4 cm around Leeds and one of radius 4 cm around Exeter. The area where they overlap should be shaded

10 a This is the perpendicular bisector of the line from York to Birmingham. It should pass just below Manchester and just through the top of Norwich
   b Sketch should show a circle of radius 7 cm around Glasgow and one of radius 5 cm around London
   c The transmitter can be built anywhere on line constructed in part **a** that is within the area shown in part **b**

11 Sketch should show two circles around Birmingham, one of radius 3 cm and one of radius 5 cm. The area of good reception is the area between the two circles

12 Sketch should show a circle of radius 6 cm around Glasgow, two circles around York, one of radius 4 cm and one of radius 6 cm and a circle around London of radius 8 cm. The small area in the Irish Sea that is between the two circles around York and inside both the circle around Glasgow and the circle around London is where the boat can be

13 Sketch should show two circles around Newcastle upon Tyne, one of radius 4 cm and one of radius 6 cm, and two circles around Bristol, one of radius 3 cm and one of radius 5 cm. The area that is between both pairs of circles is the area that should be shaded

14 Sketch should show the perpendicular bisector of the line running from Newcastle upon Tyne to Manchester and that of the line running from Sheffield to Norwich. Where the lines cross is where the oil rig is located

15 Sketch should show the perpendicular bisector of the line running from Glasgow to Norwich and that of the line running from Norwich to Exeter. Where the lines cross is where Fred's house is

16 Sketch should show the bisectors of the angles made by the piers and the sea wall at points A and B. These are the paths of each boat

17 Leeds

18 On a map, draw a straight line from Newcastle to Bristol, construct the line bisector, then the search will be anywhere on the sea along that line

Examination questions

1 Check students' drawings, top angle should be 110°

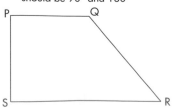

2 Check students' drawings, top angles should be 90° and 130°

3 a
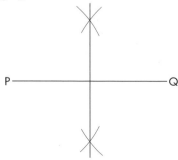

b An equal distance from P and Q

4
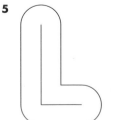

5
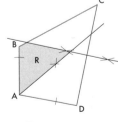

6 a

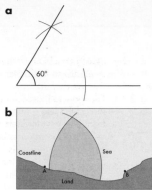

b

7 a

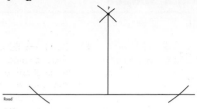

b 3 km

8

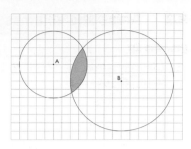

9 a Enlargement with scale factor $\frac{1}{2}$ about the point (1, 3)

b

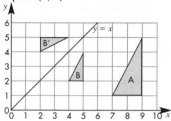

Answers to Chapter 9

Quick check

1 a 3 : 4 **b** 4 : 5 **c** 4 : 1 **d** 3 : 2
2 a 14 **b** 2.5 **c** 8 **d** 6

9.1 Similar triangles

Exercise 9A

1 2, 3
2 a Yes, 4
  b No, corresponding sides have different ratios.
3 a PQR is an enlargement of ABC
  b 1 : 3
  c Angle R
  d BA
4 a Sides in same ratio
  b Angle P   **c** PR

5 a Same angles   **b** Angle Q
  c AR
6 a 8 cm
  b 7.5 cm
  c $x = 6.67$ cm, $y = 13.5$ cm
  d $x = 24$ cm, $y = 13$ cm
  e AB = 10 cm, PQ = 6 cm
  f 4.2 cm
7 a Sides in same ratio
  b 1 : 3 **c** 13 cm **d** 39 cm

8 5.2 m
9 Corresponding sides are not in the same ratio, 12 : 15 ≠ 16 : 19
10 DE = 17.5 cm; AC : EC = BA : DE,
  5 : 12.5 = 7 : DE,
  DE = 7 × 12.5 ÷ 5 = 17.5 cm

Exercise 9B

1 a ABC and ADE; 9 cm
  b ABC and ADE; 12 cm
2 a 5 cm
  b 5 cm
3 82 m

c $x = 60$ cm, $y = 75$ cm
d $x = 45$ cm, $y = 60$ cm
e DC = 10 cm, EB = 8 cm

4 220 feet
5 15 m
6 3.3 m
7 1.8 m

8 13.5 cm
9 c

Exercise 9C

1 5 cm
2 6 cm
3 10 cm

4 $x = 6$ cm, $y = 7.5$ cm
5 $x = 15$ cm, $y = 21$ cm
6 $x = 3$ cm, $y = 2.4$ cm

9.2 Areas and volumes of similar shapes

Exercise 9D

1 a $4 : 25$ **b** $8 : 125$
2 a $16 : 49$ **b** $64 : 343$
3

Linear scale factor 2, 3, $\frac{1}{4}$, 5, $\frac{1}{10}$
Linear ratio 1 : 2, 1 : 3, 4 : 1, 1 : 5, 10 : 1
Linear fraction $\frac{2}{1}$, $\frac{3}{1}$, $\frac{1}{4}$, $\frac{5}{1}$, $\frac{1}{10}$
Area scale factor 4, 9, $\frac{1}{16}$, 25, $\frac{1}{100}$
Volume scale factor 8, 27, $\frac{1}{64}$, $\frac{1}{125}$, $\frac{1}{1000}$

4 135 cm^2
5 a 56 cm^2
  b 126 cm^2
6 a 48 m^2
  b 3 m^2
7 a 2400 cm^3
  b 8100 cm^3
8 4 litres
9 1.38 m^3
10 £6

11 4 cm
12 $8 \times 60p = £4.80$ so it is better value
13 a $3 : 4$
   b $9 : 16$
   c $27 : 64$
14 $720 \div 8 = 90$ cm^3

Exercise 9E

1 6.2 cm, 10.1 cm
2 4.26 cm, 6.74 cm
3 9.56 cm
4 3.38 m
5 8.39 cm
6 26.5 cm
7 16.9 cm
8 a 4.33 cm, 7.81 cm
  b 143 g, 839 g
9 53.8 kg
10 1.73 kg
11 8.8 cm
12 7.9 cm and 12.6 cm
13 b

Examination questions

1 4.5 cm
2 17.5 cm
3 24 cm
4 30 cm
5 $X = 125$ cm^2, $Y = 10\,800$ cm^3
6 a It doubles in three directions, $2^3 = 8$
  b Yes, $14.5 \div 8 = 1.8125$, $1.8125^3 = 5.95$

Answers to Chapter 10

Quick check

1 8.60 cm
2 13.0 cm
3 21.6°
4 8.40 cm

10.1 Some 2D problems

Exercise 10A

1 13.1 cm
2 73.7°
3 9.81 cm
4 33.5 m
5 a 10.0 cm   **b** 11.5°   **c** 4.69 cm
6 63.0°
7 774 m
8 a $\sqrt{2}$ cm

  b **i** $\frac{\sqrt{2}}{2}$ (an answer of $\frac{1}{\sqrt{2}}$ would also be accepted)

    ii $\frac{\sqrt{2}}{2}$ **iii** 1

9 14.1°

10.2 Some 3D problems

Exercise 10B

1 25.1°

2 a 58.6°   **b** 20.5 cm
   c 2049 cm^3 **d** 64.0°

3 a 3.46 m   **b** 75.5°
   c 73.2°   **d** 60.3 m^2
   e £1507.50

4 a 24.0°   **b** 48.0°
   c 13.5 cm   **d** 16.6°

5 a 3.46 m   **b** 70.5°

6 For example, the length of the diagonal of the base is $\sqrt{b^2 + c^2}$ and taking this as the base of the triangle with the height of the edge, then the hypotenuse is $\sqrt{(a^2 + (\sqrt{b^2 + c^2})^2)} = \sqrt{a^2 + b^2 + c^2}$

7 It is 44.6°; use triangle XDM where M is the midpoint of BD; triangle DXB is isosceles, as X is over the point where the diagonals of the base cross; the length of DB is $\sqrt{656}$, the cosine of the required angle is $0.5\sqrt{656} \div 18$

10.3 Solving any triangle

Exercise 10C

1 a 3.64 m   **b** 8.05 cm
   c 19.4 cm

2 a 46.6°   **b** 112.0°
   c 36.2°

3 50.3°, 129.7°

4 2.88 cm, 20.9 cm

5 a i 30°   **ii** 40°
   b 19.4 m

6 36.5 m

7 22.2 m

8 3.47 m

9 767 m

10 26.8 km/h

11 64.6 km

12 Check students' answers

13 134°

14 Check students' proof

Exercise 10D

1 a 7.71 m   **b** 29.1 cm
   c 27.4 cm

2 a 76.2°
   b 125.1°
   c 90°
   d Right-angled triangle

3 5.16 cm

4 65.5 cm

5 a 10.7 cm   **b** 41.7°
   c 38.3°   **d** 6.69 cm
   e 54.4 cm^2

6 72.3°

7 25.4 cm, 38.6 cm

8 58.4 km at 092.5°

9 21.8°

10 a 82.8°   **b** 8.89 cm

11 42.5 km

12 Check students' answers

13 111°; the largest angle is opposite the longest side

Exercise 10E

1 a 8.60 m   **b** 90°
   c 27.2 cm   **d** 26.9°
   e 41.0°   **f** 62.4 cm
   g 90.0°   **h** 866 cm
   i 86.6 cm

2 7 cm

3 11.1 km

4 19.9 knots

5 a 27.8 miles
   b 262°

6 a $A = 90°$; this is Pythagoras' theorem
   b A is acute
   c A is obtuse

7 142 m

10.4 Trigonometric ratios in surd form

Exercise 10F

1 $\frac{3}{5}$

2 $\frac{\sqrt{10}}{5}$

3 $\sqrt{19}$, $\sin x = \frac{\sqrt{6}}{\sqrt{19}}$, $\cos x = \frac{\sqrt{13}}{\sqrt{19}}$, $\tan x = \frac{\sqrt{6}}{\sqrt{13}}$

4 a $\sqrt{157}$ **b** $\sin A = \frac{6}{\sqrt{157}}$, $\cos A = \frac{11}{\sqrt{157}}$

5 $9\sqrt{3}$ cm^2

6 400 cm^2

7 $3\sqrt{6}$ cm

10.5 Using sine to find the area of a triangle

Exercise 10G

1 a 24.0 cm^2 **b** 26.7 cm^2
   c 243 cm^2 **d** 21 097 cm^2
   e 1224 cm^2

2 4.26 cm

3 a 42.3°   **b** 49.6°

4 103 cm^2

5 2033 cm^2

6 21.0 cm^2

7 a 33.2°   **b** 25.3 cm^2

8 Check students' proof

9 a $\frac{1}{\sqrt{2}}$ **b** 21 cm^2

10 726 cm^2

11 $\frac{a^2\sqrt{3}}{4}$ or $\frac{\sqrt{3}a^2}{4}$

12 c

Examination questions

1 a 13.9 cm   **b** 40.3°
2 a 6.17 cm   **b** 57.5°
3 a 6.94 cm   **b** 51.6 cm^2
4 a 15.3 cm   **b** 19.1°

5 58.0°; O is the midpoint of AC, $AO = \frac{15\sqrt{2}}{2}$,

$\angle VAO = \cos^{-1}\frac{3\sqrt{2}}{8} = 58.0°$ (3sf)

6 33.2 m

Answers to Chapter 11

Quick check

1
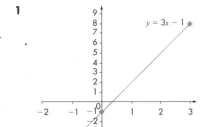

2 $y = 3x + 1$

11.1 Line graphs

Exercise 11A

1 a Values of y: 27, 12, 3, 0, 3, 12, 27
  b 6.8   **c** 1.8 or −1.8
2 a Values of y: 27, 18, 11, 6, 3, 2, 3,
     6, 11, 18, 27
  b 8.3   **c** 3.5 or −3.5
3 a Values of y: 27, 16, 7, 0, −5, −8,
     −9, −8, −5, 0, 7
  b −8.8   **c** 3.4 or −1.4
4 a Values of y: 2, −1, −2, −1, 2, 7, 14
  b 0.25   **c** 0.7 or −2.7
  d

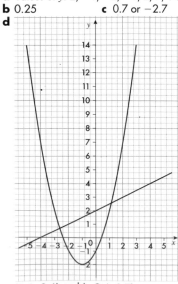

  e (1.1, 2.6) and (−2.6, 0.7)

5 a Values of y: 18, 12, 8, 6, 6, 8, 12
  b 9.75   **c** 2 or −1
  d Values of y: 14, 9, 6, 5, 6, 9, 14
  e (1, 6)
6 a Values of y: 4, 1, 0, 1, 4, 9, 16
  b 7.3   **c** 0.4 or −2.4
  d

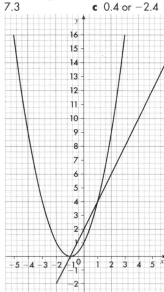

  e (1, 4) and (−1, 0)

7 a Values of y: 15, 9, 4, 0, −3, −5,
 −6, −6, −5, −3, 0, 4, 9
  b −0.5 and 3
8 Points plotted and joined should give
  parabolas
9 Points plotted and joined should give a
  parabola
10 Line A has a constant in front, so is
  'thinner' than the rest
  Line B has a negative in front, so is
  'upside down'
  Line C does not pass through the origin

11.2 The significant points of a quadratic graph

Exercise 11B

1 a Values of y: 12, 5, 0, −3, −4, −3, 0, 5, 12
  b 2 and −2
2 a Values of y: 7, 0, −5, −8, −9, −8, −5, 0, 7
  b 3 and −3
3 a The roots are positive and negative square roots of the constant term
  b Check predictions
  c Values of y: 15, 8, 3, 0, −1, 0, 3, 8, 15
  d Values of y: 11, 4, −1, −4, −5, −4, −1, 4, 11
  e 1 and −1, 2.2 and −2.2
4 a Values of y: 5, 0, −3, −4, −3, 0, 5, 12
  b −4 and 0
5 a Values of y: 16, 7, 0, −5, −8, −9, −8, −5, 0, 7, 16
  b 0 and 6
6 a Values of y: 10, 4, 0, −2, −2, 0, 4, 10, 18
  b −3 and 0
7 a The roots are 0 and the negative of the coefficient of x
  b Check predictions
  c Values of y: 10, 4, 0, −2, −2, 0, 4, 10
  d Values of y: 6, 0, −4, −6, −6, −4, 0, 6, 14
  e 0 and 3, −5 and 0

8 a Values of y: 9, 4, 1, 0, 1, 4, 9
  b −2
  c Only 1 root
9 a Values of y: 10, 3, −2, −5, −6, −5, −2, 3, 10
  b 0.6 and 5.4
10 a Values of y: 19, 6, −3, −8, −9, −6, 1, 12
  b 0.9 and −3.4
11 a (0, −4), (0, −9), (0, −1), (0, −5), (0, 0), (0, 0), (0, 0), (0, 0), (0, 0)
  b (0, −4), (0, −9), (0, −1), (0, −5), (−2, −4), (3, −9), (−1.5, −2.25), (1.5, −2.25), (−2.5, −6.25)
  c The y-intercept; the point where the x-value is the mean of the roots
12 a $y = (x − 2)^2$ **b** 0
13 a $y = (x − 3)^2 − 6$ **b** −6
14 a $y = (x − 4)^2 − 14$ **b** −14
15 a $y = −(x − 1)^2 − 5$ **b** −5
16 a The minimum point is (a, b) **b** (−5, −28)
17 $y = (x − 3)^2 − 7$, $y = x^2 − 6x + 9 − 7$, $y = x^2 − 6x + 2$
18 a (−2, −7)
  b **i** $(a, 2b − a^2)$
     ii $(2a, b − 4a^2)$

11.3 Other graphs

Exercise 11C

1
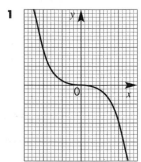

2 a Values of y: −54, −31.25, −16, −6.75, −2, −0.25, 0, 0.25, 2, 6.75, 16, 31.25, 54
  b 39.4
3 a Values of y: −24, −12.63, −5, −0.38, 2, 2.9, 3, 3.13, 4, 6.38, 11, 18.63, 30
  b 4.7   **c** −1.4 to −1.5
4 a Values of y: −16, −5.63, 1, 4.63, 6, 5.88, 5, 4.13, 4, 5.38, 9, 15.63, 26
  b **i** −2.1   **ii** (−0.8, 6)
    iii (0.7, 3.9)   **iv** (0, 5)
5 a Values of y: 10, 5, 4, 2.5, 2, 1.33, 1, 0.67, 0.5
  b **i** 0.8   **ii** −1.6
6 a Values of $5\sqrt{x}$: 0, 5 and −5, 7.1 and −7.1, 8.7 and −8.7, 10 and −10, 11.2 and −11.2
  b **i** 9.4 and −9.4   **ii** 2.6
7 a Values of y: 25, 12.5, 10, 5, 2.5, 1, 0.5, 0.33, 0.25

b
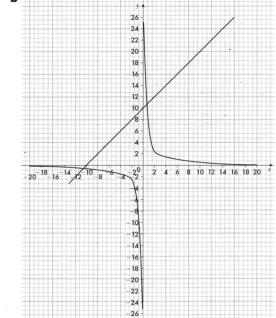

c 0.48 and −10.48

8 a Values of y: 0.01, 0.04, 0.11, 0.33, 1, 3, 9, 27
b   **c** 15.6   **d** −0.63

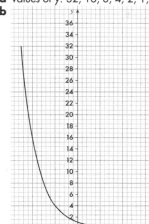

10 a Quadratic   **b** Linear   **c** Exponential
d Reciprocal   **e** None   **f** Cubic
g Linear   **h** None   **i** Quadratic

11 a The numbers go 1, 2, 4, ... which is equivalent to 2^0, 2^1, 2^2, ... so the formula is $2^{(n-1)}$
b Values of y: 1, 2, 4, 8, 16, 32, 64, 128, 256, 512
c $2^{63} = 9.22 \times 10^{18}$ **d**   £4.61×10^{14}

12 a Number of pieces: 2, 4, 8, 16, 32, 64, 128, 256
b Number of pieces = 2^n
c 1.1×10^{15} pieces   **d** 1.1×10^8 km

13 $a = 5$, $b = 3$

14

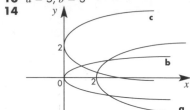

9 a Values of y: 32, 16, 8, 4, 2, 1, 0.5, 0.25, 0.13, 0.06, 0.03
b   **c** 0.18
                                         d 0.42

11.4   Trigonometric ratios of angles between 90° and 360°

Exercise 11D

1 a 36.9°, 143.1°   **b** 53.1°, 126.9°   **k** 33.6°, 146.4°   **l** 210°, 330°
c 48.6°, 131.4°   **d** 224.4°, 315.6°   **2** Sin 234°, as the others all have the
e 194.5°, 345.5°   **f** 198.7°, 341.3°   same numerical value
g 190.1°, 349.9°   **h** 234.5°, 305.5°   **3 a** 438° or 78° + 360n°
i 28.1°, 151.9°   **j** 185.6°, 354.4°   **b** −282° or 78° − 360n°

c Line symmetry about ±90n° where n is an odd integer
Rotational symmetry about ±180n° where n is an integer

Exercise 11E

1 a 53.1°, 306.9°   **b** 54.5°, 305.5°   **k** 78.7°, 281.3°   **l** 44.4°, 315.6°
c 62.7°, 297.3°   **d** 54.9°, 305.1°   **2** Cos 58°, as the others are negative
e 79.3°, 280.7°   **f** 143.1°, 216.9°   **3 a** 492° or 132° + 360n°
g 104.5°, 255.5°   **h** 100.1°, 259.9°   **b** −228° or 132° − 360n°
i 111.2°, 248.8°   **j** 166.9°, 193.1°

c Line symmetry about ±180n° where n is an integer
Rotational symmetry about ±90n° where n is an odd integer

Exercise 11F

1 a 0.707   **b** −1 (−0.9998)   **e** 60.9°, 119.1°   **f** 29.1°, 330.9°   **7** True
c −0.819   **d** 0.731   **4** 30°, 150°   **8 a** Cos 65°   **b** Cos 40°
2 a −0.629   **b** −0.875   **5** −0.755   **9 a** 10°, 130°   **b** 12.7°, 59.3°
c −0.087   **d** 0.999   **6 a** 1.41   **b** −1.37   **10** 38.2°, 141.8°
3 a 21.2°, 158.8°   **b** 209.1°, 330.9°   **c** −0.0367   **d** −0.138
c 50.1°, 309.9°   **d** 150.0°, 210.0°   **e** 1.41   **f** −0.492

Exercise 11G

1 a 14.5°, 194.5°   **b** 38.1°, 218.1°   **m** 160.5°, 340.5°   **n** 130.9°, 310.9°   **3 a** 425° or 65° + 180n°, $n \geqslant 2$
   c 50.0°, 230.0°   **d** 61.9°, 241.9°   **o** 76.5°, 256.5°   **p** 116.0°, 296.0°   **b** −115° or 65° − 180n°
   e 68.6°, 248.6°   **f** 160.3°, 340.3°   **q** 174.4°, 354.4°   **r** 44.9°, 224.9°   **c** No line symmetry
   g 147.6°, 327.6°   **h** 135.4°, 315.4°   **s** 50.4°, 230.4°   **t** 111.8°, 291.8°   Rotational symmetry about ±180n°
   i 120.9°, 300.9°   **j** 105.2°, 285.2°   **2** Tan 235°, as the others have a   where n is an integer
   k 54.4°, 234.4°   **l** 42.2°, 222.2°   numerical value of 1

11.5   The circular function graphs

Exercise 11H

1 115°   **c** Sin x = cos (90 − x)°   **11 a** 1.1307
2 327°   **d** Cos x = sin (90 − x)°   **b** Error
3 324°   **8 a** 64°   **b** 206°, 334°   **c** If you tried to draw this triangle
4 195°   **c** 116°, 244°   accurately then you would see that
5 210°, 330°   **9 a** −0.384   **b** 113°   the line that is 12 long does not
6 135°, 225°   **10 a** 0.822 **b** 55.3   intersect with the base
7 a Say 32°, sin 32° = 0.53, cos 58° =   **c** No   **12 a** to **e** All true
      0.53   **d** The calculator has given the value of
   b Say 70°, sin 70° = 0.94, cos 20° =   the acute angle but the angle 124.7°
      0.94   has the same positive sign

11.6   Solving equations, one linear and one non-linear, with graphs

Exercise 11I

1 a (0.7, 0.7), (−2.7, −2.7)   **h** (2.6, 1.6), (−1.6, −2.6)   **3 a** There is no solution
   b (6, 12), (−1, −2)   **2 a** (1, 0)   **b** The graphs do not intersect
   c (4, −3), (−3, 4)   **b** Only one intersection point   **c** $x^2 + x + 4 = 0$
   d (0.8, 1.8), (−1.8, −0.8)   **c** $x^2 + x(3 − 5) + (−4 + 5) = 0$ **d** $b^2 − 4ac = −15$
   e (4.6, 8.2), (0.5, 0)   **d** $(x − 1)^2 = 0 \Rightarrow x = 1$ **e** No solution as the discriminant is
   f (3, 6), (−2, 1)   **e** Only one solution as line is a   negative and there is no square root
   g (4.8, 6.6), (0.2, −2.6)   tangent to curve   of a negative number

11.7   Solving equations by the method of intersection

Exercise 11J

1 a i −1.4, 4.4   **7**
   ii −2, 5
   iii −0.6, 3.6
   b 2.6, 0.4
2 a −5, 1
   b i −5.3, 1.3
   ii −4.8, 0.8
   iii −3.4, −0.6
3 a i 0, 6
   ii 4.3, 0.7
   b i 4.8, 0.2
   ii 5.4, −0.4
4 a i −1.6, 2.6
   ii 1.4, −1.4
   b i 2.3, −2.3
   ii 2, −2
5 a 0, 2   **b** 2.5
   c −0.6, 1, 1.6   **d** 2.8
   e −0.8, 0.6, 2.2
6

7

a 1.6, −1.6
b −1.2, 1.2

8

a 2.2, −2.2
b −1.8, 2.8

a −0.4, 4.4
b −1, 5

9

a 3.3, −0.3
b 4.8, 0.2

10

a 2
b 2.5

11 **a** C and D   **b** A and D   **12** **a** $(x + 2)(x - 1) = 0$
     c $x^2 + 4x - 1 = 0$ **b** $5 - -2 = +7$, not -7
     d $(-1.5, -10.25)$ **c** $y = 2x + 7$

Examination questions

1 **a** $-3, 7$ **b** Correct graph
     c Read from the x-axis
2 Graph 1 is equation D, Graph 2 is equation A, Graph 3 is
     equation E, Graph 4 is equation C
3 **a** $110°$ **b** 250 and 290
     c   **d** 35, 55, 215, 235

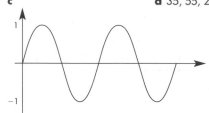

4 **a** $(2x - 5)^2 = 0$, $x = \frac{5}{2}$

     b Sketch 2, as the line only just touches the curve
5 **a** Draw $y = 1$, $x = 0.8$ and -3.8
     b Draw $y = x - 1$, $x = 0.4$, -2.4

6 **a** $(0, -5)$ and $(4, 3)$
     b Circle radius 5 centre the origin; solutions in (a) are
       intersections of graphs
7 **a**

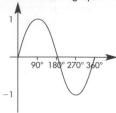

     b Any of the following: $y = \sin(x - 180°)$,
       $y = \sin(x + 180°)$, $y = \cos(x + 90°)$,
       $y = \cos(x - 270°)$
8 Draw $y = x - 1$: $x = 1.6$ or -2.6
9 $(4.5, 4.5)$
10 **a** $290°$ **b** $110°$ and $250°$

Answers to Chapter 12

Quick check

1 **a** 25   **b** 9   **c** 27   **d** 4   **2** **a** 48   **b** $\frac{1}{2}$

12.1 Direct variation

Exercise 12A

1 **a** 15   **b** 2
2 **a** 75   **b** 6
3 **a** 150   **b** 6
4 **a** 22.5   **b** 12
5 **a** 175 miles   **b** 8 hours

6 **a** £66.50   **b** 175 kg
7 **a** 44   **b** 84 m^2
8 **a** 33 spaces
     b 66 spaces since new car park has 366 spaces
9 17 minutes 30 seconds

Exercise 12B

1 **a** 100   **b** 10
2 **a** 27   **b** 5
3 **a** 56   **b** 1.69
4 **a** 192   **b** 2.25
5 **a** 25.6   **b** 5
6 **a** 80   **b** 8
7 **a** £50   **b** 225
8 **a** 3.2 °C   **b** 10 atm

9 **a** 388.8 g   **b** 3 mm
10 **a** 2 J   **b** 40 m/s
11 **a** £78   **b** 400 miles
12 4000 cm^3
13 £250
14 **a** B   **b** A   **c** C
15 **a** B   **b** A

12.2 Inverse variation

Exercise 12C

1	$Tm = 12$	**a** 3	**b** 2.5
2	$Wx = 60$	**a** 20	**b** 6
3	$Q(5 - t) = 16$	**a** −3.2	**b** 4
4	$Mt^2 = 36$	**a** 4	**b** 5
5	$W\sqrt{T} = 24$	**a** 4.8	**b** 100
6	$x^3 y = 32$	**a** 32	**b** 4
7	$gp = 1800$	**a** £15	**b** 36
8	$td = 24$	**a** 3 °C	**b** 12 km

9 $ds^2 = 432$ **a** 1.92 km   **b** 8 m/s
10 $p\sqrt{h} = 7.2$ **a** 2.4 atm   **b** 100 m
11 $W\sqrt{F} = 0.5$ **a** 5 t/h   **b** 0.58 t/h
12 B – This is inverse proportion, as x increases y decreases

13

x	8	27	64
y	1	$\frac{2}{3}$	$\frac{1}{2}$

14 4.3 miles

Examination questions

1

x	25	100	400
y	10	20	40

2 a $E = 4000v$ **b** 3.6 m/s

3 a $y = 4x^{-\frac{1}{3}}$ or $y = \dfrac{4}{\sqrt[3]{x}}$

   b i 20   **ii** 8

4 19.4 cm

5 128

6 a $y = 2x^2$

   b
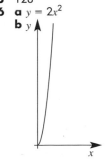

7 Statement 1 matches table B, Statement 2 matches table C, Statement 3 matches table A
8 a 2.5   **b** 0.25   **c** 250   **d** 50, −50
9 a 10   **b** 3.375
10 a 48π **b** 9
11 27 Hz
12 a $V = 0.5h^3$
    b 13 500 cubic metres
    c 21.5 m
13 40

Answers to Chapter 13

Quick check

a $\begin{pmatrix} 1 \\ 3 \end{pmatrix}$ **b** $\begin{pmatrix} 3 \\ 0 \end{pmatrix}$ **c** $\begin{pmatrix} 2 \\ -1 \end{pmatrix}$ **d** $\begin{pmatrix} -1 \\ -2 \end{pmatrix}$

13.1 Properties of vectors

Exercise 13A

1 a Any three of: $\vec{AC}$, $\vec{CF}$, $\vec{BD}$, $\vec{DG}$, $\vec{GI}$, $\vec{EH}$, $\vec{HJ}$, $\vec{JK}$
   b Any three of: $\vec{BE}$, $\vec{AD}$, $\vec{DH}$, $\vec{CG}$, $\vec{GJ}$, $\vec{FI}$, $\vec{IK}$
   c Any three of: $\vec{AO}$, $\vec{CA}$, $\vec{FC}$, $\vec{IG}$, $\vec{GD}$, $\vec{DB}$, $\vec{KJ}$, $\vec{JH}$, $\vec{HE}$
   d Any three of: $\vec{BO}$, $\vec{EB}$, $\vec{HD}$, $\vec{DA}$, $\vec{JG}$, $\vec{GC}$, $\vec{KI}$, $\vec{IF}$

2 a 2**a**   **b** 2**b**   **c** **a** + **b**
   d 2**a** + **b**   **e** 2**a** + 2**b**   **f** **a** + 2**b**
   g **a** + **b**   **h** 2**a** + 2**b**   **i** 3**a** + **b**
   j 2**a**   **k** **b**   **l** 2**a** + **b**

3 a Equal   **b** $\vec{AI}$, $\vec{BJ}$, $\vec{DK}$
4 a $\vec{OJ} = 2\vec{OD}$ and parallel   **b** $\vec{AK}$ **c** $\vec{OF}$, $\vec{BI}$, $\vec{EK}$

5

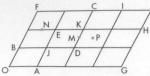

6 a Lie on same straight line
 b All multiples of **a** + **b** and start at O
 c H
 d i $\overrightarrow{OQ} = \mathbf{a} + \frac{1}{2}\mathbf{b}$ **ii** $\overrightarrow{OR} = 3\mathbf{a} + \frac{3}{2}\mathbf{b}$
 e $n\mathbf{a} + \frac{n}{2}\mathbf{b}$

7 a $-\mathbf{b}$ **b** $3\mathbf{a} - \mathbf{b}$ **c** $2\mathbf{a} - \mathbf{b}$
 d $\mathbf{a} - \mathbf{b}$ **e** $\mathbf{a} + \mathbf{b}$ **f** $-\mathbf{a} - \mathbf{b}$
 g $2\mathbf{a} - \mathbf{b}$ **h** $-\mathbf{a} - 2\mathbf{b}$ **i** $\mathbf{a} + 2\mathbf{b}$
 j $-\mathbf{a} + \mathbf{b}$ **k** $2\mathbf{a} - 2\mathbf{b}$ **l** $\mathbf{a} - 2\mathbf{b}$

8 a Equal but in opposite directions
 b Any three of: $\overrightarrow{DA}$, $\overrightarrow{EF}$, $\overrightarrow{GJ}$, $\overrightarrow{FI}$, $\overrightarrow{AH}$

9 a Opposite direction and $\overrightarrow{AB} = -\frac{1}{2}\overrightarrow{CK}$
 b $\overrightarrow{BJ}$, $\overrightarrow{CK}$
 c $\overrightarrow{EB}$, $\overrightarrow{GO}$, $\overrightarrow{KH}$

10

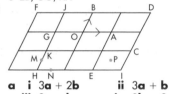

11 a i $3\mathbf{a} + 2\mathbf{b}$ **ii** $3\mathbf{a} + \mathbf{b}$
 iii $2\mathbf{a} - \mathbf{b}$ **iv** $2\mathbf{b} - 2\mathbf{a}$
 b $\overrightarrow{DG}$ and $\overrightarrow{BC}$

12 a Any three of: $\overrightarrow{MJ}$, $\overrightarrow{AG}$, $\overrightarrow{HC}$, $\overrightarrow{BD}$, $\overrightarrow{OH}$, $\overrightarrow{NA}$, $\overrightarrow{PO}$, $\overrightarrow{KB}$, $\overrightarrow{IE}$
 b Any three of: $\overrightarrow{DG}$, $\overrightarrow{HJ}$, $\overrightarrow{AL}$, $\overrightarrow{EH}$, $\overrightarrow{BA}$, $\overrightarrow{OM}$, $\overrightarrow{FB}$, $\overrightarrow{IO}$, $\overrightarrow{KN}$
 c Any three of: $\overrightarrow{GD}$, $\overrightarrow{HE}$, $\overrightarrow{BF}$, $\overrightarrow{JH}$, $\overrightarrow{AB}$, $\overrightarrow{OI}$, $\overrightarrow{LA}$, $\overrightarrow{MO}$, $\overrightarrow{NK}$
 d Any three of: $\overrightarrow{CH}$, $\overrightarrow{DB}$, $\overrightarrow{EI}$, $\overrightarrow{GA}$, $\overrightarrow{HO}$, $\overrightarrow{BK}$, $\overrightarrow{JM}$, $\overrightarrow{AN}$, $\overrightarrow{OP}$
 e Any three of: $\overrightarrow{FH}$, $\overrightarrow{EG}$, $\overrightarrow{IA}$, $\overrightarrow{BJ}$, $\overrightarrow{KM}$, $\overrightarrow{OL}$
 f Any three of: $\overrightarrow{JD}$, $\overrightarrow{AE}$, $\overrightarrow{OF}$, $\overrightarrow{LH}$, $\overrightarrow{MB}$, $\overrightarrow{NI}$
 g i $\overrightarrow{FG}$, $\overrightarrow{IJ}$ or $\overrightarrow{KL}$ **ii** $\overrightarrow{OC}$, $\overrightarrow{KD}$, $\overrightarrow{NG}$, $\overrightarrow{PH}$
    iii $\overrightarrow{FJ}$ or $\overrightarrow{IL}$ **iv** $\overrightarrow{FL}$
    v $\overrightarrow{LF}$ **vi** $\overrightarrow{PC}$
    vii $\overrightarrow{CP}$ **viii** Same as part **d** of this question
    ix Same as part **a** of this question

13 Parts **b** and **d** could be, parts **a** and **c** could not be

14 a Any multiple (positive or negative) of $3\mathbf{a} - \mathbf{b}$
 b Will be a multiple of $3\mathbf{a} - \mathbf{b}$

15 For example, let ABCD be a quadrilateral as shown
 Then $\overrightarrow{AD} = \overrightarrow{AB} + \overrightarrow{BD} = \mathbf{a} + (\mathbf{b} + \mathbf{c})$.
 But $\overrightarrow{AD} = \overrightarrow{AC} + \overrightarrow{CD} = (\mathbf{a} + \mathbf{b}) + \mathbf{c}$.
 Hence $\mathbf{a} + (\mathbf{b} + \mathbf{c}) = (\mathbf{a} + \mathbf{b}) + \mathbf{c}$.

16 a i $2\mathbf{b} - 2\mathbf{a}$ **ii** $\mathbf{a} - \mathbf{c}$
    iii $2\mathbf{c} - 2\mathbf{b}$ **iv** $\mathbf{b} + \mathbf{c} - \mathbf{a}$
 b $\overrightarrow{RQ} = \mathbf{a} - \mathbf{c} = \overrightarrow{SP}$, so two opposite sides are equal and parallel, hence PQRS is a parallelogram

13.2   Vectors in geometry

Exercise 13B

1 a i $-\mathbf{a} + \mathbf{b}$
   ii $\frac{1}{2}(-\mathbf{a} + \mathbf{b})$
   iii

   iv $\frac{1}{2}\mathbf{a} + \frac{1}{2}\mathbf{b}$
 b i $\mathbf{a} - \mathbf{b}$
   ii $\frac{1}{2}\mathbf{a} - \frac{1}{2}\mathbf{b}$
   iii

   iv $\frac{1}{2}\mathbf{a} + \frac{1}{2}\mathbf{b}$
 c

 d M is midpoint of parallelogram of which OA and OB are two sides.

2 a i $-\mathbf{a} - \mathbf{b}$
   ii $-\frac{1}{2}\mathbf{a} - \frac{1}{2}\mathbf{b}$
   iii (diagram)
   iv $\frac{1}{2}\mathbf{a} - \frac{1}{2}\mathbf{b}$
 b i $\mathbf{b} + \mathbf{a}$
   ii $\frac{1}{2}\mathbf{b} + \frac{1}{2}\mathbf{a}$
   iii (diagram)
   iv $\frac{1}{2}\mathbf{a} - \frac{1}{2}\mathbf{b}$
 c (diagram)
 d N is midpoint of parallelogram of which OA and OC are two sides

3 a i $-\mathbf{a} + \mathbf{b}$
   ii $\frac{1}{3}(-\mathbf{a} + \mathbf{b})$
   iii $\frac{2}{3}\mathbf{a} + \frac{1}{3}\mathbf{b}$
 b $\frac{3}{4}\mathbf{a} + \frac{1}{4}\mathbf{b}$

4 a i $\frac{2}{3}\mathbf{b}$
   ii $\frac{1}{2}\mathbf{a} + \frac{1}{2}\mathbf{b}$
   iii $-\frac{2}{3}\mathbf{b}$
 b $\frac{1}{2}\mathbf{a} - \frac{1}{6}\mathbf{b}$
 c $\overrightarrow{DE} = \overrightarrow{DO} + \overrightarrow{OE}$
    $= \frac{3}{2}\mathbf{a} - \frac{1}{2}\mathbf{b}$
 d $\overrightarrow{DE}$ parallel to $\overrightarrow{CD}$ (multiple of $\overrightarrow{CD}$) and D is a common point

5 a (diagram)
    $\overrightarrow{CD} = -\mathbf{a} + \mathbf{b} = \mathbf{b} - \mathbf{a}$
    (diagram)
 b i $-\mathbf{a}$
   ii $-\mathbf{b}$
   iii $\mathbf{a} - \mathbf{b}$
 c 0, vectors return to starting point

d i $2\mathbf{b}$
   ii $2\mathbf{b} - 2\mathbf{a}$
   iii $-2\mathbf{a}$
   iv $2\mathbf{b} - \mathbf{a}$
   v $-\mathbf{a} - \mathbf{b}$

6 a (diagram)
    $\overrightarrow{CX} = \sqrt{1^2 + 1^2}\mathbf{b} = \sqrt{2}\mathbf{b}$
    $\overrightarrow{CD} = \overrightarrow{CX} + \overrightarrow{XD}$
      $= \sqrt{2}\mathbf{b} - \mathbf{a}$
 b (diagram)
    $\overrightarrow{YE} = \sqrt{1^2 + 1^2}\mathbf{a} = \sqrt{2}\mathbf{a}$
    $\overrightarrow{DE} = \overrightarrow{DY} + \overrightarrow{YE}$
      $= \mathbf{b} - \sqrt{2}\mathbf{a}$
 c i $-\mathbf{a}$
   ii $-\mathbf{b}$
   iii $\mathbf{a} - \sqrt{2}\mathbf{b}$
   iv $\sqrt{2}\mathbf{a} - \mathbf{b}$
   v $\sqrt{2}\mathbf{a} + \mathbf{a}$
   vi $\sqrt{2}\mathbf{b} + \mathbf{b}$
   vii $2\mathbf{b} + \sqrt{2}\mathbf{b} - \mathbf{a} - \sqrt{2}\mathbf{a}$
   viii $2\mathbf{b} + \sqrt{2}\mathbf{b} - 2\mathbf{a} - \sqrt{2}\mathbf{a}$

7 a i $-\mathbf{a} + \mathbf{b}$

   ii $\frac{1}{2}(-\mathbf{a} + \mathbf{b}) = -\frac{1}{2}\mathbf{a} + \frac{1}{2}\mathbf{b}$

   iii $\frac{1}{2}\mathbf{a} + \frac{1}{2}\mathbf{b}$

 b i $\frac{1}{2}\mathbf{b} + \mathbf{c}$

   ii $-\frac{1}{2}\mathbf{a} + \frac{1}{2}\mathbf{c}$

 c i $-\frac{1}{2}\mathbf{a} + \frac{1}{2}\mathbf{c}$

   ii Equal

   iii Parallelogram

d $\overrightarrow{AC} = -\mathbf{a} + \mathbf{c} = 2(-\frac{1}{2}\mathbf{a} + \frac{1}{2}\mathbf{c})$
    $= 2\overrightarrow{QM}$

8 a i $\frac{1}{2}\mathbf{a}$

   ii $\mathbf{c} - \mathbf{a}$

   iii $\frac{1}{2}\mathbf{a} + \frac{1}{2}\mathbf{c}$

   iv $\frac{1}{2}\mathbf{c}$

 b i $-\frac{1}{2}\mathbf{a} + \frac{1}{2}\mathbf{b}$

   ii $-\frac{1}{2}\mathbf{a} + \frac{1}{2}\mathbf{b}$

c Opposite sides are equal and parallel

d NMRQ and PNLR

9 a $-\frac{1}{2}\mathbf{a} + \frac{1}{2}\mathbf{b}$

 b i Rhombus

   ii They lie on a straight line, $\overrightarrow{OM} = \frac{1}{2}\overrightarrow{OC}$

10 $k = 8$

13.3 Geometric proof

Exercise 13C

1 a Angles ABC and ACB are both $54°$, hence triangle ABC is isosceles

 b $\angle DFE = 180° - (90° + \frac{x}{2}°) = 90° - \frac{x}{2}°$

   $\angle DEF = 180° - x° - (90° - \frac{x}{2}°) = 90° - \frac{x}{2}°$

   $\angle DFE = \angle DEF$ hence triangle DEF is isosceles.

2 The exterior angle of a triangle is equal to the sum of the opposite 2 interior angles.

   $x° = \frac{x}{2}° + \frac{x}{2}°$, hence the triangle is isosceles

3 a $\angle DAB = 50°$, $\angle DCB = 130°$

 b $\angle AOC = 2x°$, hence $\angle ADC = x°$

   reflex angle $AOC = 2y°$, hence $\angle ADC = y°$

   But $2x° + 2y° = 360°$ (angles around a point)

   hence $2(x° + y°) = 360°$

   giving $x° + y° = 180°$

4 a $x = 40°$

 b $\angle CED + \angle AEC = 180°$ (angles on a straight line)

   $\angle ABC + \angle AEC = 180°$ (cyclic quadrilateral)

   But $\angle ABC = \angle ACB$ (isosceles triangle)

   Hence $\angle ACB = \angle CED$

5 PS = QR, RS = PQ, both triangles share side QS hence by SSS triangles are congruent

6 Join O to C and C to B to form a triangle. Let X be the point where the perpendicular bisector meets OB. Then OX = BX. By pythagoras OC = CB. But OC = OB (both radii). Hence OBC is equilateral

7 $\overrightarrow{AB} = \mathbf{b} - \mathbf{a}$, $\overrightarrow{EF} = 3\mathbf{b} - 3\mathbf{a} = 3(\mathbf{b} - \mathbf{a}) = 3\overrightarrow{AB}$ hence $\overrightarrow{AB}$ is parallel to $\overrightarrow{EF}$

8 a Check students' proofs

 b By the alternate segment theorem $\angle TXA = \angle TYB$ hence AX is parallel to BY

9 $\angle QAT = \angle QTA$ (isosceles triangle)

   $\angle PTB = \angle QTA$ (vertically opposite angles)

   $\angle PTB = \angle PBT$ (isosceles triangle)

   Hence $\angle PBT = \angle QAT$ and PB is parallel to AQ

10 a $\overrightarrow{YW} = \overrightarrow{YZ} + \overrightarrow{ZW} = 2\mathbf{a} + \mathbf{b} + \mathbf{a} + 2\mathbf{b} = 3\mathbf{a} + 3\mathbf{b}$

   $= 3(\mathbf{a} + \mathbf{b}) = 3\overrightarrow{XY}$

 b $3 : 1$

 c They lie on a straight line.

 d Points are A(6, 2), B(1, 1) and C(2, −4). Using Pythagoras' theorem, $AB^2 = 26$, $BC^2 = 26$ and $AC^2 = 52$ so $AB^2 + BC^2 = AC^2$ hence $\angle ABC$ must be a right angle

Examination questions

1 $\frac{1}{4}\mathbf{s} + \frac{3}{4}\mathbf{t}$

2 a $2\mathbf{b} - 2\mathbf{a}$

 b $2\mathbf{c} - 2\mathbf{b}$

 c $\overrightarrow{EF} = \frac{1}{2}\overrightarrow{AB} + \frac{1}{2}\overrightarrow{BC}$

   $= \frac{1}{2}(2\mathbf{b} - 2\mathbf{a}) + \frac{1}{2}(2\mathbf{c} - 2\mathbf{b})$

   $= \mathbf{c} - \mathbf{a}$

 d $\overrightarrow{DG} = \overrightarrow{EF} = \mathbf{c} - \mathbf{a}$

3 a i $5\mathbf{b} - 5\mathbf{a}$

   ii $2\mathbf{b} - \mathbf{a}$

 b $\overrightarrow{QR} = 6\mathbf{b} - 3\mathbf{a} = 3\overrightarrow{PQ}$

4 a $2\mathbf{b} - 2\mathbf{a}$

 b $\overrightarrow{PQ} = \overrightarrow{PA} + \frac{1}{4}\overrightarrow{AB} = \mathbf{a} + \frac{1}{4}(2\mathbf{b} - 2\mathbf{a})$

 c $\mathbf{a} + \mathbf{b}$

 d $\overrightarrow{PQ} = \frac{1}{2}\overrightarrow{OM}$ hence sides are parallel

5 a i $\mathbf{a} + \frac{3}{2}\mathbf{b}$

   ii $\mathbf{a} - \frac{1}{2}\mathbf{b}$

   iii $\frac{1}{2}\mathbf{a} - \frac{1}{4}\mathbf{b}$

   iv $\frac{1}{2}\mathbf{a} + \frac{3}{4}\mathbf{b}$

 b They lie on a straight line, with N the midpoint of OQ.

6 a i $\frac{3}{2}\mathbf{b} - 3\mathbf{a}$

   ii $\frac{3}{2}\mathbf{a} + \frac{3}{2}\mathbf{a} + \frac{3}{2}\mathbf{b}$

   iii $\mathbf{b} - 2\mathbf{a}$

 b $2 : 1$

Answers to Chapter 14

Quick check

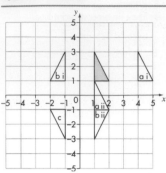

14.1 Transformations of the graph $y = f(x)$

Exercise 14A

1 a–d

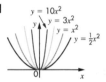

$y = 10x^2$
$y = 3x^2$
$y = x^2$
$y = \frac{1}{2}x^2$

e Stretch sf in y-direction: 3, $\frac{1}{2}$, 10

2 a–d

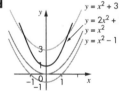

$y = x^2 + 3$
$y = 2x^2 + 1$
$y = x^2$
$y = x^2 - 1$

e b Translation $\begin{pmatrix} 0 \\ 3 \end{pmatrix}$

c Translation $\begin{pmatrix} 0 \\ -1 \end{pmatrix}$

d Stretch sf 2 in y-direction, followed by translation $\begin{pmatrix} 0 \\ 1 \end{pmatrix}$

3 a–d

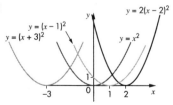

$y = (x - 1)^2$
$y = (x + 3)^2$
$y = 2(x - 2)^2$
$y = x^2$

e b Translation $\begin{pmatrix} -3 \\ 0 \end{pmatrix}$

c Translation $\begin{pmatrix} 1 \\ 0 \end{pmatrix}$

d Stretch sf 2 in y-direction, followed by translation $\begin{pmatrix} 2 \\ 0 \end{pmatrix}$

4 a–c

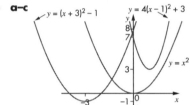

$y = (x + 3)^2 - 1$
$y = 4(x - 1)^2 + 3$
$y = x^2$

d b Translation $\begin{pmatrix} -3 \\ -1 \end{pmatrix}$

c Translation $\begin{pmatrix} 1 \\ 3 \end{pmatrix}$ followed by stretch sf 4 in y-direction

5 a–d

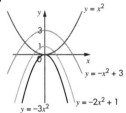

$y = x^2$
$y = -x^2 + 3$
$y = -3x^2$
$y = -2x^2 + 1$

e b Reflection in x-axis, followed by translation $\begin{pmatrix} 0 \\ 3 \end{pmatrix}$

c Reflection in the x-axis, followed by stretch sf 3 in y-direction

d Reflection in x-axis, followed by stretch sf 2 in y-direction and translation $\begin{pmatrix} 0 \\ 1 \end{pmatrix}$

6 a-d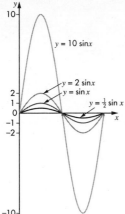

e Stretch sf in y-direction: 2, $\frac{1}{2}$, 10

7 a-d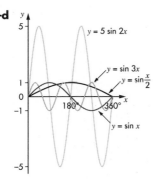

e *b* Stretch sf $\frac{1}{3}$ in x-direction

c Stretch sf 2 in x-direction

d Stretch sf 5 in y-direction, followed by stretch sf $\frac{1}{2}$ in x-direction

8 a-d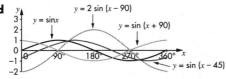

e *b* Translation $\begin{pmatrix} -90 \\ 0 \end{pmatrix}$

c Translation $\begin{pmatrix} 45 \\ 0 \end{pmatrix}$

d Stretch sf 2 in y-direction followed by translation $\begin{pmatrix} 90 \\ 0 \end{pmatrix}$

9 a-d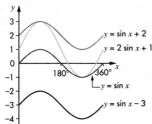

e *b* Translation $\begin{pmatrix} 0 \\ 2 \end{pmatrix}$

c Translation $\begin{pmatrix} 0 \\ -3 \end{pmatrix}$

d Stretch sf 2 in y-direction followed by translation $\begin{pmatrix} 0 \\ 1 \end{pmatrix}$

10 a-d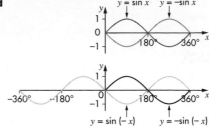

e *b* Reflection in x-axis
c Reflection in y-axis
d This leaves the graph in the same place and is the identity transformation

11 a-d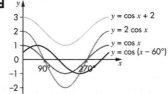

e *b* Stretch sf 2 in y-direction

c Translation $\begin{pmatrix} 60 \\ 0 \end{pmatrix}$

d Translation $\begin{pmatrix} 0 \\ 2 \end{pmatrix}$

12 All of them.

13 a **i** Stretch sf 4 in y-direction
ii Stretch sf 9 in y-direction
iii Stretch sf 16 in y-direction

b **i** Stretch sf $\frac{1}{2}$ in x-direction
ii Stretch sf $\frac{1}{3}$ in x-direction
iii Stretch sf $\frac{1}{4}$ in x-direction

c Stretch sf a^2 in y-direction, or stretch sf $\frac{1}{a}$ in x-direction

14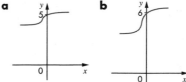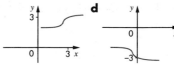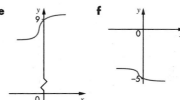

15 a $y = 5x^2$ **b** $y = x^2 + 7$
c $y = (x+3)^2$ **d** $y = (x+2)^2 - 3$
e $y = 3x^2 + 4$ **f** $y = -3x^2$

16 a $y = 6 \cos x$
　　b $y = \cos x + 3$
　　c $y = \cos (x + 30°)$
　　d $y = \cos (x - 45°) - 2$
　　e $y = 3 \cos x - 2$

17 a

　　b i 　　**ii**

　　iii 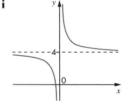　　**iv**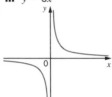

　　c i $y = -x^3$　　**ii** $y = x^3 - 2$
　　　iii $y = 3x^3$　　**iv** $y = (x + 2)^3$

18 a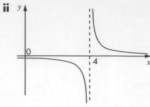

　　b i

ii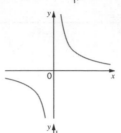

iii

iv

　　c i $y = \dfrac{1}{x} + 4$

　　　ii $y = \dfrac{1}{x - 4}$

　　　iii $y = \dfrac{3}{x}$

　　　iv $y = \dfrac{1}{2x}$

19 No, as $f(-x) = (-x)^2 = x^2$, and $-f(x) = -(x)^2 = -x^2$
20 a $y = x^2 + 2$　　　　**b** $y = (x - 2)^2$
　　c $y = 2x^2$　　　　　**d** $y = -x^2 + 4$
21 a $y = 2 \sin x$　　　　**b** $y = \sin(x - 30°)$
　　c $y = 2\sin(x - 60°)$　　**d** $y = \sin 2x$
22 a Translation
　　b i Equivalent　　　　**ii** Equivalent
　　　iii Not equivalent
23 i A　　　　　　　　**ii** D
　　iii E　　　　　　　**iv** C
　　v B

Examination questions

1 **a**
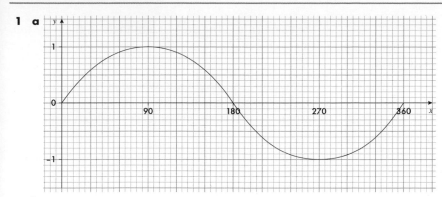

b $y = -\sin x$

2 **a** $y = \cos x + 1$ **b** $y = 2\cos x$

    c $y = \cos 2x$ **d** $y = \cos (x - 90)$ or $y = \sin x$

GLOSSARY

3D   A solid shape that has three dimensions (height, width, depth).

adjacent side   In a triangle, rectangle or square, the side adjacent to (next to) the angle or side being worked on.

alternate segment   The 'other' segment. In a circle divided by a chord, the alternate segment lies on the other side of the chord.

angle   The space, usually measured in degrees (°), between two intersecting lines or surfaces (planes). The amount of turn needed to move from one line or plane to the other.

angle bisector   A straight line or plane that divides an angle in half.

angle of depression   The angle you have to turn downwards from looking along the horizontal to look at the ground or sea from the top of a tower, tree, cliff, etc.

angle of elevation   The angle you have to turn upwards from looking along the horizontal to look at the top of a tree, cliff, flagpole, etc.

anticlockwise   Turning in the opposite direction to the movement of the hands of a clock. (Opposite of *clockwise*)

apex   The highest vertex in the given orientation of a polygon such as a triangle or a 3D shape.

arc   A curve forming part of the circumference of a circle.

area   Measurement of the flat space a shape occupies. Usually measured in square units or hectares. (See also *surface area*.)

area ratio   The ratio of the areas of two similar shapes is equal to the ratio of the squares of their corresponding lengths. The area ratio, or area scale factor, is the square of the length ratio.

area scale factor   See *area ratio*.

area sine rule   The area of a triangle is given by $\frac{1}{2}ab$ sin$C$.

asymptote   A straight line whose perpendicular distance from a curve decreases to zero as the distance from the origin increases without limit.

average   A single number that represents or typifies a collection of values. (The three commonly used averages are mode, mean and median.)

balance   Equality on either side of an equation.

bearing   The direction relative to a fixed point.

best buy   A purchase that gives best value for money spent.

better value   A purchase that costs less in terms of weight or size, or that can be purchased in a greater quantity than another product, but at the same price.

bisect   To divide into two equal parts, or in half. You can bisect a line or an angle.

brackets   The symbols '(' and ')' which are used to separate part of an expression. This may be for clarity or to indicate a part to be worked out individually. When a number and/or value is placed immediately before an expression or value inside a pair of brackets, the two are to be multiplied together. For example, $6a(5b + c) = 30ab + 6ac$.

centre of enlargement   The fixed point of an enlargement. The distance of each image point from the centre of enlargement is the distance of object point from centre of enlargement x scale factor. In simple terms, the centre of enlargement is used to change the size of an object without changing its shape, and can be compared to a projector magnifying an image. (See also *enlargement*, *image* and *scale factor*.)

centre of rotation   The fixed point around which a shape is rotated or turned.

check   Calculations can be checked by carrying out the inverse operation. Solutions to equations can be checked by substituting values of the variable(s).

chord   A line joining two points on the circumference of a circle.

circle   A circle is the path of a point that is always equidistant from another point (the centre).

circular function   A function with a repeating set of values, such as sine and cosine, where the values cycle through from 0 to 1 to 0 to –1 to 0, and repeat.

circumference   The outline of a circle. The distance all the way around this outline.

clockwise   Turning in the same direction as the movement of the hands of a clock. (Opposite of *anticlockwise*)

coefficient   The number in front of an unknown quantity (the letter) in an algebraic term. For example, in $8x$, 8 is the coefficient of x.

comment   A note whether a result in a trial and improvement problem is too high or too low.

compasses   Also called a pair of compasses, an instrument used for drawing circles and measuring distances.

congruent   Exactly alike in shape and size.

constant of proportionality, k   This describes the situation when the probability of an event is dependent upon the outcome of another event. For example, the probability of the colour of a second ball drawn from a bag is conditional to the colour of the first ball drawn from the bag – if the first ball is not replaced.

constant term   A term in an algebraic expression that does not change because it does not contain a variable, the number term. For example, in $6x^2 + 5x + 7$, 7 is the constant term.

construct   To draw angles, lines or shapes accurately, according to given requirements.

cosine   The ratio of the adjacent side to the hypotenuse in a right-angled triangle.

cosine rule   A formula used to find the lengths of sides or the size of an angle in a triangle. $a^2 = b^2 + c^2 - 2bc \cos A$.

cross-section   The shape of a slice through a solid. Depending on where the cut is made, the cross-section of a cone could be a circle, a triangle, an ellipse, or a parabola.

cubic   A cubic expression or equation contains an 'x^3' term.

cyclic   Arranged as if on a circle.

cyclic quadrilateral   A quadrilateral whose vertices lie on a circle.

cylinder   A solid or hollow prism with circular ends and uniform (unchanging) cross-section. The shape of a can of baked beans or a length of drainpipe.

decagon   A polygon with 10 straight sides. The internal angles add up to 1440°.

decimal place   Every digit in a number has a place value (hundreds, tens, ones, etc.). The places after (to the right of) the decimal point have place values of tenths, hundredths, etc. These place values are called the decimal places.

demonstration   Logically presented proof of how a theory generates a certain result.

density   The ratio of the mass of an object to its volume. The mass per unit volume.

diameter   A straight line across a circle, from circumference to circumference and passing through the centre. It is the longest chord of a circle and two radii long. (See also *radius*.)

direct proportion   Two values or measurements may vary in direct proportion. That is, if one increases, then so does the other.

direct variation   Another name for *direct proportion*.

direction   The way something is facing or pointing. Direction can be described using the compass points (north, south, south-east, etc.) or using bearings (the clockwise angle turned from facing north). The direction of a vector is given by the angle it makes with a line of reference. Two vectors that differ only in magnitude will be parallel.

discriminant   The quantity $(b^2 - 4ac)$ in the quadratic formula is called the discriminant.

distance   The separation (usually along a straight line) of two points.

do the same to both sides   To keep an equation balanced, you must do the same thing to both sides. If you add something to one side, you must add the same thing to the other side. If you double one side, you must double the other side, etc. If you are manipulating a fraction, you must do the same thing to the numerator and the denominator to keep the value of the fraction unchanged. However you can only multiply or divide the numbers. Adding or subtracting will alter the value of the fraction. See also *equation*.

eliminate   To remove a quantity such as a variable from an equation.

enlargement   A transformation of a plane figure or solid object that increases the size of the figure or object by a scale factor but leaves it the same shape, that is, the figure or object remains in the same ratio. (See also *scale factor*.)

equation   A number sentence where one side is equal to the other. An equation always contains an equals sign (=).

equidistant   The same distance apart.

equilateral triangle   A triangle with three equal sides (and three equal angles – each of which is 60°).

expand   Make bigger. Expanding brackets means you must multiply the terms inside a bracket by the number or letters outside. This will take more room to write, so you have 'expanded' the expression.

expand and simplify   An expression involving brackets can be expanded (remove the brackets) and the resulting terms may contain like terms that can then be simplified.

exponential function   Non-linear equations that have the form $y = k^x$, where k is a positive number.

expression   Collection of symbols representing a number. These can include numbers, variables (x, y, etc.), operations (+, ×, etc.), functions (squaring, cosine, etc.), but there will be no equals sign (=).

exterior angle   The exterior angles of a polygon are outside the shape. They are formed when a side is produced (extended). An exterior angle and its adjacent interior angle add up to 180°.

factor   A whole number that divides exactly into a given number. For example, factors of 30 are 1, 2, 3, 5, 6, 10, 15 and 30. Or, a number or term that divides exactly into an algebraic expression.

factorisation   (noun) Finding one or more factors of a given number or expression. (verb: factorise)

formula   (plural: formulae) An equation that enables you to convert or find a measurement from another known measurement or measurements. For example, the conversion formula from the Fahrenheit scale of temperature to the more common Celsius scale is $\frac{C}{5} = \frac{F-32}{9}$ where C is the temperature on the Celsius scale and F is the temperature on the Fahrenheit scale.

frustum   The base of a cone or pyramid. The shape obtained by removing the top of a cone or pyramid.

function   A function of x is any algebraic expression in which x is the only variable. This is often represented by the function notation f(x) or 'function of x'.

guess   Using mathematical knowledge to make an estimate of an answer and then using this as a starting point in a trial and improvement problem.

heptagon   A polygon with seven sides. The sum of all the interior angles of a heptagon is 900°. A regular heptagon has sides of equal length.

hexagon   A polygon with six sides. The sum of all the interior angles of a hexagon is 720°. A regular hexagon has sides of equal length and each of the interior angles is 120°.

hypotenuse   The longest side of a right-angled triangle. The side opposite the right angle.

identity   An identity is similar to an equation, but is true for all values of the variable(s). Instead of the usual equals (=) sign, ≡ is used. For example, $2x \equiv 7x - 5x$.

image   In geometry the 'image' is the result of a transformation. A good way to remember this is to relate it to the 'cut and paste' function on your computer.

included angle   The angle between two lines or sides of a polygon.

intercept   The point where a line or graph crosses an axis.

interior angle   An angle between the sides inside a polygon; an internal angle.

inverse   Inverse operations cancel each other out or reverse the effect of each other. The inverse of a number is the reciprocal of that number.

inverse cosine   The reverse of the cosine function. It tells you the value of the angle with that cosine. $\text{Cos}^{-1}A$.

inverse operations   Operations that reverse or cancel out the effect of each other. For example, addition is the inverse of subtraction, division is the inverse of multiplication.

inverse proportion   Two quantities vary in inverse proportion when one quantity is directly proportional to the reciprocal of the other. As one quantity increases, the other decreases.

inverse sine   The reverse of the sine function. It tells you the value of the angle with that sine. $\text{Sin}^{-1}A$.

inverse variation   Another name for inverse proportion.

isosceles triangle   A triangle with two sides that are equal. It also has two equal angles.

kite   A quadrilateral with two pairs of adjacent sides (i.e. the sides meet) that are equal in length. A kite has equal angles where the pairs meet, and the diagonals are perpendicular, but only one of them bisects the kite.

length ratio   The ratio of lengths in similar figures.

like terms   Terms in algebra that are the same, apart from their numerical coefficients. For example, $2ax^2$ and $5ax^2$ are a pair of like terms but $5x^2y$ and $7xy^2$ are not. Like terms can be combined by adding together their numerical coefficients so $2ax^2 + 5ax^2 = 7ax^2$.

line bisector   A point, a straight line or a plane that divides a line in half.

line symmetry   Symmetry that uses a line to divide a figure or shape into halves, such that both halves are an exact mirror image of each other. Many shapes have more than one line of symmetry.

linear   Forming a line.

linear scale factor   Also called the *scale factor* or *length ratio*. The ratio of corresponding lengths in two similar shapes is constant.

loci   See *locus*.

locus   (plural: loci) The locus of a point is the path taken by the point following a rule or rules. For example, the locus of a point that is always the same distance from another point is the shape of a circle.

magnitude   Size. Magnitude is always a positive value.

mass   The mass is the amount of 'stuff' an object consists of. It does not vary if the object is moved somewhere else. The weight of an object is closely related to mass but depends on the effect of gravity. The weight of an object will be different on the Earth to what it is on the Moon. Its mass will remain constant.

maximum   The greatest value of something. The turning point or point at which the graph of a parabola $y = -ax^2 + bx + c$ is at its highest.

minimum   The smallest value of something. The turning point or point at which the graph of a parabola $y = ax^2 + bx + c$ is at its lowest.

mirror line   A line on which a shape is reflected exactly on the other side.

nonagon   A polygon with nine sides. A regular nonagon has all its sides of equal length, and each of its interior angles measures 140°.

non-linear   An expression or equation that does not form a straight line. The highest power of x, is greater than 1.

object   (in maths) You carry out a transformation on an object to form an image. The object is the original or starting shape, line or point. (See also *enlargement*.)

octagon   A polygon that has eight sides. A regular octagon has all its sides of equal length, and each of its interior angles measures 135°.

opposite side   In a triangle, rectangle or square, the side opposite (or, on the other side of) the angle or side being worked on.

parabola   The shape of a graph potted from an equation such as $5x^2 - 7x + 2 = 0$. The equation will have an 'x^2' term.

parallelogram   A four-sided polygon with two pairs of equal and parallel opposite sides.

pentagon   A polygon that has five sides. A regular pentagon has all its sides of equal length, and each of its interior angles measures 108°.

perpendicular bisector   A line drawn at a right angle to a line segment which also divides it into two equal parts.

point of contact   The point where a tangent touches a circle.

polygon   A closed shape with three or more straight sides.

prism   A 3D shape that has a uniform or constant cross-section; the shape of the slice formed by cutting perpendicular to its length is always the same.

proof   An argument that establishes a fact about numbers or geometry for all cases. Showing that the fact is true for specific cases is a demonstration.

prove   The process of explaining a proof. (See also *proof*.)

pyramid   A polyhedron on a triangular (see *triangle*), square, or polygonal (see *polygon*) base, with triangular faces meeting at a vertex. The volume, V, of a pyramid of base area A and perpendicular height h, is given by the formula: $V = \frac{1}{3}A \times h$.

Pythagoras' theorem   The theorem states that the square on the hypotenuse of a right-angled triangle is equal to the sum of the squares on the other two sides.

quadratic   An expression, equation or formula involving an x^2 term.

quadratic expansion   Expanding two brackets $(x + a)(x + b)$ to give a quadratic expression. (See also *expand* and *expression*.)

quadratic formula   A formula for solving quadratic equations. The solution of the equation $ax^2 + bx + c = 0$ is given by: $x = \frac{-b \pm \sqrt{b^2 - 4ac}}{2a}$

radius   (Plural: radii) The distance from the centre of a circle to its circumference.

ratio   The ratio of A to B is a number found by dividing A by B. It is written as A : B. For example, the ratio of 1 m to 1 cm is written as 1 m : 1 cm = 100 : 1. Notice that the two quantities must both be in the same units if they are to be compared in this way.

rearrange   See *rearrangement*.

rearrangement   To change the arrangement of something. An equation can be rearranged using the rules of algebra to help you solve it. Data can be rearranged to help you analyse it.

reciprocal   The reciprocal of any number is 1 divided by the number. The effect of finding the reciprocal of a fraction is to turn it upside down. The reciprocal of 3 is $\frac{1}{3}$. The reciprocal of $\frac{1}{4}$ is 4. The reciprocal of $\frac{10}{3}$ is $\frac{3}{10}$.

reflection   The image formed after being reflected. The process of reflecting an object.

regular polygon   A polygon that has sides of equal length and angles of equal size.

rhombus   A parallelogram that has sides of equal length. A rhombus has two lines of symmetry and a rotational symmetry of order 2. The diagonals of a rhombus bisect each other at right angles and they bisect the figure.

roots   The roots of a quadratic equation are the values of x when $y = 0$. (They are the solution to the equation.) They can be seen on a graph where the parabola crosses the x-axis.

rotation   Turning. A geometrical transformation in which every point on a figure is rotated through the same angle.

rotational symmetry   A shape which can be turned about a point so that it coincides exactly with its original position at least twice in a complete rotation.

scale   A scale on a diagram shows the scale factor used to make the drawing. The axes on a graph or chart will use a scale depending on the space available to display the data. For example, each division on the axis may represent 1, 2, 5, 10, 100, etc. units. (See also *scale factor*.)

scale factor   The ratio by which a length or other measurement is increased or deceased.

sector   A region of a circle, like a slice of a pie, bounded by an arc and two radii.

segment   A part of a circle between a chord and the circumference.

semicircle   Half a circle.

side   1. A straight line forming part of the perimeter of a polygon. For example, a triangle has three sides.

   2. A face (usually a vertical face) of a 3D object, such as the side of a box. (See also *3D*.)

similar   The same shape but a different size.

similar triangles   Triangles with the same size angles. The lengths of the sides of the triangles are different but vary in a constant proportion.

simplify   To make an equation or expression easier to work with or understand by combining like terms or cancelling down. For example, $4a - 2a + 5b + 2b = 2a + 7b$, $\frac{12}{18} = \frac{2}{3}$.

simultaneous equations   Two or more equations that are true at the same time.

sine   The ratio of the opposite side to the hypotenuse in a right-angled triangle.

sine rule   In a triangle, the ratio of the length of a side to the sine of the opposite angle is constant, hence $\frac{a}{\sin A} = \frac{b}{\sin B} = \frac{c}{\sin C}$.

slant height   The distance along the sloping edge of a cone or pyramid.

soluble   Something that can be solved.

solution   The result of solving a mathematical problem. Solutions are often given in equation form.

solve   Finding the value or values of a variable (x) that satisfy the given equation or problem.

speed   How fast something moves.

sphere   A three-dimensional round body. All points of its surface are equidistant from its centre.

stretch   An enlargement that takes place in one direction only. It is described by a scale factor and the direction of the stretch.

substitute   When a letter in an equation, expression or formula is replaced by a number, we have substituted the number for the letter. For example, if $a = b + 2x$, and we know $b = 9$ and $x = 6$, we can write $a = 9 + 2 \times 6$. So $a = 9 + 12 = 17$.

subtend   Standing on. An angle made by two radii at the centre of a circle is the angle subtended by the arc which joins the points on the circumference at the ends of the radii.

subtended   Standing on. An angle made by two radii at the centre of a circle is the angle subtended by the arc which joins the points on the circumference at the ends of the radii.

surd   A number written as $\sqrt{x}$. For example, $\sqrt{7}$.

surd form   The square root sign is left in the final expression when $\sqrt{x}$ is an irrational number.

surface area   The area of the surface of a 3D shape, such as a prism. The area of a net will be the same as the surface area of the shape.

tangent   1. A straight line that touches the circumference of a circle at one point only.

2. The ratio of the opposite side to the adjacent side in a right-angled triangle.

term   1. Each quantity or expression in a ratio or fraction.

2. In an equation, any of the quantities connected to each other by an addition or subtraction sign.

three-figure bearing   The angle of a bearing is given with three digits. The angle is less than 100°, a zero (or zeros) is placed in front, such as 045° for north-east.

time   How long something takes. Time is measured in days, hours, seconds, etc.

transform   To change.

transformation   An action such as translation, reflection or rotation. (See also *translation*, *reflection* and *rotation*.)

translation   A transformation in which all points of a plane figure are moved by the same amount and in the same direction.

trapezium   A quadrilateral with one pair of parallel sides.

trial and improvement   Some problems can be solved or estimated by making an educated guess. This guess can then be refined to get a more accurate answer. This is known as trial and improvement.

trigonometry   The branch of mathematics that shows how to explain and calculate the relationships between the sides and angles of triangles.

unit cost   The cost of one unit of a commodity, such as the cost per kilogram.

value for money   The best purchase that a certain amount of money can get.

variable   A quantity that can have many values. These values may be discrete or continuous. They are often represented by x and y in an expression. (See also *expression*.)

vector   A quantity with magnitude and direction. (See also *magnitude* and *direction*.)

vertex   1. The points at which the sides of a polygon or the edges of a polyhedron meet.

2. The turning point (maximum or minimum) of a graph. (See also *maximum* and *minimum*.)

vertical height   The perpendicular height from the base to the apex of a triangle, cone, or pyramid.

volume   The amount of space occupied by a substance or object or enclosed within a container.

volume ratio   The ratio of the volumes of two similar shapes is equal to the ratio of the cubes of their corresponding lengths. The volume ratio, or volume scale factor, is the cube of the length ratio.

volume scale factor   See *volume ratio*.

π   Pronounced 'pie', the numerical value of the ratio of the circumference of a circle to its diameter (approximately 3.14159).

INDEX

William Collins' dream of knowledge for all began with the publication of his first book in 1819. A self-educated mill worker, he not only enriched millions of lives, but also founded a flourishing publishing house. Today, staying true to this spirit, Collins books are packed with inspiration, innovation and practical expertise. They place you at the centre of a world of possibility and give you exactly what you need to explore it.

Collins. Freedom to teach.

Published by Collins
An imprint of HarperCollins*Publishers*
77–85 Fulham Palace Road
Hammersmith
London
W6 8JB

> Browse the complete Collins catalogue at
> www.collinseducation.com

© HarperCollins*Publishers* Limited 2010

10 9 8 7 6 5 4 3 2 1

ISBN-13 978-0-00-734013-2

Kevin Evans, Keith Gordon, Trevor Senior, Brian Speed and Chris Pearce assert their moral rights to be identified as the authors of this work.

British Library Cataloguing in Publication Data

A Catalogue record for this publication is available from the British Library.

Commissioned by Katie Sergeant
Project managed by Priya Govindan
FM and PS pages project managed by Alexandra Riley
Edited and proofread by Joan Miller, Karen Westall and Brian Asbury
Indexing by Esther Burd
Answers checked by Amanda Dickson
Glossary by Marian Bond
Cover design by Angela English
Content design by Nigel Jordan
Typesetting by Jordan Publishing Design
FM and PS pages designed by EMC Design and Jerry Fowler
Production by Arjen Jansen
Printed and bound by L.E.G.O. S.p.A. Italy

AQA has checked that the content and level of this publication are appropriate for its GCSE Mathematics (4360) specification.

Acknowledgements

The publishers have sought permission from AQA to reproduce questions from past GCSE Mathematics papers.

The publishers wish to thank the following for permission to reproduce photographs. Every effort has been made to trace copyright holders and to obtain their permission for the use of copyright material. The publishers will gladly receive any information enabling them to rectify any error or omission at the first opportunity.

p.6 A/W Nigel Jordan, © iStockphoto.com/Patricia Burch, © iStockphoto.com/Terry Wilson, © iStockphoto.com/Jaroslaw Wojcik, A/W Robert Gray; p.24 A/W Jerry Fowler; p.62 © iStockphoto.com/Graeme Purdy, © iStockphoto.com/Darren Pearson, © iStockphoto.com/Andrew Howe, A/W Lesley Gray; p.81 © iStockphoto.com/Robert Churchill, © iStockphoto.com/ Wendell Franks; p.108 © iStockphoto.com/fotoVoyager, © iStockphoto.com/Martin Vegh, © iStockphoto.com/Matthias Weinrich, © iStockphoto.com/Stefan Weichelt; p.150–151 © BG David Martyn Hughes (Dr), © Eric Simard (Dr), © BR Jun Mu (Dr); p.152 © iStockphoto.com/Henryk Sadura, © iStockphoto.com/mbbirdy; p.180–181 © Dreamstime.com/ Jonnycwh, © Dreamstime.com/Jaroslaw Grudzinski, © Dreamstime.com/Mark Fairey; p.182 © iStockphoto.com/ Roberto Gennaro, © iStockphoto.com/Andrey Prokhorov; p.212 © iStockphoto.com/Branko Miokovic, © iStockphoto.com/ Sam Valtenbergs; p.240 © iStockphoto.com/sculpies, © iStockphoto.com/Luis Carlos Torres, © iStockphoto.com/ magaliB, Eagle Nebula image taken from Hubble telescopy ©NASA; p.262 © iStockphoto.com/Lukasz Laska, © iStockphoto.com/Paul Cowan, Canadarm2 robotic manipulator ©NASA; p.292 © iStockphoto.com/Philip Beasley, © iStockphoto.com/Andreas Weber; p.338 © iStockphoto.com/ Ivan Kmit, © iStockphoto.com/Scott Leigh, © iStockphoto.com/ zxvisual, © iStockphoto.com/Dan Barnes, © iStockphoto.com/ SilentWolf, © iStockphoto.com/Soundsnaps, © iStockphoto.com/porcorex, © iStockphoto.com/ Ivan Stevanovic, © iStockphoto.com/Gary Martin; p.354 A/W Jerry Fowler, © iStockphoto.com/Mark Evans, © iStockphoto.com/David Joyner, © iStockphoto.com/Stefan Weichelt; p.378 © iStockphoto.com/marc brown

With thanks to Chris Pearce, Samantha Burns, Naomi Norman, Claire Beckett, Andy Edmonds, Anton Bush (Gloucester High School for Girls), Matthew Pennington (Wirral Grammar School for Girls), James Toyer (The Buckingham School), Gordon Starkey (Brockhill Park Performing Arts College), Laura Radford and Alan Rees (Wolfreton School) and Mark Foster (Sedgefield Community College).